Binding and Linkage

Binding and Linkage

FUNCTIONAL CHEMISTRY OF BIOLOGICAL MACROMOLECULES

Jeffries Wyman and Stanley J. Gill

UNIVERSITY OF COLORADO
BOULDER, COLORADO

UNIVERSITY SCIENCE BOOKS
Mill Valley, California

University Science Books
20 Edgehill Road
Mill Valley, CA 94941

Production manager: Mary Miller
Manuscript editor: Aidan Kelly
Text and jacket designer: Robert Ishi
Compositor: Polyglot Pte. Ltd.
Printer and binder: Maple-Vail Book Manufacturing Group

Library of Congress Catalog Number: 90-070275

ISBN 0-935702-56-3

Printed in the United States of America
10 9 8 7 6 5 4 3 2 1

We wish to dedicate this book to John Tileston Edsall.

Contents

Preface

The origin of this book goes back to discussions between the two authors during the course of a La Cura Conference held at Varenna on Lake Como in 1973. Our idea was to bring together in one place concepts and procedures applicable to ligand binding by biological macromolecules, then scattered among various journals and reviews covering a period of nearly 40 years, and, perhaps more importantly, to show from what minimum set of general principles, physical and mathematical, they arise. Our project might be described as an endeavor to present the allosteric hypothesis about regulation and control of biological systems in simple form. The manuscript has grown in the course of writing. Every time we have come back to it, we have found something to change or add—some new way of looking at things—with no limit in sight. We must stop somewhere; so we present the book as it stands. Voltaire once remarked that he could write a book in one year in two volumes, or in two years in one volume. Our experience has been somewhat the same.

Acknowledgments

This book represents the results of discussion and interaction with a large number of colleagues among whom we are particularly indebted to friends and hosts in Rome and in Boulder. Eraldo Antonini played a key role to my (J. W.) coming to Rome in the first place (1960), and the collaboration with the Rome group presided over by Alexando Rossi-Fanelli, Eraldo Antonini, Maurizio Brunori, Melina Chiancone, Galtano Fichero, Clara and Enrico Bucci and their students provided a stimulating environment for thought and work. The same exciting atmosphere drew the other author (S. J. G.), beginning in 1972 and continued with many visits when the ideas of linkage thermodynamics were discussed and applied. The La Cura meetings, which drew many colleagues with similar interests, played a major role in the development of our thoughts. Jim Murray gave great impetus to ideas on non-equilibrium processes. For the last fifteen years we have benefitted greatly from friends in Boulder, particularly Paul Phillipson, Bill Briggs and Ed King along with many students and postdoctoral fellows. Various chapters have been read by colleagues and students and their advice and help, particularly by Chuck Robert and Enrico Di Cera, has been invaluable in the preparation of the book. Lana Hope has contended with the many revisions of the manuscript preparation and Elaine Black has helped with many details of the final stage of assembly. We are indebted to the National Science Foundation and the National Institutes of Health for research grants that have played a key role in the development of many ideas in this book.

John Edsall has followed the development of the book since its early stages and has encouraged us when progress flagged. His critical comments and historical perspective have added clarity and breadth to many sections of the book. His interest and encouragement have been a critical factor in the completion of the book.

Binding and Linkage

Introduction 1

Life as we know it, or indeed as we can conceive it, is restricted to a very narrow range of environmental conditions, particularly of pressure and temperature.* We cannot seriously imagine that a gas or a crystal could be alive. In the billions of worlds in the expanding universe, although there may be many regions where life exists, these must be a very small fraction of the total. The essential feature of a world of living systems must be that it allows the formation of molecules, and all the chemistry in which they are involved. Moreover, there must be a suitable matrix to hold together other, more complex constituents of organisms in solution. In our world it is water that plays this essential role, and it is indeed difficult to imagine how any other substance could substitute for water in other worlds that contain life. For life as we know it, it is primarily the properties of water that set the limits of pressure and temperature within which life can exist. Recent findings of strange bacteria, flourishing at great depths in some of the "hot spots" in the Pacific, show that some primitive forms of life, at least, can live under extremes of pressure and temperature that most of us previously thought were impossible. The halobacteria that live in the very high salt concentrations of the Dead Sea, or the sulfur bacteria that thrive under conditions of high acidity, are further examples of adaptation to extreme conditions. But the basic medium is still water.

However, only when a special group of very large molecules has formed can those complex binding, linkage, and feedback phenomena exist that lead to control of complex metabolic processes. It is these phenomena that we shall

---

* L. J. Henderson (1913) in his provocative book, *The Fitness of the Environment*, specified the essential characteristics of life as complexity, regulation, and metabolism, and he emphasized the unique properties of water as the matrix in which life could occur.

study here. Although linkage and control occur in the realms of both equilibrium and nonequilibrium phenomena, we shall here be concerned with systems at equilibrium.

Hemoglobin, the abundant oxygen carrier in many organisms, has played a key role for more than a century in elucidating fundamental ideas about the functioning of biological macromolecules. By considering some of the pertinent chemical properties of myoglobin and hemoglobin, the first proteins whose detailed structures were discovered by x-ray crystallography, we shall set the stage to develop the mathematics of regulation and control as they apply to macromolecules in biological systems. Before turning to mathematical formulations in subsequent chapters, we shall briefly look at a collection of diverse examples that illustrate the strong relationship between molecular form and function.

1.1 FUNCTION

1.1.1 Binding Curves

In characterizing various aspects of macromolecular phenomena in living systems, reversible binding of smaller molecules is of fundamental importance. This is illustrated by the binding of oxygen to hemoglobin and myoglobin. The amount of oxygen reversibly bound is determined by its partial pressure. The transport of oxygen by hemoglobin is described by a binding curve, which relates the amount of oxygen bound per unit of hemoglobin to the oxygen concentration to which blood is exposed in the lungs and tissues. Early investigators found the functional relationship between oxygen saturation and partial pressure, as shown by the curves presented in three alternative ways for hemoglobin and myoglobin in Figure 1-1.

Three principal ways of representing the binding of a small molecule by a macromolecule are shown in this figure. The sigmoid shape of the oxygen-saturation curve of hemoglobin (Figure 1-1a) is in marked contrast to the rectangular hyperbola found for myoglobin. The functional chemistry of these two macromolecules in relation to oxygen is clearly very different. Myoglobin has a much higher affinity than hemoglobin, and displays a simpler, hyperbolic binding curve. These curves explain the way in which oxygen drawn from the lungs into the blood (hemoglobin) is made available to the tissues (myoglobin) by the concerted action of the two proteins.

A more rational way of plotting the oxygen-binding data is as a function, not of the partial pressure itself, but of its logarithm, since the logarithm of the partial pressure is proportional to the chemical potential, which is the more fundamental variable.* When plots are made in this way, we obtain the curves

---

* For an introductory discussion of the concept of chemical potential, see Edsall and Gutfreund (1983).

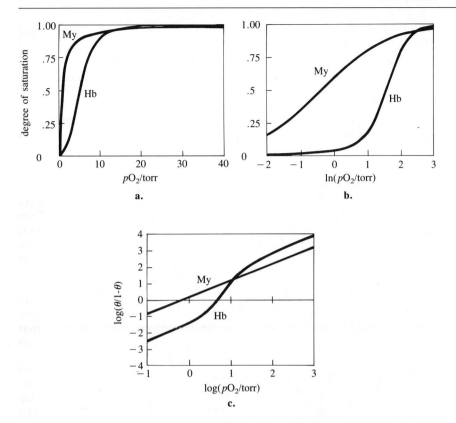

Figure 1-1.
Reversible oxygen-binding curves for myoglobin (Rossi-Fanelli and Antonini, 1958) and hemoglobin at 25°C and pH 7.4 (Imai and Yonetani, 1975a). (a) Degree of saturation vs. pO_2. (b) Degree of saturation vs. $\log(pO_2/\text{torr})$. (c) Hill plot.

for myoglobin and hemoglobin shown in Figure 1-1b. We shall reserve the term *binding curve* for such plots. In these plots we see that the oxygen binding curve is everywhere steeper for hemoglobin than it is for myoglobin.

The relative steepness of the binding curve is brought out in the Hill plot (Figure 1-1c). The Hill plot is made by taking the logarithm of the ratio of ligated sites to unligated sites, and plotting this quantity against the logarithm of the ligand activity. The degree of saturation θ measures the fraction of sites occupied. The Hill plot for myoglobin yields a straight line of unit slope, whereas the curve for hemoglobin shows a slope that is greater than one in the mid-saturation range and that approaches asymptotes of unit slope at the two ends. The slopes (or first derivatives) of the binding curve and the Hill plot in Figure 1-1b and c are depicted in Figure 1-2.

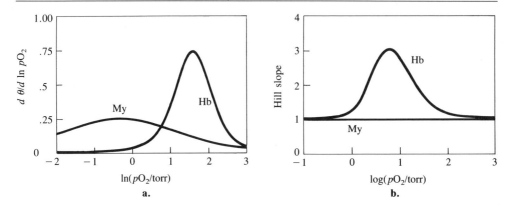

Figure 1-2.
Slope of binding curve (a) and Hill plot (b) for situations depicted in Figure 1-1.

The derivative of the binding curve is analogous to the heat capacity (or compressibility) of a simple system, and is called the *binding capacity* (Di Cera *et al.*, 1988b). We see that hemoglobin exhibits a much larger value for the binding capacity than myoglobin. This feature just suggests that oxygen binds cooperatively to hemoglobin. The slope of the Hill plot, n_H, brings out the cooperative feature of the binding process even more directly, as is seen in Figure 1-2b. The cooperativity for oxygen binding to hemoglobin implies that successive oxygen binding in hemoglobin is facilitated if some oxygen is already bound. Clearly this phenomenon can happen only when there is more than one binding site in the macromolecule. In hemoglobin there are four binding sites, whereas in myoglobin there is only one. This shows that somehow the oxygen-binding sites in hemoglobin interact positively as oxygen is bound.

Binding of other ligands (CO_2, CO, protons, electrons, organic phosphates) to hemoglobin can be described in a similar manner. When one considers the electron as a ligand, i.e., in a reduction reaction, then the voltage of a suitable electrochemical cell provides a measure of the activity of the electron. The functional chemistry of the macromolecule is embodied in such curves as they are affected by various conditions, such as temperature and pH.

1.1.2   Linked Functions

(a) *Chemical ligand linkage.* An oxygen-binding curve, such as that in Figure 1-1, reveals the effect of interaction between the four binding sites in hemoglobin for oxygen. Because the interactions are between sites that bind the same ligand, they are called *homotropic*. There may also be interaction between sites that bind different ligands. Such interactions are called *heterotropic*. The classical example of this is the influence of pH on the oxygen-binding curve of hemoglobin shown in Figure 1-3a.

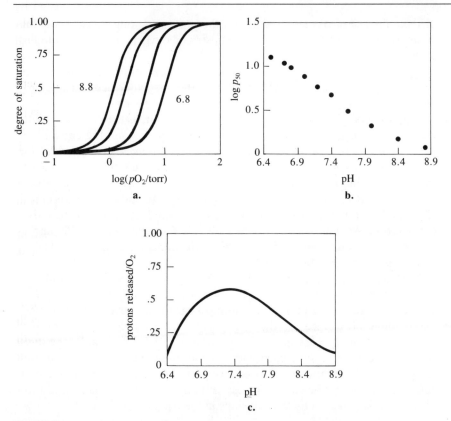

Figure 1-3.
(a) Effect of pH on oxygen-binding curves of hemoglobin A at 25°C curves from left
to right at pH values of 8.8, 8.0, 7.4 and 6.8. (b) The logarithm of the half-saturation
oxygen pressure (p_{50}) plotted as a function of pH. (c) Change in protons per mole
of oxygen bound (Data taken from Imai and Yonetani, 1975b).

The influence of the binding of one ligand upon the binding of another is
described as *linkage*, and thus there are two general kinds of ligand linkage,
homotropic and heterotropic. Either one may be either positive or negative:
positive when the binding of one ligand facilitates the binding of the other (or
next) ligand; and negative when the binding of one opposes the binding of the
other. In hemoglobin the position of the binding curve shifts with pH. The
shift, often depicted by a plot of $\log p_{50}$, the logarithm of the oxygen partial
pressure at half-saturation, versus the pH, as shown in Figure 1-3b, depends
on the difference in the amount of proton bound per mole of oxygen bound.
The slope of the plot of $\log p_{50}$ versus pH corresponds to change in the moles
of proton bound at each pH, as given in Figure 1-3c. In the physiological pH
range, the heterotropic linkage is negative. That is, the binding of protons
leads to the liberation of oxygen, and conversely the binding of oxygen leads
to the release of protons. The same phenomena can be characterized in terms

of the influence of oxygen pressure on the proton-binding curve. These sets of figures represent the functional chemistry of oxygen and proton binding to hemoglobin.

Such ideas regarding proton and oxygen linkage were first proposed by Bohr, Hasselbalch, and Krogh (1904), and the particular heterotropic linkage shown in Figure 1-3 is known as the *Bohr effect*. The physiological consequence of the proton-oxygen Bohr effect is that, as the blood circulates through the lungs, it picks up oxygen and gives off protons, thereby making the solution more acid. At the same time the blood gives off CO_2, which in turn lowers the acidity. The combination of these oxygen-linked effects keeps the pH of the blood nearly constant. The reverse effect, of course, operates in the tissues, where CO_2 is taken up, oxygen given off, and protons absorbed. Hemoglobin thus can also bind CO_2, and the binding process is linked to oxygenation. Actually, there are other ligands that affect oxygen binding as well. Chloride ion is one, and diphosphoglycerate is especially important in regulating the oxygen-binding process.

A particularly simple type of ligand linkage occurs when two different ligands bind competitively at the same site. This type of linkage is known as *identical linkage*. For example, the binding of carbon monoxide competes with the binding of oxygen to the heme irons in hemoglobin. A Hill plot representing this process under full saturation conditions graphs the logarithm of the ratio of sites filled with carbon monoxide to those filled with oxygen against the ratio of the respective partial pressures of the gases. With hemoglobin the replacement process is noncooperative under saturation conditions, as indicated by.the unit slope in the Hill plot of Figure 1-4.

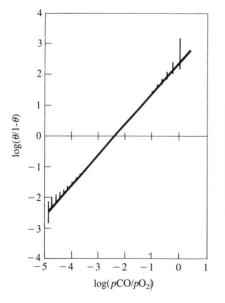

Figure 1-4.
Hill plot of the carbon monoxide replacement of oxygen in fully saturated human hemoglobin at pH 9.1, 25°C (Wyman *et al.*, 1982). Data points are represented by vertical lines of length given by four times the standard error of θ. Note how the error in the Hill plot is magnified at the ends.

(b) *Physical ligand linkage: Enthalpy and volume.* In addition to the linkage of chemical ligands to one another, there can also be physical linkage effects, where a physical parameter such as temperature or pressure influences the ligand-binding properties of a macromolecule. The parallel to ligand-linkage phenomena enables us to express all these phenomena from a common viewpoint. For example, the influence of temperature on the binding curve is controlled by the enthalpy changes of the binding reactions, as commonly expressed through the van't Hoff equation. You will readily see the parallel between the effect of temperature and the effect of a second ligand (e.g., protons) if you compare the shift in the oxygen-binding curves caused by changes in pH in Figure 1-3 to the temperature-induced shift shown in Figure 1-5.

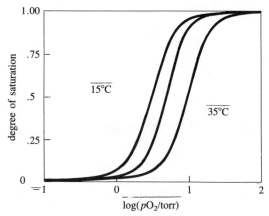

Figure 1-5.
Temperature dependence of the oxygen-binding curve for human hemoglobin at pH 7.4, 0.1 M Cl⁻ at 15°C, 25°C, and 35°C (adapted from Imai and Yonetani, 1975a).

Here the magnitude and direction of the shift of the binding curve with increase in temperature are determined by the negative enthalpy change for the reaction with oxygen. The analogous effect may be looked for if there is a change in pressure; the shift in the binding curve will depend on the change in volume for the oxygenation process.

(c) *Polysteric linkage.* So far we have tacitly assumed that the macromolecule does not dissociate or aggregate. There are many interesting natural phenomena in which ligand-binding effects are linked to the aggregation state of a system, a phenomenon called *polysteric linkage* (Colosimo et al., 1976). An example of polysteric linkage is the dissociation of the hemoglobin $\alpha_2\beta_2$ tetramer into two $\alpha\beta$ dimers, a process which is sensitive to both hemoglobin and oxygen concentration. This is illustrated in Figure 1-6 by the oxygen-saturation curves at different hemoglobin concentrations. At high concentrations the curves represent the cooperative binding of oxygen to the

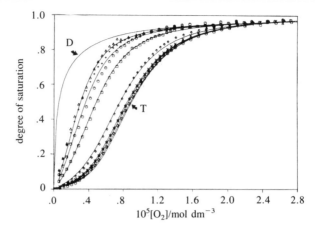

Figure 1-6.
Hemoglobin concentration dependence of the oxygen-saturation curve for human hemoglobin at pH 7.4, 0.1 M Cl$^-$, 21.5°C. Experiments performed for heme concentrations ranging from 10^{-8} M (left) to 10^{-4} M (Mills *et al.*, 1976).

tetramer (T), and at very low concentrations one approaches the curve for the dimer (D), which is apparently noncooperative.

(d) *Polyphasic linkage.* Another general type of linkage known as *polyphasic linkage* (Wyman and Gill, 1980) occurs where the system consists of two or more phases, such as solid and solution phases, and the relative amounts of the phases are sensitive to ligand concentration. A striking example of polyphasic linkage is that of oxygen binding to sickle-cell hemoglobin HbS, where at high HbS concentrations a gel phase will appear below a critical oxygen partial pressure. Curves for oxygen binding to sickle-cell hemoglobin under two different concentrations are shown in Figure 1-7. The left curve represents the system when it is dilute enough never to form the gel phase. The right curve for highly concentrated HbS shows the break (the crisis point) where the gel phase forms in increasing amounts as the oxygen pressure is reduced. In a broad sense, the solvent itself plays a principal role as a ligand in both polyphasic and polysteric processes.

(e) *Generalized linkage phenomena.* The chemistry of linked functions involves coupling various chemical reactions through their interaction with macromolecular systems. These may be studied under equilibrium, transient, or steady-state conditions. By all odds the most precise relations prevail under equilibrium conditions, such as those involved in the binding curves just presented, where the static system can be described in terms of thermodynamic potential theory, with all the power that it brings. This presents a contrast to time-dependent situations, where complex kinetic equations are required. For the latter analytical solutions are difficult, though usually possible. Although equilibrium is an ideal limiting case, the study of linkage under such condi-

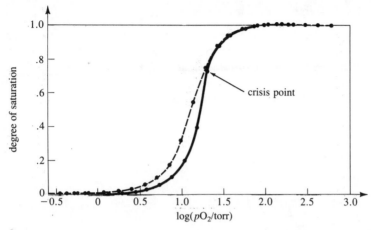

Figure 1-7.
Dotted line shows oxygen-binding curve of sickle hemoglobin HbS under non-gelling conditions (0.15 g/ml). Solid line shows the binding curve when concentration is high enough (0.3 g/ml) for polyphasic equilibrium effects to be seen as the gel phase forms (Wyman and Gill, 1980).

tions provides the background information needed to understand steady-state and transient behavior. This has been expressed eloquently by Segrè (1980):

> Thermodynamics has the same degree of certainty as its postulates. Reasoning in thermodynamics is often subtle, but is absolutely solid and conclusive. We shall see how Planck and Einstein built on it with absolute trust and how they considered thermodynamics the only absolutely firm foundation in which to build a physical theory. Whenever they were confronted by formidable obstacles they turned to it.

1.2 THE RELATION BETWEEN STRUCTURE AND FUNCTION

The complex functions of various macromolecular systems reflect the intrinsic properties of the macromolecules involved. Knowledge of the structure of the macromolecule has proven to be invaluable for understanding how ligands influence one another's binding, as mediated by the macromolecule. We have collected a gallery of macromolecules whose structural features suggest the basis for their functional properties. This is by no means an exhaustive list, but it will illustrate the subtle relationships between molecular form and function (the details of which must still be unraveled).

1.2.1   The Respiratory Proteins

(a) *Myoglobin.* The myoglobin molecule contains a single oxygen-binding site at a centrally located heme group. The oxygen-binding curve of this molecule has been shown in Figure 1-1, and the Hill plot reveals the simplicity of the binding process. The Hill plot, along with the graphic representation of the molecular structure of myoglobin and the oxygen binding site, is shown in Figure 1-8.

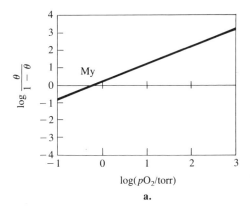

a.

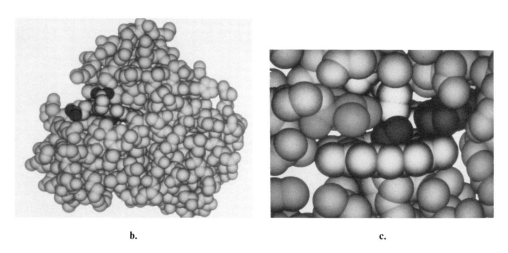

b.   c.

Figure 1-8.
Myoglobin: (a) Oxygen binding function depicted by Hill plot, data from Rossi-Fanelli and Antonini (1958); (b, c) Structural features represented by spaced filled models of complete molecule (b) and heme binding site filled with oxygen (c). Computer graphic pictures provided by John S. Olson, Rice University. Original structure determinations were made by Kendrew and coworkers (1961).

(b) *Hemoglobin A.* The human hemoglobin tetramer consists of four subunits, each roughly resembling an entire myoglobin molecule. Each subunit contains five stretches of α-helix that encompass the oxygen-binding heme group (Dickerson and Geis, 1983). A representation of the four subunit chains in the oxygenated state and the relatively complex Hill plot for oxygen binding are shown in Figure 1-9. The progressive increase in oxygen affinity with degree of oxygenation for hemoglobin seems to result from a change in the structure of the molecule, as shown in Figure 1-9. Consideration of such structural change permits us to explain the functional properties seen in the Hill plot by attributing different oxygen affinities to the different structural forms presumed to be in equilibrium in solution throughout the binding process. An explanation of this type is described as an *allosteric mechanism,* the simplest of which involves only two conformations. The large structural changes involving both translation and rotation between subunits are known as *quaternary* changes.* In general, where there is no change in molecular weight, the term *allosteric* (*allo* = different, *steric* = spatial) *change* is used to describe any structural change at any level, either within or between subunits. The term *allosteric* (Monod and Jacob, 1961) was originally used to describe long-range interaction between spatially remote ligand-binding sites mediated by the structure of a macromolecule. The concept has been broadened to describe ligand control of conformational equilibria.

(c) *Hemocyanins.* The first structure of a respiratory arthropod protein, spiny lobster hemocyanin of *Panulirus interruptus,* was solved in the laboratory of Wim Hol in 1984 (Gaykema *et al.*, 1984), and further refinement has been reported (Gaykema *et al.*, 1985) utilizing the sixfold symmetry of the hexamer. The oxygen binding occurs at a binuclear copper site surrounded by six histidines of the four alpha helices that form part of the polypeptide chain of one of the six subunits (Figure 1-10a on page 14). Each subunit, with a molecular weight of 75,000, consists of three domains of the polypeptide chain, but only one of these domains contains the oxygen-binding site (Figure 1-10b). Each subunit of the hexamer is in contact with four neighboring subunits (Figure 1-10c). Particularly well-fitting contacts occur between three pairs of subunits called the "dimers" of the hexamer. Less extensive contacts occur between three subunits described by a threefold axis of symmetry and called the "trimers" of the hexamer. The oxygen-binding cooperativity, shown in the form of a Hill plot in Figure 1-10d, presumably results from changes in the interaction between subunits as oxygen is bound, since a noncooperative Hill plot occurs when the subunits are dissociated.

The hexameric structure of panilirus hemocyanin seems to be the basic structural building block for higher aggregates found in other arthropod species. For example, the hemocyanin from the tarantula *Eurypelma californicum* is susceptible to preparation in various hexameric (some oligomers are

---

* For a discussion of primary, secondary, tertiary, and quaternary structures, consult Cantor and Schimmel (1980).

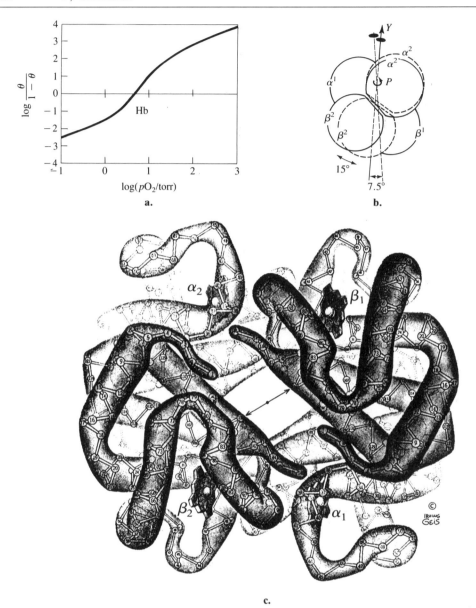

Figure 1-9.
Hemoglobin: (a) Function represented by Hill plot of oxygen binding results to
human hemoglobin (Imai and Yonetani, 1975a); (b) Gross structural changes of
α and β subunits upon deoxygenation (Baldwin and Chothia, 1979); (c, d) Detailed
structural change of subunit chains, viewed down the symmetry axes, for the oxy
(c) and deoxy (d) states, as determined by X-ray crystallography (Perutz, 1960), and
illustrated by Irving Geis (Dickerson and Geis, 1969, 1983); (e) Ribbon representation of the hemoglobin molecule (drawing by Jane Richardson, 1989).

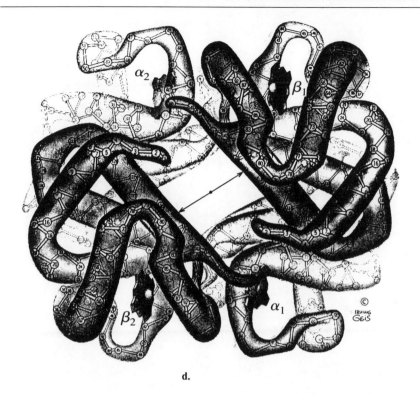

d.

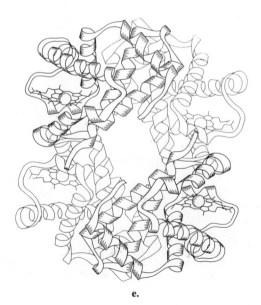

e.

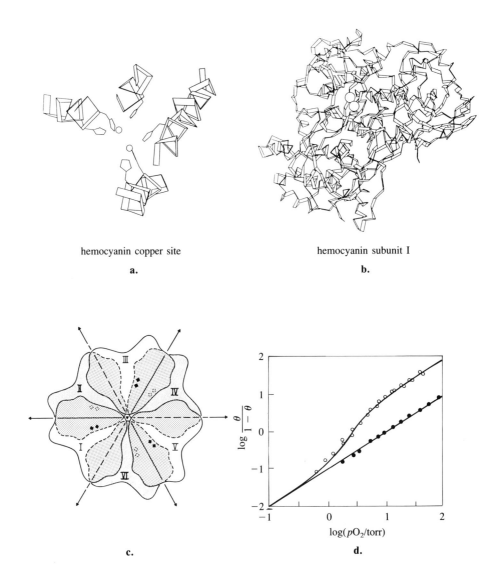

hemocyanin copper site

a.

hemocyanin subunit I

b.

c.

d.

Figure 1-10.
Structure and functional properties of the hemocyanin from the spiny lobster
Panulirus interruptus. Structure (Gaykema *et al.*, 1985): (a) dinuclear copper site
within one subunit; (b) backbone of single subunit; and (c) schematic arrangement
of six subunits which form the hexamer. Function: (d) Hill plot for oxygen binding
under hexamer conditions (pH 9.6 and 20°C in the presence of 10 mM $CaCl_2$) (○),
and dissociated subunit conditions (no $CaCl_2$) (●) (Kuiper *et al.*, 1977).

found with an additional subunit as well) aggregated forms, which show increasing cooperativity with increasing size of the aggregate (Figure 1-11).

Hemocyanins of even larger aggregates with an entirely different structural motif are found in mollusks. An electron micrograph of the hemocyanin from the snail *Helix pomatia* and a schematic representation of the subunit packing arrangement are shown in Figure 1-12. The basic polypeptide subunit is a string of eight dinuclear copper-containing binding sites (Figure 1-12a).

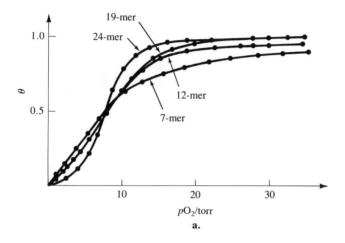

a.

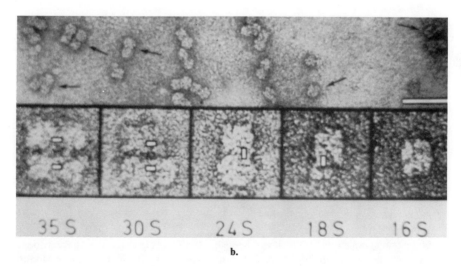

b.

Figure 1-11.
(a) Binding curves of tarantula *Eurypelma* Hc in different states of aggregation (Savel, 1984). (b) Electron micrographs under conditions which lead to particles with indicated sedimentation coefficients (Markl *et al.*, 1981).

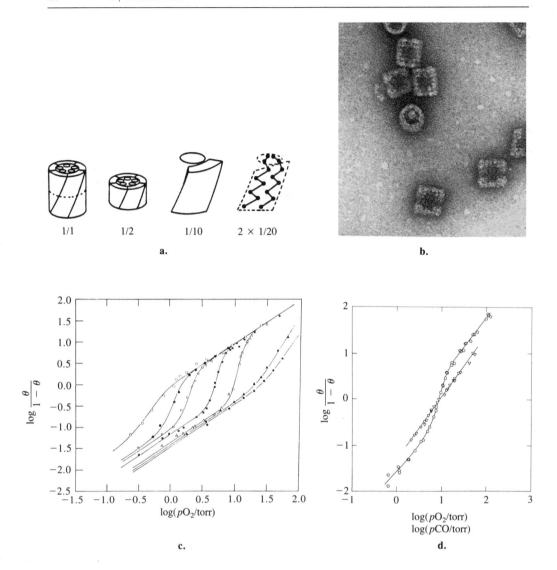

Figure 1-12.
Hemocyanin from the snail *Helix pomatia*: (a) a model representative for the subunit chain arrangement (E. F. J. van Bruggen, 1983); (b) electron micrograph (side
and end on views). Courtesy of E. F. J. van Bruggen. (c) Hill plots of oxygen binding
(β-Hc) as a function of pH (17 mM CaCl$_2$), ($\bigcirc$) pH 7.00, ($\bullet$) pH 7.04, ($\square$) pH 7.10,
($\blacksquare$) pH 7.18, ($\triangle$) pH 7.40, ($\blacktriangle$) pH 8.00, (*) pH 9.00 (Zolla *et al.*, 1978); (d) Hill plots
for α-Hc with different ligands ($\bigcirc$) oxygen, ($\triangle$) carbon monoxide (pH 8.2, 10 mM
CaCl$_2$) (Kuiper *et al.*, 1976).

Twenty of these polypeptide chains interact to build a unique structure with 160 oxygen-binding sites, as seen in an electron micrograph (Figure 1-12b). These large aggregates of oxygen-carrying sites are extremely sensitive to external conditions of pH and calcium-ion concentration. Hill plots of oxygen binding to the β-Hc of *Helix pomatia* as a function of pH are shown in Figure 1-12c. The Hill slope approaches values of nearly seven in some situations. A marked contrast exists between binding of oxygen and carbon monoxide. Figure 1-12d shows the large difference in cooperativity between O_2 and CO binding, which is actually quite typical of all hemocyanins. Carbon monoxide, which also binds with the same stoichiometry as O_2, does not promote significant structural changes.

The detection of aggregated states of different degrees for both the arthropod and the molluscan hemocyanins has been characterized by sedimentation properties, as summarized in Figure 1-13a (Bonaventura and

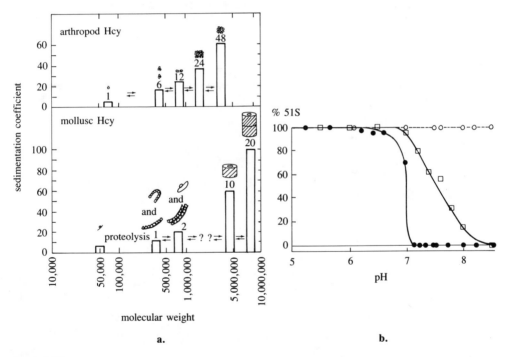

Figure 1-13.
(a) Dependence of sedimentation coefficients on various states of aggregation for typical arthropod and molluscan hemocyanins (Bonaventura and Bonaventura, 1980). (b) Dependence on pH of the amount of decameric (51S) *Octopus* aggregate in equilibrium with dimeric (20S) and monomeric (11S) forms: (○) with 10 mM Ca^{2+} and 50 mM Mg^{2+}; (●) without Ca^{2+} or Mg^{2+} ions, in air; (□) without Ca^{2+} or Mg^{2+}, deoxygenated (van Holde and Miller, 1986).

Bonaventura, 1980). It has sometimes been possible to study the equilibria between various forms. For example, the molluscan hemocyanin from *Octopus
dofleini* exists in the hemolymph as a decamer (51S) of subunits of a single
polypeptide chain of seven linked oxygen-binding sites (11S) (van Holde and
Miller, 1985). As seen in Figure 1-13b, the percent of the decamer is extremely
sensitive to pH; dissociation to dimer (22S) and monomer (11S) to various
extents depends also on the partial pressure of oxygen.

   (d) *Erythrocruorins*. Large aggregates of polypeptide chains that contain
heme oxygen-binding units have been found in annelids, such as earthworms.
The large molecular weight (4×10^6) particle (a double-layered hexagon) can
be dissociated into twelve particles, each of which consists of a hexameric
group of three polypeptide chains, only two of which contain hemes. Thus the
total number of oxygen-binding sites is 144. A model scheme of the aggregated
structure is shown in Figure 1-14a, and an electron micrograph of the
erythrocruorin molecules in a monolayer two-dimensional array is shown
in Figure 1-14b. The functional properties of oxygen binding are shown in
Figure 1-14c, illustrating the highly cooperative nature of the oxygen-binding
process achieved by this structure.

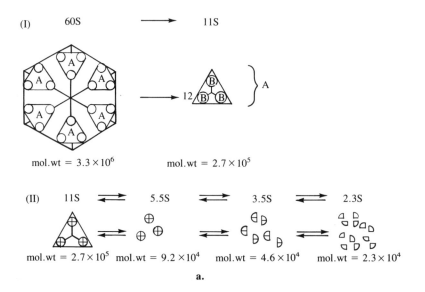

a.

Figure 1-14.
Erythrocruorin, the heme-containing respiratory protein from earthworms:
(a) model of subunit structure and dissociation scheme (Chiancone *et al.*, 1972);
(b) electron micrograph of crystalline monolayers (*Ophelia bicornis*) erythrocruorin
(Magaldi *et al.*, 1986); (c) Hill plots of oxygen binding to *octolasium complanatum*
erythrocruorin (Santucci *et al.*, 1984).

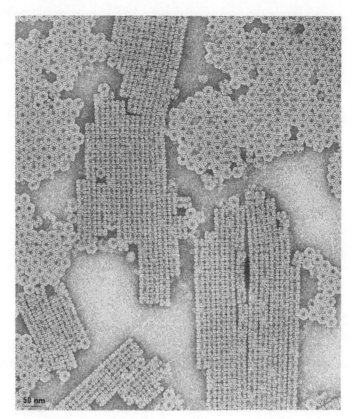

b.

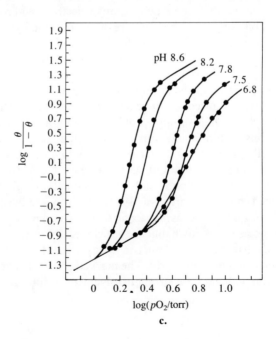

c.

19

(e) *Hemerythrin*. An entirely different non-heme, iron-containing protein also serves as an oxygen carrier. These are the hemerythrin proteins. Interestingly, the oxygen-binding site is a binuclear iron group with a μ-oxo bridge, and the iron atoms are coordinated to two carboxy and five histidine groups, somewhat as in the binuclear copper-binding site in hemocyanin. The active center is shown in Figure 1-15, along with a Hill plot of oxygen binding at several values of pH. A clear indication of positive cooperativity is found for this particular hemerythrin species, but in general, the cooperativity is low.

The respiratory proteins, due to their wide availability and simple function as oxygen carriers, have served as key examples in broadening our understanding of linkage and binding properties of multi-subunit proteins.

1.2.2 Electron-Binding Proteins

A variety of proteins play important roles in oxidation-reduction processes, where the electron plays the role of a control ligand. For example, the heme-centered cytochromes serve as active participants in electron-transport processes. For many of these, we do not yet know much about the electron-binding processes, or how they depend on solution conditions and other ligands. The structure of cytochrome c from tuna fish shows conformational changes in its reduced and oxidized form. The principal side chains that move in the vicinity of the heme are shown in Figure 1-16. Electromotive force measurements as a function of pH show that different acid and base groups are strongly involved with the electron-binding process.

Four-heme cytochromes have been found to exhibit oxidation-reduction properties that suggest cooperative electron-binding effects between the different binding sites. The structure of one of these, cytochrome c_3 from the sulfate-reducing bacterium *Desulfovibrio desulfuricans*, is shown in Figure 1-17, along with an electron-binding curve. The observed binding curve is less steep than the symmetric reference curve generated for identical binding sites, and shows that the binding is noncooperative.

Oxidation-reduction processes are involved in the iron-storage process, in which the multisubunit protein ferritin is able to carry as many as 4,500 iron atoms within a single protein molecule. The protein consists of a spherical shell composed of 24 structurally equivalent polypeptide subunits with an internal cavity of about 80 Å diameter. Access to the interior is by either six equivalent hydrophobically lined channels or eight equivalent hydrophilically lined channels (Ford *et al.*, 1984). The iron is taken from solution in the ferrous form and stored as the ferric form. The nature of the oxidation-reduction process is unknown, but the stoichiometry of the iron-storage process can be established by coulometric measurements of the oxidation process, as indicated in Figure 1-18. The marked pH dependence of the electron binding again indicates the strong involvement or linkage of protons in this process.

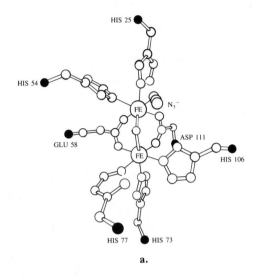

a.

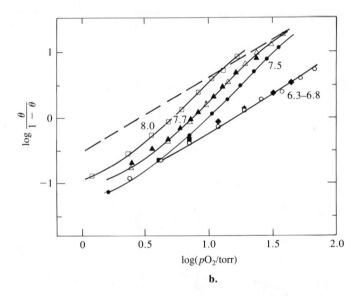

b.

Figure 1-15.
(a) X-ray structure of active center of hemerythrin (azidomet) (Sheriff *et al.*, 1982).
(b) Hill plot of oxygen binding to the native octamer form of *Lingula reevii* hemerythrin at indicated pH values in phosphate buffer at 23°C (Richardson *et al.*, 1983).

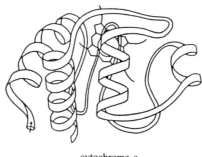

cytochrome c

a.

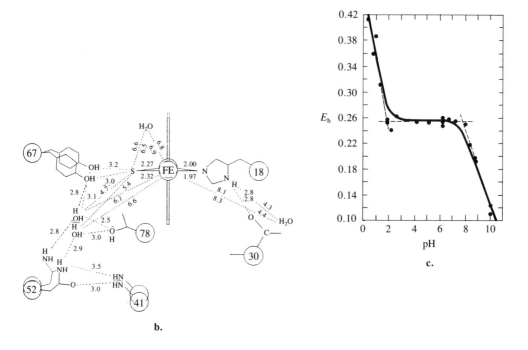

b.

c.

Figure 1-16.
(a) Main chain of ferrocytochrome c with central heme (drawing by Jane Richardson).
(b) Schematic drawing of side-chain motion for cytochrome c in the region of the heme for reduced form (heavy lines) and oxidized form (light lines) including hydrogen bond (----) and inter-atomic distances (····) (Takano and Dickerson, 1981).
(c) Dependence of oxidation potential on pH (Rodkey and Ball, 1950).

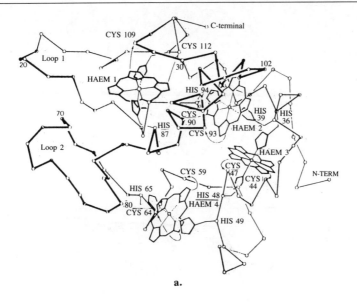

a.

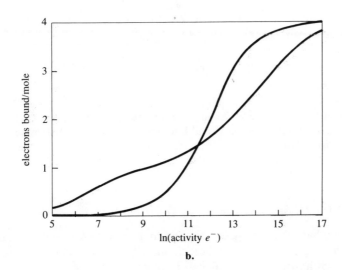

b.

Figure 1-17.
(a) Three-dimensional structure of cytochrome c_3 from *Desulfovibrio desulfuricans*
(Haser *et al.*, 1979). (b) The undulating electron-binding curves to the four
heme groups which bind electrons independently were generated from half-potentials
of $-170\,mV$, $-310\,mV$, $-360\,mV$, and $-400\,mV$ by Bianco and Haladjian (1981).
The symmetric reference curve shows how electrons would bind to identical binding
sites. The logarithm of the electron activity is also given by $-FE/RT$, where E is the
applied potential.

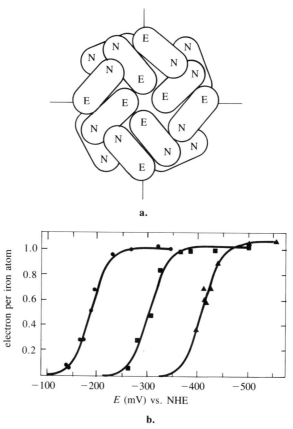

a.

b.

Figure 1-18.
(a) Model of ferritin molecule viewed down a molecular fourfold axis. Each of 24 subunits is labeled at ends as N and E to indicate location of N-terminal and carboxyl terminal of polypeptide chain (Ford *et al.*, 1984). (b) Coulometric determination of the oxidation process that occurs as ferric iron is stored within the ferritin molecule (Watt *et al.*, 1985).

1.2.3   Other Allosteric Systems

Structural changes upon ligand binding first revealed by x-ray crystallography for hemoglobin have now been found for several other proteins. These findings emphasize the general nature of structure and of ligand control. Hexokinase undergoes a significant conformational change when complexed with glucose (Bennett and Steitz, 1978). The structure has been solved in the presence and absence of glucose, and shows movements of the polypeptide backbone as large as 8 Å. The conformational change presumably facilitates the enzymatic reaction, in which the glucose is phosphorylated. The structure in the two conformations (with and without glucose) is depicted in Figure 1-19. The functional stability of the protein changes in the presence of glucose, as is revealed by scanning calorimetry in the presence and the absence of glucose (Takahashi *et al.*, 1981).

24

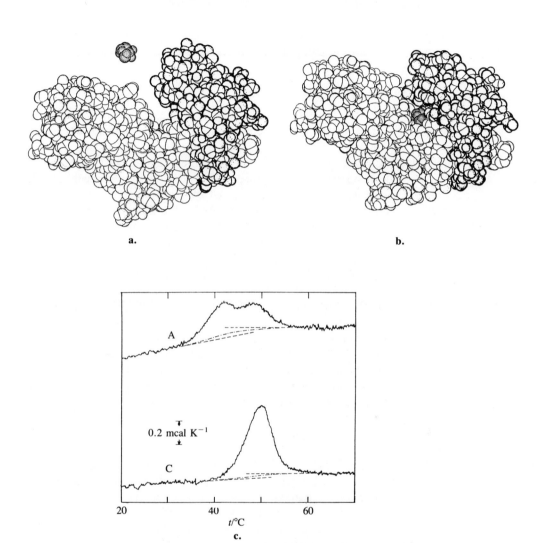

Figure 1-19.
Structural change of hexokinase in the absence (a) and presence (b) of glucose.
The shaded lobe moves to virtually enclose the glucose molecule (Bennett and Steitz, 1980). (c) Thermal denaturation of hexokinase as revealed by heat capacity measurements in the absence (A) and presence (C) of 20 mM glucose with approximately 2 mg of protein per mL (Takahashi *et al.*, 1981). The two thermal peaks in the absence of glucose indicate different stability and possible independence of the two lobes, while the single peak in the presence of glucose indicates a cooperative melting of the whole molecule under such conditions.

One of the most striking examples of structural change mediated by ligand control is that of aspartate transcarbamylase. The gross structural changes are indicated for this multiple subunit protein in Figure 1-20, along with some of the physical and enzymatic property changes that occur through ligand binding under various solution conditions.

1.2.4 Nucleic-Acid Binding Processes

Regulatory proteins involved in molecular reproduction involve a series of allosteric control mechanisms. The lac repressor protein, which binds to the lac operon region of DNA, is allosterically controlled by the presence of the sugar lactose, or of its more conveniently studied analog, IPTG (isopropyl-β,D-thiogalactoside) (O'Gorman et al., 1980). The functional chemistry of this macromolecule is quantitatively illustrated by the binding curve shown in Figure 1-21 for IPTG binding under reversible conditions in the presence and absence of operator fragment. The system shows distinct positive co-operativity in the presence of operon; hence this suggests there are allosteric structural changes that are controlled by ligand concentration. Although structural details of the lac repressor DNA complex are still unknown, structures of other DNA complexes such as the Cro protein (Takeda et al., 1983) and the tryptophan repressor complex (Zhang et al., 1987) have been solved, and some of their interesting features are shown in Figure 1-21c. The formation of these complex structures is mediated by small control ligands.

Cooperative interactions have been revealed between repressor molecules bound to adjacent operators, allowing fine control of the associated gene expression. Examination of specific site binding has been possible by special methods developed by Ackers and coworkers (1983). A schematic diagram of the equilibria between repressors and the three operator sites is shown in Figure 1-22a, and the repressor binding curves for each of the three operator sites are shown in Figure 1-22b.

Structural transitions in both DNA and double-helical RNA can be induced by binding of cationic ligands. In the most extreme cases the actual handedness of the helix changes, as is revealed by circular dichroic studies. In Figure 1-23 the right-handed B form and left-handed Z form of DNA are shown, and the dependence of the fraction of molecules in each form is shown as a function of salt concentration.

The widespread existence of ligand-controlled structural transitions is also revealed for proteins and nucleic acids by the use of temperature-scanning measurements (Privalov, 1979), which measure the excess heat capacity of the macromolecule as a function of temperature; when the molecule undergoes a conformational change, there is a significant increase in the heat capacity. The shape of such curves reveals the cooperative nature of the transition process. A complex allosteric situation is exposed by the

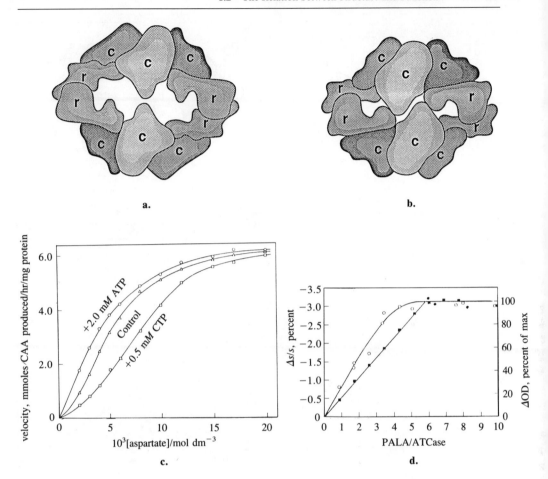

Figure 1-20.
Structural and functional properties of aspartate transcarbamylase are regulated by
conversion of allosteric forms upon ligand binding. A gross allosteric change from
the T (a) to the R (b) conformation occurs upon binding of PALA, a substrate that
mimics carbamyl phosphate and aspartate, to its binding site on one of the six catalytic chains (designated by c). (Drawings from W. N. Lipscomb, Harvard.) The six
regulatory chains (designated by r) provide further enzymatic control through binding of allosteric effectors ATP and CTP (Kantrowitz and Lipscomb, 1988). This is
seen in (c), where the velocity of the reaction as a function of aspartate is lowered in
the presence of CTP but raised in the presence of ATP with attendant changes in
cooperativity (Gerhart, 1970). The lack of synchrony of the allosteric changes upon
PALA binding is shown in (d) by careful sedimentation measurements ($\bigcirc$) that
follow a complex curve, while the optical changes ($\square$) accompanying substrate binding follow a simple linear curve (Howlett and Schachman, 1977).

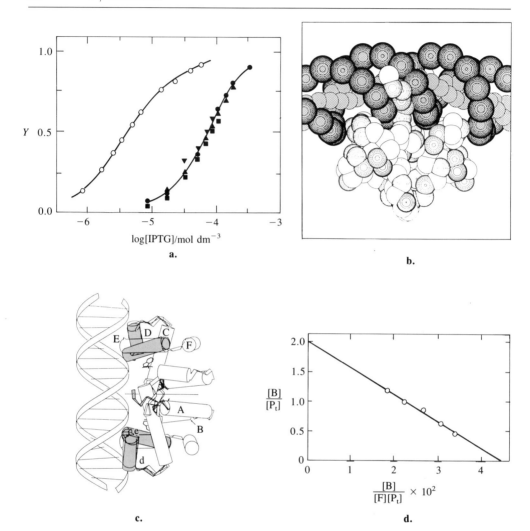

Figure 1-21.
(a) Binding plots of inducer (isopropylthiogalactoside, IPTG) binding to lac repressor protein, a tetrameric molecule, in the presence (filled symbols) and absence
(open symbols) of DNA operator fragment (O'Gorman *et al.*, 1980). The cooperativity is enhanced with the presence of the operator fragment. (b) The structure of lac
repressor is unknown but structural details of a smaller dimeric protein, Cro, that also
binds to DNA and represses transcription, are shown in a possible mode of binding
to DNA (Takeda *et al.*, 1983). (c) The structure of trp repressor, another DNA binding protein, has been solved under various ligand conditions and is shown in two
configurations in the presence and absence (grey shading) of L-tryptophan.
Enhanced contact of reading heads to DNA occurs in the presence of the tryptophan control ligand (Zhang *et al.*, 1987). (d) Scatchard plot of L-tryptophan binding
to trp aporepressor in the absence of DNA. The intercept of 2 signifies two binding
sites and straight line fit shows each site binds independently with the same binding
constant. The following symbols define the plot: B, bound ligand; F, free ligand;
P_t, protein concentration (Avidson *et al.*, 1986). Unit of concentration is one μM.

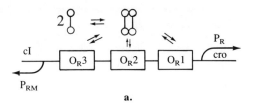

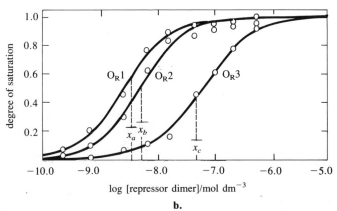

Figure 1-22.
(a) Schematic representation of interactions of bacteriophage λ repressor molecules
($\bigcirc-\bigcirc$) with the three binding sites of the right operator in the bacteriophage
lambda (Ackers *et al.*, 1982). (b) Repressor binding curves for each site (Ackers *et al.*,
1983) O_R1, O_R2, and O_R3 as measured by footprinting autoradiograms. Solid
curves are calculated from theoretical interaction model.

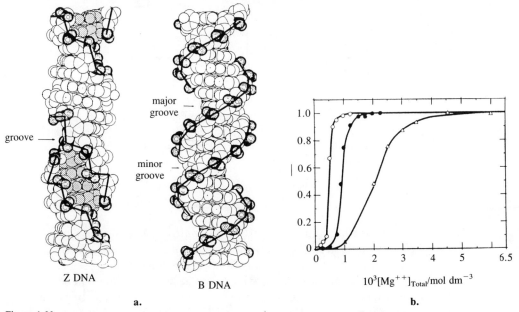

Figure 1-23.
(a) Right-handed (B form) and left-handed (Z form) structures of the DNA double
helix (Rich *et al.*, 1984). (b) Mg^{++} dependence of extent of conversion from B to Z
form at 40°C ($\triangle$), 25°C ($\bullet$) and 10°C ($\bigcirc$) (Chaires, 1986).

29

temperature-scanning curves in Figure 1-24 for tRNA, which shows the presence of multiple transitions between various allosteric forms. The populations of underlying allosteric species are affected in a complex way by different magnesium-ion concentrations. The structure of the low-temperature magnesium-stabilized form is shown in Figure 1-24 (left). The form of higher-temperature intermediates is unknown.

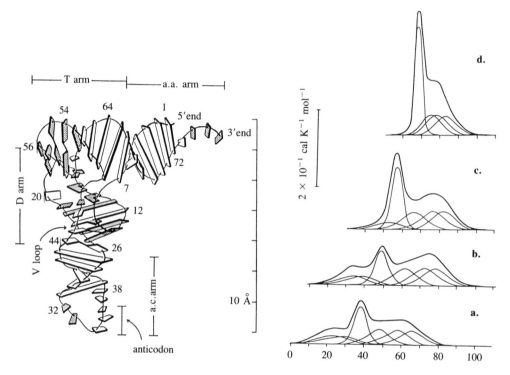

Figure 1-24.
Structure of t-RNA (left) (Kim, 1978) with scanning calorimetry trace of denaturation process (right) indicating multiple transition species under different salt conditions: (a) salt-free; (b) 150 mM NaCl; (c) 150 mM NaCl and 1 mM $MgCl_2$; and (d) 1 mM $MgCl_2$ (Privalov, 1976).

At an even higher level of structural control, one finds the regulation of the nucleosome structure of chromatin. Here histone subunits (H1, H2, H1A, H2A) aggregate to form an octameric core, which provides an extensive binding site around the octamer on which double-stranded DNA can be wrapped with a single turn. The formation of this octamer core has been shown to be a cooperative process (Benedict et al., 1984). One can well imagine that the cooperative assembly of the core and the binding of the DNA is subject to environmental control in accordance with the needs of the cell.

1.3   SUMMARY

In this introductory chapter we have seen how the functional properties of biological molecules are controlled through ligand-binding processes. The regulation and cooperativity interaction between distant binding sites is mediated by sensitive modulation of different structural forms available to the macromolecular complex. Specific conformations provide unique surfaces and forms for enzymatic reactions, for aggregation to higher-order molecular complexes, and for selected binding of various ligands. In a broad sense the macromolecule functions as a molecular transducer, responding to the presence of control ligands and modulating a set of subsequent reaction processes. In subsequent chapters we shall be concerned with quantitative formulation of the principles involved in describing binding reactions and allosteric changes, in order to arrive at models that can be invoked to explain experimental observations.

Properties of Binding Curves 2

The functional chemistry of macromolecules is described by their binding reactions. In order to describe these reactions, we examine the relation between the amount of ligand bound, at various activities of the ligand, expressed in the form of binding curves. The interpretation of binding curves in terms of fundamental equilibrium equations is then the first step in obtaining a quantitative analysis of the binding processes. We shall first consider some of the properties of binding curves that result from binding ligands to macromolecules with one or two binding sites. Here we limit ourselves to reversible binding describable by the law of mass action. In this chapter we shall give an elementary treatment of the quantitative nature of binding processes for some special cases. In this way we hope to set the stage for a more detailed and general treatment of linkage phenomena to come later.

2.1 BINDING OF LIGAND X TO A SINGLE SITE

The reaction of oxygen to myoglobin is a reaction between a small molecule (the ligand) and a macromolecule with a single binding site. The site of the reaction is at the heme group, as shown in Figure 2-1. What type of binding curve is predicted for such a reaction? Let us denote the macromolecule by M and the ligand by X. The reaction equation is written as

$$M + X \rightarrow MX. \tag{2.1}$$

The mass-action law gives the equilibrium constant K for this reaction in terms of the species activities a_X, a_M, and a_{MX}:

$$K = \frac{a_{MX}}{a_M a_X}. \tag{2.2}$$

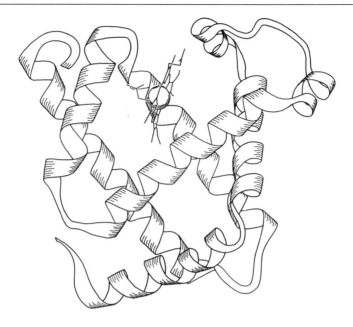

Figure 2-1.
Structure of myoglobin, showing the oxygen-binding site at the heme.
Courtesy of Jane Richardson.

We assume that the ratio of activities of M and MX is determined by the ratio of their concentrations, $[MX]/[M]$, and that the equilibrium constant can be written as

$$K = \frac{[MX]}{[M]x},$$

(2.3)

where for brevity we replace a_X with x.

The degree of binding, $\bar{X}$, is defined by the moles of X bound per mole of macromolecule. Here we derive it from the concentrations $[M]$ and $[MX]$ as

$$\bar{X} = \frac{[MX]}{[M] + [MX]}.$$

(2.4)

Replacing $[MX]$ by equation (2.3) gives

$$\bar{X} = \frac{Kx}{1 + Kx},$$

(2.5)

or, upon rearrangement,

$$\frac{\bar{X}}{1 - \bar{X}} = Kx. \tag{2.6}$$

These are the simple relations between the amount of ligand bound and the ligand activity for a single site reaction. The form of equation (2.5) shows that, at low x, $\bar{X} \rightarrow 0$, and at large x, $\bar{X} \rightarrow 1$. Further, at half-saturation, i.e., when $\bar{X} = 1/2$, then $Kx_{(1/2)} = 1$. The value of the activity $x_{(1/2)}$ at half-saturation provides a convenient definition of K. These properties are illustrated in Figure 2-2.

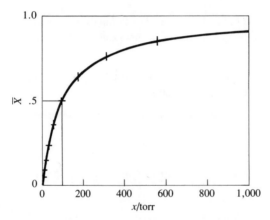

Figure 2-2.
Single-site X-binding curve showing hyperbolic relation between $\bar{X}$ and ligand activity, x. Note that the reciprocal of the half-saturation activity $x_{1/2}$ gives the binding constant K, in this case, 0.0100 torr^{-1}. The vertical error lines at chosen points represent an error of ± 0.02 in $\bar{X}$.

As we saw in the first chapter, there are other ways of displaying binding curves (Edsall and Wyman, 1958). The plot shown in Figure 2-2 gives one branch of a rectangular hyperbola. Taking the reciprocal of equation (2.5) gives the form

$$\frac{1}{\bar{X}} = 1 + \frac{1}{K}\frac{1}{x}. \tag{2.7}$$

This results in the double reciprocal plot made by plotting $1/\bar{X}$ versus $1/x$. This plot is linear, with a slope of $1/K$, as seen in Figure 2-3.

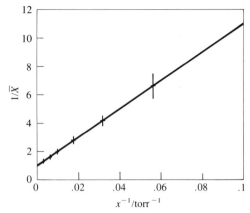

Figure 2-3.
Double reciprocal plot: $1/\bar{X}$ versus $1/x$. Simulation of same data as given in Figure 2-2. Note how length of error lines differs in this mode of plotting.

Scatchard (1949) employed a different type of plot, obtained by multiplying equation (2.6) by $(1 - \bar{X})/x$, which gives

$$\frac{\bar{X}}{x} = K - K\bar{X}. \tag{2.8}$$

A plot of $\bar{X}/x$ as the ordinate against $\bar{X}$ as the abscissa gives a straight line, as seen in Figure 2-4.

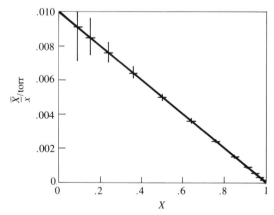

Figure 2-4.
The Scatchard plot, $\bar{X}/x$ versus $\bar{X}$, is linear for single-site reaction with a slope of $-K$ and intercepts of 1 and K. Error range on points corresponds to fixed error of ± 0.02 in $\bar{X}$ as given in Figure 2-2.

The fraction of sites filled is given by $\bar{X}$, and the fraction of sites empty is given by $1 - \bar{X}$, for a single-site reaction. The ratio of filled to empty sites is then $\bar{X}/(1 - \bar{X})$, and by equation (2.6) this is equal to Kx. A plot of $\bar{X}/(1 - \bar{X})$

versus x is thus linear with the slope of K. This mode of plotting is shown in Figure 2-5.

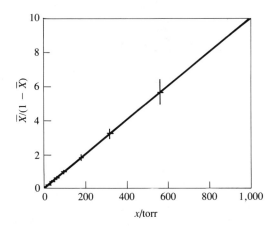

Figure 2-5.
Plot of the ratio of filled ($\bar{X}$) and empty sites ($1 - \bar{X}$) versus the ligand activity x. The slope of the plot gives K.

The Hill plot (Hill, 1910) is obtained by plotting $\log(\bar{X}/(1 - \bar{X}))$ against $\log x$. As seen by equation (2.6) for a single-site reaction, we have

$$\log\frac{\bar{X}}{1 - \bar{X}} = \log K + \log x. \qquad (2.9)$$

This relation gives a straight line with a slope of unity, as seen in Figure 2-6.

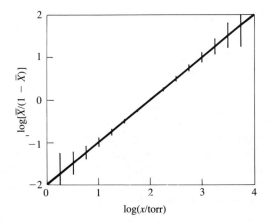

Figure 2-6.
Hill plot of a single-site reaction. The logarithm of the ratio of filled ($\bar{X}$) to unfilled sites ($1 - \bar{X}$) is plotted against the logarithm of the ligand activity x. Note how the error increases greatly in the end regions when the data are plotted in this way.

The most fundamental representation of the binding curve is obtained by a plot of $\bar{X}$ versus $\log x$, because the logarithm of the ligand activity is proportional to the chemical potential of the ligand. We might call this way of plotting the *titration binding curve*, since the data are typically obtained by a titration experiment in which the amount of ligand bound, for example, protons, is plotted against the pH as acid or base is added to the system. The data used in the previous examples along with error bars are plotted in this way in Figure 2-7.

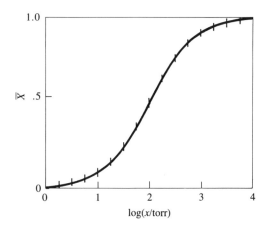

Figure 2-7.
Titration binding curve obtained by plotting $\bar{X}$ versus $\log x$ for a single-site reaction where $K = 0.01$. Error of data points is ± 0.02 in $\bar{X}$. Compare with plots shown in Figures 2-2 through 2-6.

All these plots are merely different illustrations of the mass law for the simplest case, that of a one-site macromolecule. The different types of plots bring out different features of the underlying binding processes. As we shall see in further development, the Hill plot and the normal titration curve ($\bar{X}$ versus $\log x$) depict directly the cooperativity and thermodynamic functional chemistry of macromolecular binding processes.

Values of $\bar{X}$ are obtained from experiments in several ways: (1) where there is a change in absorption spectra when the binding of X occurs, (2) by dialysis measurements where the concentration bound is indicated by the difference in ligand concentration between the two sides of the dialysis cell, or (3) by titration results using suitable electrodes to measure ligand activity. The activity x is given quite closely by the free concentration of X; for a gas the activity is given by its partial pressure, or for an ion the activity may be measured with a suitable ion-sensitive electrode. As a general principle, to measure the activity of a ligand, we must introduce another phase, such as a gas, dialyzate, or electrode, in equilibrium with the system, and in which the measurement of the ligand activity can be made.

2.2   BINDING OF LIGAND X TO A MACROMOLECULE CONTAINING TWO SITES

As we have seen, myoglobin, with its single heme oxygen-binding site, has provided an important biological example of a single-site reaction. Other heme proteins contain multiple subunits that perform specific biochemical functions. An interesting species of molecules thought to be involved in electron transport is the cytochromes c′ from the photosynthetic bacteria (Bartsch, 1978). They are typically dimeric with two heme binding sites. A high-resolution structure of one of these was worked out by Weber and Salemme (1982), and is shown schematically in Figure 2-8. There are two

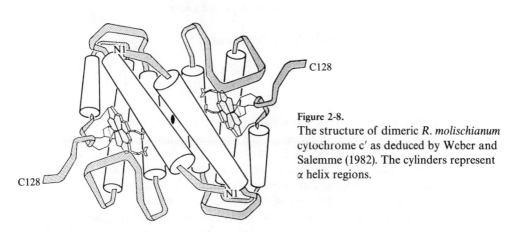

Figure 2-8.
The structure of dimeric *R. molischianum* cytochrome c′ as deduced by Weber and Salemme (1982). The cylinders represent α helix regions.

ligand-binding reactions for such a molecule. These give rise to stepwise reactions with constants K_1 and K_2 described as

$$M + X \rightarrow MX, \qquad K_1 = \frac{[MX]}{[M]x},$$

$$\tag{2.10}$$

$$MX + X \rightarrow MX_2, \qquad K_2 = \frac{[MX_2]}{[MX]x}.$$

Alternatively, we can describe the binding process in terms of overall reactions to the unreacted macromolecule by constants β_1 and β_2 defined as

$$M + X \rightarrow MX, \qquad \beta_1 = \frac{[MX]}{[M]x},$$

$$\tag{2.11}$$

$$M + 2X \rightarrow MX_2, \qquad \beta_2 = \frac{[MX_2]}{[M]x^2}.$$

The two representations are related by $K_1 = \beta_1$ and $K_1 K_2 = \beta_2$.

The moles of X bound per macromolecule M in all forms gives the degree of binding,

$$\bar{X} = \frac{[MX] + 2[MX_2]}{[M] + [MX] + [MX_2]}. \tag{2.12}$$

The factor 2 arises because two moles of X are bound for each mole of MX_2. In terms of the stepwise reactions (2.10), we find

$$\bar{X} = \frac{K_1 x + 2K_1 K_2 x^2}{1 + K_1 x + K_1 K_2 x^2}. \tag{2.13}$$

Likewise in terms of the overall reactions (2.10) we obtain

$$\bar{X} = \frac{\beta_1 x + 2\beta_2 x^2}{1 + \beta_1 x + \beta_2 x^2}. \tag{2.14}$$

Either of these two equations describes how the amount of X bound varies with activity of X in terms of the reaction constants. There is no simple algebraic manipulation, such as we found for single-site reactions, which yields a linear plot. We can evaluate the binding constants, however, by nonlinear data-fitting methods. Furthermore, we can prepare Hill plots (or Scatchard plots) that allow evaluation of the binding parameters.

The Hill plot is formed by taking the ratio of sites filled to sites empty; for two sites, this is $\bar{X}/(2 - \bar{X})$. In terms of the ligand activity the ratio is found from equation (2.13) as

$$\frac{\bar{X}}{2 - \bar{X}} = \frac{K_1 x + 2K_1 K_2 x^2}{2 + K_1 x}. \tag{2.15}$$

At low saturations, i.e., $x \to 0$, we obtain the ratio

$$\frac{\bar{X}}{2 - \bar{X}} = \frac{1}{2} K_1 x, \tag{2.16}$$

and at high saturation, i.e., $x \to \infty$, we obtain

$$\frac{\bar{X}}{2 - \bar{X}} = 2K_2 x. \tag{2.17}$$

The Hill plot, formed by taking $\log \bar{X}/(2 - \bar{X})$ versus $\log x$, thus becomes linear at these extremes, with y-axis intercepts of $\log((1/2)K_1)$ and $\log(2K_2)$ for these low- and high-saturation asymptotes. Such results are illustrated in Figure 2-9. The Hill plot becomes linear, i.e., the asymptotes become the

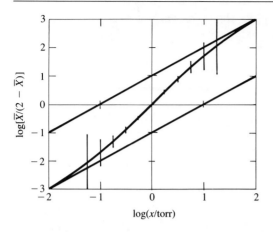

Figure 2-9.
Hill plot for a two-site macromolecule showing the passage from a lower to a higher asymptote. Note that the lower asymptote is determined by $(1/2)K_1$ and the higher asymptote by $2K_2$. In this plot $(1/2)K_1 = 0.1$ and $2K_2 = 10$. Error range of points is indicated for error in $\bar{X}$ of ± 0.02.

same, when $(1/2)K_1$ is equal to $2K_2$. At half-saturation $\bar{X} = 1$ and the ratio $\bar{X}/(2 - \bar{X}) = 1$. The ligand activity at this point is denoted by $x_{1/2}$, and from either (2.14) or (2.15) we find

$$\beta_2 x_{1/2}^2 = 1$$

or (2.18)

$$K_1 K_2 x_{1/2}^2 = 1.$$

One final point is to note the symmetry of both the titration curve and the Hill plot about $x_{1/2}$. This is a necessary property of a two-site macromolecule. A Hill plot of oxygen binding to a dimeric hemoglobin found in the bivalve mollusk *Scapharca inaequivalvis* shows a high cooperativity (Hill-plot slope of approximately 1.5) and a symmetric shape, which is necessary for a two-site reaction (see Figure 2-10).

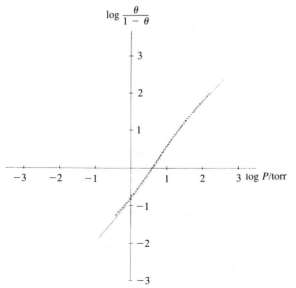

Figure 2-10.
Hill plot of O_2 binding a dimeric clam hemoglobin (Ikeda-Saito, *et al.*, 1983).

2.3   THE BINDING PARTITION FUNCTION OR BINDING POLYNOMIAL

Binding reactions are conveniently described by means of the binding partition function. This partition function represents the sum of the concentrations of all the different macromolecular species found in the system relative to some reference species, such as the unligated form. We shall denote the partition function by Q, and describe the concentrations of the various ligated states of the macromolecule by the bracketed terms as

$$Q = \frac{[M] + [MX] + [MX_2] + \cdots}{[M]}. \tag{2.19}$$

This expression is equivalent to the denominator of the extent-of-binding equation [e.g., equation (2.14)]. For the single-site reaction in equation (2.5), Q is given as

$$Q = 1 + Kx. \tag{2.20}$$

For two-site reactions [see (2.13) and (2.14)], we obtain

$$Q = 1 + K_1 x + K_1 K_2 x^2 = 1 + \beta_1 x + \beta_2 x^2. \tag{2.21}$$

These equations for Q are polynomials in x; hence for this situation Q is called *the binding polynomial* and expressed by the symbol P. The concentrations of the various species relative to the unligated species are given by the successive terms of the polynomial.

The ligand-binding curve is obtained from the derivative of the binding polynomial P. Specifically, the degree of binding, $\bar{X}$, is found by taking the derivative of $\ln P$ with respect to $\ln x$. (Strictly, we should use the partial derivative, since β_1, etc. will depend on other variables, such as temperature, pressure, and other ligand activities; but for simplicity we shall assume these other variables are fixed.) Then

$$\bar{X} = \frac{d \ln P}{d \ln x} = \frac{x}{P} \frac{dP}{dx}. \tag{2.22}$$

For the single-site binding polynomial, this differentiation is carried out explicitly as follows:

$$\bar{X} = \frac{d \ln(1 + Kx)}{d \ln x} = \frac{x}{1 + Kx}\left(\frac{d(1 + Kx)}{dx}\right) = \frac{Kx}{1 + Kx}. \tag{2.23}$$

Thus we recover the same result as in equation (2.5). Similar operation on the binding polynomial for two sites ($P = 1 + \beta_1 x + \beta_2 x^2$) yields equation (2.14).

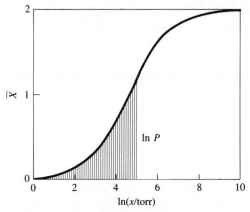

Figure 2-11.
General titration curve for a two-site macromolecule, showing the relation between the area under the binding curve (A_u) and the logarithm of the binding polynomial (P).

The reverse operation, namely, the integration of $\bar{X}$ with respect to $\ln x$, must give $\ln P$. This is graphically represented by the area under the binding curve, as seen in Figure 2-11. Integration of equation (2.22) from $x = 0$ to x gives $\ln P$ as follows:

$$\int_{-\infty}^{\ln x} \bar{X}\, d\ln x = \int_{0}^{\ln P} d\ln P = \ln P = A_u, \tag{2.24}$$

where A_u is the area under the binding curve. The partition function is then given by the exponential of A_u:

$$P = e^{A_u}. \tag{2.25}$$

The partition function is also directly related to the fraction of unligated macromolecule denoted by α_0. This fraction, α_0, is the reciprocal of the partition function:

$$\alpha_0 = \frac{1}{P}. \tag{2.26}$$

Since the area under the ligand binding curve, A_u, is related logarithmically to P, we may write

$$A_u = \ln P = -\ln \alpha_0; \tag{2.27}$$

so the fraction α_0 falls off exponentially with A_u as

$$\alpha_0 = e^{-A_u}. \tag{2.28}$$

This equation shows that when the area under the curve is small, i.e., at small x, α_0 approaches unity, showing that nearly all the macromolecules are unligated. As x becomes larger, A_u increases, and α_0 declines, until at high saturations α_0 disappears.

More generally, the fractions of species of macromolecules with i ligands bound are proportional to their represented terms in P. Thus

$$\alpha_i = \frac{\beta_i x^i}{P}. \tag{2.29}$$

This expression shows that the fraction of the fully ligated form increases to 1 as $x \to \infty$, and intermediate forms pass through a maximum value at some intermediate value of x. For a single site, the unligated fraction is $\alpha_0 = 1/(1 + Kx)$, which is the same as $1 - \bar{X}$, and the ligated fraction is $\alpha_1 = Kx/(1 + Kx)$, which is the same as $\bar{X}$. The logarithm of the ratio α_1/α_0 leads directly to the Henderson-Hasselbalch equation for proton binding to single sites, which is the same as a simple titration curve.

2.4   INDEPENDENT-SITE BINDING REACTIONS

The binding polynomial given in equation (2.21) describes general two-site binding reactions. There is a simple class of reactions where each reaction is assumed to be independent of the other. Consider an example in which two sites (denoted by subscripts a and b) bind independently of each other, each with a single-site binding constant, given by κ_a and κ_b. Then the total amount of X bound per unit of macromolecule, i.e., $\bar{X}$, is the sum of the amount bound to each site, which is described by its appropriate single-site binding reaction, i.e.,

$$\bar{X} = \frac{\kappa_a x}{1 + \kappa_a x} + \frac{\kappa_b x}{1 + \kappa_b x}. \tag{2.30}$$

When this is multiplied out, we see

$$\bar{X} = \frac{(\kappa_a + \kappa_b)x + 2\kappa_a\kappa_b x^2}{1 + (\kappa_a + \kappa_b)x + \kappa_a\kappa_b x^2}. \tag{2.31}$$

The partition function P is then identified by the denominator

$$P = 1 + (\kappa_a + \kappa_b)x + \kappa_a\kappa_b x^2, \tag{2.32}$$

and the various coefficients can be identified with stoichiometric reaction constants $(\beta_1, \beta_2, K_1, K_2)$ as follows:

$$\beta_1 = \kappa_a + \kappa_b = K_1,$$

$$\beta_2 = \kappa_a \kappa_b = K_1 K_2. \tag{2.33}$$

The first stepwise binding constant, K_1, is thus the sum of the independent site constants, $\kappa_a + \kappa_b$, and the second stepwise constant, K_2, is found by elimination of K_1 between equations (2.33):

$$K_2 = \frac{\kappa_a \kappa_b}{\kappa_a + \kappa_b} = \frac{1}{\dfrac{1}{\kappa_a} + \dfrac{1}{\kappa_b}}. \tag{2.34}$$

The partition function given by equation (2.32) is also expressed as the product of the two individual-site binding polynomials:

$$P = (1 + \kappa_a x)(1 + \kappa_b x). \tag{2.35}$$

This result can, of course, be generalized to any number of independent reaction sites, and we see that the factors of the binding polynomial lead by equation (2.22) to the extent of binding given by the sum of the independent site contributions, i.e., the terms in the sum given by equation (2.30).

If the two sites are identical, then $\kappa_a = \kappa_b = \kappa$ and

$$K_1 = 2\kappa, \qquad K_2 = \kappa/2. \tag{2.36}$$

The explanation of these numerical factors lies in the statistical features of the presence of multiple sites. There are two sites available for binding the first ligand, which can then be removed in only one way; this gives a factor of two for the probability of formation of MX. On the other hand, there is only one way to add a second ligand to MX, and two ways to remove X from MX_2, which gives the statistical factor of $1/2$ to the term κ_2.

In any experimental two-site binding situation, we actually determine values of K_1 and K_2, or more generally β_1 and β_2. The question then arises: can we express κ_a and κ_b in terms of K_1 and K_2? If we can, then the ligand binding can be considered to be attributed to independent sites with affinities κ_a and κ_b. In order to establish when this occurs, we form the quadratic equation using

$$\kappa_a = K_1 - \kappa_b \tag{2.37}$$

and from (2.33)

$$K_1 K_2 = \kappa_a \kappa_b = K_1 \kappa_b - \kappa_b^2. \tag{2.38}$$

Hence

$$\kappa_b^2 - K_1\kappa_b + K_1K_2 = 0. \tag{2.39}$$

We can then solve for κ_b and κ_a, as follows:

$$\kappa_b = \frac{K_1 - (K_1^2 - 4K_1K_2)^{1/2}}{2}, \tag{2.40}$$

$$\kappa_a = \frac{K_1 + (K_1^2 - 4K_1K_2)^{1/2}}{2}. \tag{2.41}$$

Now we note the interesting situation that some experimental values of K_1 and K_2 will give imaginary values of κ_a. Clearly, when this happens, our assumption of site independence must be invalid. The condition is easily found. The values of κ_a and κ_b will be real if $K_1^2 - 4K_1K_2$ or $K_1 - 4K_2$ is positive. If $K_1 - 4K_2$ is negative, then it is not possible to explain the binding curve in terms of two independent reaction sites. Equivalently, the binding polynomial cannot then be factored into linear terms with real coefficients. We shall see that this situation corresponds to a positive cooperative process.

On the other hand, when the binding polynomial can be factored into linear terms with affinities κ_a and κ_b, this situation can be attributed either to heterogeneous independent sites, as already mentioned, or to negative interactions between sites, defined as negative cooperativity. The discrimination between these two interpretations requires additional information on the binding properties of each site that is not revealed by simple overall binding curves.

2.5 COOPERATIVITY AS MEASURED BY BINDING CURVES

A measure of cooperativity is given by comparing the slope of an observed binding curve with the slope predicted for a curve based on identical and independent binding sites. The degree of binding $\bar{X}$ is found by extension of equation (2.30) to the situation where one has t identical binding sites. The binding curve of a molecule with t equivalent independent sites with binding constant κ is expressed as

$$\bar{X} = \frac{t\kappa x}{1 + \kappa x}, \tag{2.42}$$

and the slope of this curve is obtained by differentiation:

$$\frac{d\bar{X}}{dx} = \frac{t\kappa}{(1 + \kappa x)} - \frac{t\kappa^2 x}{(1 + \kappa x)^2}, \tag{2.43}$$

which, upon multiplying by x, yields

$$\frac{x \, d\bar{X}}{dx} = \frac{t\kappa x}{(1 + \kappa x)} - \frac{t\kappa^2 x^2}{(1 + \kappa x)^2}. \tag{2.44}$$

With equation (2.42) we find

$$\frac{d\bar{X}}{d \ln x} = \bar{X} - (\bar{X})^2/t = \bar{X}(1 - \bar{X}/t). \tag{2.45}$$

The maximum slope occurs at $\bar{X} = t/2$, and is equal to $t/4$. The effect of cooperativity is illustrated for a two-site situation in Figure 2-12, where binding curves and their derivatives are shown.

The cooperativity can now be assessed for any actual binding situation by comparison with the independent equivalent site example. If this comparison leads to a slope greater than the reference curve, then we have positive cooperativity, and if less than the reference curve, then we have negative cooperativity. Our comparison of slopes depends on what $\bar{X}$ value is taken; so a given binding curve may exhibit various values of cooperativity when measured in this way.

There is one method of plotting binding-curve results which gives this comparison of slopes directly; this is the Hill plot referred to previously. To see this most clearly, we express the binding curve in terms of fractional saturation θ defined simply as

$$\theta = \bar{X}/t. \tag{2.46}$$

In terms of θ the slope of the reference curve [equation (2.45)] is

$$\frac{d\theta}{d \ln x} = \theta(1 - \theta). \tag{2.47}$$

The Hill plot of the real binding curve may be expressed as $\ln [\theta/(1 - \theta)]$ versus $\ln x$, and the slope of the Hill plot, n_H, is then given as

$$n_H = \frac{d \ln (\theta/(1 - \theta))}{d \ln x} = \frac{d \ln \theta}{d \ln x} - \frac{d \ln (1 - \theta)}{d \ln x} \tag{2.48}$$

or

$$n_H = \left(\frac{1}{\theta} + \frac{1}{1 - \theta}\right)\frac{d\theta}{d \ln x}, \tag{2.49}$$

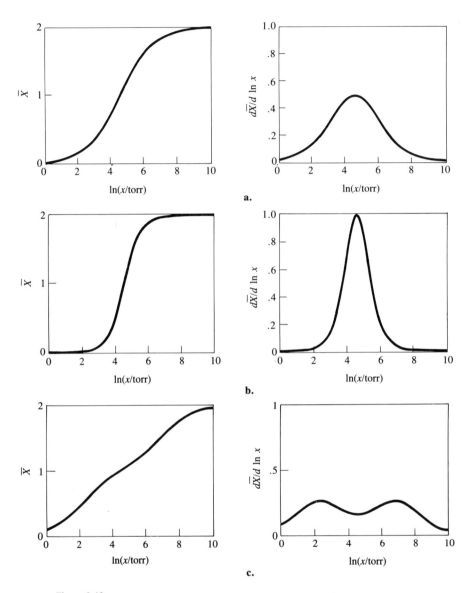

Figure 2-12.
Binding curves and their slopes for two-site binding. (a) Noncooperative case
($\beta_1 = .02$ torr^{-1}, $\beta_2 = .0001$ torr^{-2}). (b) Maximum cooperativity, i.e., no single-
site ligated species ($\beta_1 = 0$, $\beta_2 = .0001$ torr^{-2}). (c) Negative cooperativity
($\beta_1 = .10$ torr^{-1}, $\beta_2 = .0001$ torr^{-2}).

and thus

$$n_{\mathrm{H}} = \frac{1}{\theta(1-\theta)} \frac{d\theta}{d\ln x}. \tag{2.50}$$

Thus the slope of the Hill plot is determined by the slope of the binding curve $(d\theta/d\ln x)$ divided by $\theta(1-\theta)$; the latter term gives the slope of the reference curve [see equation (2.47)]. Thus the Hill-plot slope gives a direct measure of the cooperativity of any given point along the binding curve. Of course, when the slope of the binding curve is the same as that of the reference curve, then $n_{\mathrm{H}} = 1$, and the cooperativity is zero. This occurs everywhere for a single-site binding curve, and for multiple sites is always applicable in the asymptotic limits. Thus the asymptotes can be interpreted as representing independent site reactions.

2.6   ALLOSTERIC EFFECTS: SINGLE-LIGAND SPECIES

The observation of positive cooperativity from steep binding curves or Hill plots of oxygen and hemoglobin has been a key point in developing various molecular models to account for such properties. Here we briefly examine the consequences of the allosteric model (Monod *et al.*, 1965), which leads directly to predictions of positive cooperativity.

We consider that the macromolecule can exist in two conformations, specified by R and T. We first suppose that a single X-binding site is present on these forms, and the reaction with the ligand X, as well as the equilibrium between R and T forms, is specified as follows.

The two binding reactions are

$$M_R + X \rightarrow M_R X, \qquad \kappa_R = \frac{[M_R X]}{[M_R]x},$$

$$M_T + X \rightarrow M_T X, \qquad \kappa_T = \frac{[M_T X]}{[M_T]x}, \tag{2.51a}$$

and the allosteric equilibrium between unligated forms is

$$M_R \rightarrow M_T, \qquad L_0 = \frac{[M_T]}{[M_R]}. \tag{2.51b}$$

Here κ_R, κ_T, and L_0 are the equilibrium constants for the respective reactions. Then the degree of binding is given as

$$\bar{X} = \frac{[M_R X] + [M_T X]}{[M_R] + [M_T] + [M_R X] + [M_T X]}, \tag{2.52}$$

which yields, upon substitution of the equilibria equations,

$$\bar{X} = \frac{\kappa_R x + L_0 \kappa_T x}{1 + L_0 + \kappa_R x + L_0 \kappa_T x}. \tag{2.53}$$

By normalizing with respect to the sum of the unligated species concentrations, $[1 + L_0]$, to give a leading term of unity in the denominator, we have

$$\bar{X} = \frac{\left(\dfrac{\kappa_R + L_0 \kappa_T}{1 + L_0}\right) x}{1 + \left(\dfrac{\kappa_R + L_0 \kappa_T}{1 + L_0}\right) x}. \tag{2.54}$$

This expression has exactly the same form as the degree of binding [see equation (2.5)] for single-site binding, with an average affinity given by

$$\bar{\kappa} = \frac{\kappa_R + L_0 \kappa_T}{1 + L_0}. \tag{2.55}$$

The binding curve will be indistinguishable from that with a single binding constant where there is no allosteric change.

The binding polynomial (or partition function) is given by the expression

$$P = 1 + \left(\frac{\kappa_R + L_0 \kappa_T}{1 + L_0}\right) x = \frac{1}{1 + L_0}(1 + \kappa_R x) + \frac{L_0}{1 + L_0}(1 + \kappa_T x). \tag{2.56}$$

We see that for an allosteric reaction the partition function is the fractionally weighted sum of R and T binding polynomials. The binding curve for the allosteric reaction is intermediate between the $\bar{X}_R$ and $\bar{X}_T$ curves. The functional binding constant $\bar{\kappa}$ is given by the fractionally weighted sum of κ_R and κ_T as

$$\bar{\kappa} = \frac{\kappa_R}{1 + L_0} + \frac{L_0 \kappa_T}{1 + L_0}. \tag{2.57}$$

The factors $1/(1 + L_0)$ and $L_0/(1 + L_0)$ represent the fractions of unligated R and T species, and may be designated as α_R^0 and α_T^0. In these terms the binding polynomial may be written as

$$P = 1 + \bar{\kappa} x,$$

where

$$\bar{\kappa} = \alpha_R^0 \kappa_R + \alpha_T^0 \kappa_T. \tag{2.58}$$

And with $\alpha_R^0 + \alpha_T^0 = 1$ we obtain

$$\bar{\kappa} = \kappa_T - \alpha_T^0(\kappa_T - \kappa_R). \tag{2.59}$$

Thus the binding curve is displaced from the pure $\bar{X}_T$ curve by an amount that depends on the fraction α_T^0 and the spacing of the pure $\bar{X}_T$ and $\bar{X}_R$ curves. An example is shown in Figure 2-13.

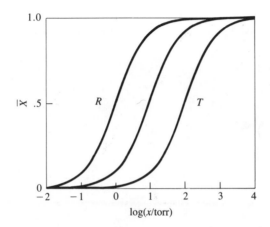

Figure 2-13.
Single-site allosteric macromolecules with R and T forms. The extreme curves show binding to the pure R and pure T forms denoted by T and R, and the intermediate binding curve is obtained for the two binding to allosteric forms in equilibrium ($\alpha_R^0 = 1/10$). Note that the allosteric curve remains a simple titration curve. Since there is only one binding site, there can be no cooperativity.

The amounts of the different forms as ligation proceeds are of special interest. The fraction of the R form is given as

$$\alpha_R = \frac{[M_R] + [M_RX]}{[M_R] + [M_T] + [M_RX] + [M_TX]}, \tag{2.60}$$

and with equations (2.51) we have the result

$$\alpha_R = \frac{1 + \kappa_R x}{1 + \kappa_R x + L_0(1 + \kappa_T x)}. \tag{2.61}$$

The expression for α_T is

$$\alpha_T = \frac{L_0(1 + \kappa_T x)}{1 + \kappa_R x + L_0(1 + \kappa_T x)}. \tag{2.62}$$

In this allosteric model, as ligation proceeds, there will be a change in the fraction of R or T species. Consider the fraction α_R described by equation (2.61) in the limits of very small and very large values of x. Let these be denoted by α_R^0 and α_R^∞ respectively. We rearrange equation (2.61) as

$$\alpha_R = \frac{1}{1 + L_0\left(\dfrac{1 + \kappa_T x}{1 + \kappa_R x}\right)}. \tag{2.63}$$

In the limits of small and large values of x, we find

$$\alpha_R^0 = \frac{1}{1 + L_0}, \qquad x \to 0 \tag{2.64}$$

and

$$\alpha_R^\infty = \frac{1}{1 + \dfrac{\kappa_T}{\kappa_R}L_0}, \qquad x \to \infty. \tag{2.65}$$

Thus if L_0 is large, then α_R^0 must be small, but α_R^∞ can approach unity provided $\kappa_T L_0/\kappa_R$ is sufficiently small, in which case the concentration of X ligand changes the population of macromolecules from essentially all T form to all R form. This is illustrated in Figure 2-14.

When the two allosteric forms (T and R) contain more than one X-binding site, then the binding process takes on additional interesting features, in particular the display of cooperativity. We consider the situation where each form has t binding sites, and each form has identical independent binding sites with binding constants κ_R and κ_T. The binding polynomial is given by the sum

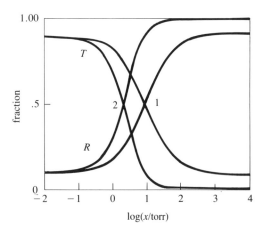

Figure 2-14.
Fractions of allosteric forms, α_R and α_T, as a function of ligand activity for the binding constants given in Figure 2-13. Note that the transition for the two-site situation (2) is much sharper and covers a larger change in the fraction of the form than that for the single-site case (1).

of binding polynomials for each form weighted by the fractions of unligated forms, exactly as we saw for the single-site case. The result is

$$P = \frac{1}{1 + L_0}(1 + \kappa_R x)^t + \frac{L_0}{1 + L_0}(1 + \kappa_T x)^t. \qquad (2.66)$$

The binding curve is then given by the logarithmic derivative, which gives

$$\bar{X} = \frac{t(1 + \kappa_R x)^{t-1}\kappa_R x + tL_0(1 + \kappa_T x)^{t-1}\kappa_T x}{P(1 + L_0)}. \qquad (2.67)$$

If $\kappa_R \neq \kappa_T$, this curve has a slope greater than the noncooperative t-site reference curve for either the T or R forms. The maximum steepness depends on the choice of the model parameters. This positive cooperativity is also a direct manifestation of the fact that this binding polynomial cannot be factored into linear terms. The fraction of R allosteric forms is given by writing equation (2.63) with t sites:

$$\alpha_R = \frac{1}{1 + L_0\left(\dfrac{1 + \kappa_T x}{1 + \kappa_R x}\right)^t}. \qquad (2.68)$$

The effect of combining t binding sites is to amplify the effect of ligand activity, so that the fraction of a given allosteric form is more rapidly changed for a given change in x. See the two situations depicted in Figure 2-14. The highly aggregated forms of respiratory proteins, such as the hemocyanins, may have developed because they achieved in this way efficient transport of oxygen by a highly cooperative molecular mechanism.

Interestingly, although each R and T form has by itself noncooperative binding, the shifting equilibrium between the two forms gives rise to a steeper binding curve, as seen in Figure 2-15.

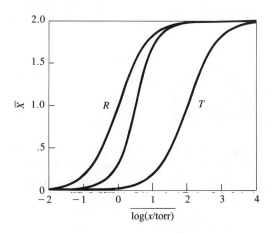

log(x/torr)

Figure 2-15.
Effect of the allosteric transition on the binding curves for a two-site macromolecule with $\kappa_R = 1$, $\kappa_T = .01$, and $L_0 = 9$.

2.7   MIXTURE OF MACROMOLECULES

If the allosteric transition were to be repressed, so that the R and T forms remain frozen in their original proportions, α_R^0, α_T^0, then the resulting titration curve would always be less steep than either the pure R or T titration curves. Such a situation is defined to be negatively cooperative. For a single site the binding curve is the sum of the fractional contribution of binding to each form:

$$\bar{X} = \frac{\alpha_R^0 \kappa_R x}{1 + \kappa_R x} + \frac{\alpha_T^0 \kappa_T x}{1 + \kappa_T x}. \tag{2.69}$$

The binding polynomial must then consist of single-site factors weighted by the mole fractions. For this situation,

$$\bar{X} = \frac{d \ln P}{d \ln x} = \alpha_R^0 \frac{d \ln P_R}{d \ln x} + \alpha_T^0 \frac{d \ln P_T}{d \ln x}, \tag{2.70}$$

which integrates to

$$\ln P = \alpha_R^0 \ln (1 + \kappa_R x) + \alpha_T^0 \ln (1 + \kappa_T x), \tag{2.71}$$

and the partition function is then

$$P = (1 + \kappa_R x)^{\alpha_R^0} (1 + \kappa_T x)^{\alpha_T^0}. \tag{2.72}$$

The nature of the cooperativity for this system is again a function of the derivative of $\bar{X}$ with respect to $\ln x$. This is the second derivative of $\ln P$, i.e.,

$$\frac{d\bar{X}}{d \ln x} = \frac{d^2 \ln P}{(d \ln x)^2}. \tag{2.73}$$

With equation (2.71) we obtain

$$\frac{d^2 \ln P}{(d \ln x)^2} = \frac{\alpha_R^0 \kappa_R x}{(1 + \kappa_R x)^2} + \frac{\alpha_T^0 \kappa_T x}{(1 + \kappa_T x)^2}. \tag{2.74}$$

This represents the sum of the appropriately weighted slopes of the two R and T binding processes. This sum will be less than that for a single-binding-site reaction. Thus the cooperativity is negative except at the ends, where it approaches neutral cooperativity. We can see this graphically in Figure 2-16.

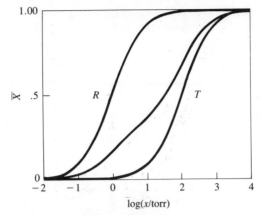

Figure 2-16.
Binding curve for a frozen mixture of single-site R and T molecules with fixed fractions α_R^0 and α_T^0 chosen as $1/3$ and $2/3$. $\bar{X}_R$ and $\bar{X}_T$ curves are multiplied by fractional amounts α_R^0 and α_T^0 and then added together to give an overall curve that has a slope everywhere less than that of the single-site curves.

2.8 BINDING OF TWO DIFFERENT LIGANDS (X AND Y): HETEROTROPIC EFFECTS

2.8.1 Identical Linkage: Two Ligands, Single Site

We shall next consider the simple situation of binding two different ligands (X and Y) to a macromolecule M, where we assume that the macromolecule M has one binding site that binds either X or Y. This is termed competitive binding or identical linkage (Wyman, 1948). This would be the situation for the binding of O_2 or CO to myoglobin. The binding reactions [see equation (2.1)] are

$$M + X \rightarrow MX, \qquad \kappa_X = \frac{[MX]}{[M]x}, \qquad (2.75)$$

$$M + Y \rightarrow MY, \qquad \kappa_Y = \frac{[MY]}{[M]y}, \qquad (2.76)$$

and the molar amounts of X and Y bound per mole of macromolecule M are

$$\bar{X} = \frac{[MX]}{[M] + [MX] + [MY]} = \frac{\kappa_X x}{1 + \kappa_X x + \kappa_Y y}, \qquad (2.77)$$

$$\bar{Y} = \frac{[MY]}{[M] + [MX] + [MY]} = \frac{\kappa_Y y}{1 + \kappa_X x + \kappa_Y y}. \qquad (2.78)$$

Here we note there is a simple partition of X and Y given by $\bar{X}/\bar{Y} = (\kappa_X/\kappa_Y)(x/y)$. As we have seen before, the binding polynomial is the denominator, or

$$P = 1 + \kappa_X x + \kappa_Y y. \tag{2.79}$$

Again the successive terms of the binding polynomial represent the relative concentrations of the three species, and the binding parameters $\bar{X}$ and $\bar{Y}$ are given by the appropriate partial derivatives as follows:

$$\bar{X} = \left(\frac{\partial \ln P}{\partial \ln x}\right)_y, \tag{2.80}$$

$$\bar{Y} = \left(\frac{\partial \ln P}{\partial \ln y}\right)_x. \tag{2.81}$$

The logarithm of the binding polynomial is the sum of areas under the $\bar{X}$ vs. $\ln x$ and $\bar{Y}$ vs. $\ln y$ binding curves. We see this by writing the differential of $\ln P$,

$$d \ln P = \left(\frac{\partial \ln P}{\partial \ln x}\right)_y d \ln x + \left(\frac{\partial \ln P}{\partial \ln y}\right)_x d \ln y, \tag{2.82}$$

and from equations (2.80) and (2.81) we find

$$d \ln P = \bar{X} d \ln x + \bar{Y} d \ln y. \tag{2.83}$$

Upon integration from a reference state of zero X and Y ligand activity, where $P = 1$,

$$\ln P = \int_0^x \bar{X} d \ln x + \int_0^y \bar{Y} d \ln y. \tag{2.84}$$

This equation shows how the sum of areas beneath the respective binding curves determines the partition function.

The effect of the presence of one ligand upon the binding properties of the other is known as the *linkage effect*, and can be assessed from the heterotropic derivative properties of the partition function. The heterotropic second derivatives of $\ln P$ with respect to $\ln y$ and $\ln x$ are equal, since the order of differentiation is immaterial if $\ln P$ is well-behaved and continuous:

$$\frac{\partial^2 \ln P}{\partial \ln y \partial \ln x} = \frac{\partial^2 \ln P}{\partial \ln x \partial \ln y}. \tag{2.85}$$

With (2.80) and (2.81) we then obtain the general linkage relation

$$\left(\frac{\partial \bar{X}}{\partial \ln y}\right)_x = \left(\frac{\partial \bar{Y}}{\partial \ln x}\right)_y. \tag{2.86}$$

For the example of identical linkage given by equations (2.77) and (2.78), we obtain

$$\left(\frac{\partial \bar{X}}{\partial \ln y}\right)_x = y\left(\frac{\partial \bar{X}}{\partial y}\right)_x = \frac{-\kappa_X x \kappa_Y y}{(1 + \kappa_X x + \kappa_Y y)^2} = -\bar{X}\bar{Y} \tag{2.87}$$

and

$$\left(\frac{\partial \bar{Y}}{\partial \ln x}\right)_y = x\left(\frac{\partial \bar{Y}}{\partial x}\right)_y = \frac{-\kappa_X x \kappa_Y y}{(1 + \kappa_X x + \kappa_Y y)^2} = -\bar{X}\bar{Y}. \tag{2.88}$$

We see that the two linkage derivatives are equal, as they must be, and in this example of ligand competition we see that these derivatives are negative, since the product $\bar{X}\bar{Y}$ is always a positive quantity. This situation is termed *negative heterotropic cooperativity*. An example of it is the competitive binding of oxygen and carbon monoxide to single subunits of lobster hemocyanin (Richey *et al.*, 1985). The linkage derivative [see (2.87) or (2.88)] is shown in Figure 2-17 as a function of oxygen and carbon monoxide pressure. Note the linkage derivative is everywhere negative with a maximum value at $x = 1/\kappa_X$ and $y = 1/\kappa_Y$.

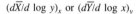

$(d\bar{X}/d \log y)_x$ or $(d\bar{Y}/d \log x)_y$

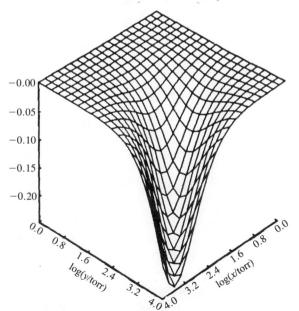

Figure 2-17.
Heterotropic linkage derivative for oxygen and carbon monoxide binding to isolated subunits of the hemocyanin from the lobster *Homarus americanus*, generated from binding constants reported in Richey *et al.* (1985): $\kappa_X = 0.009$ torr^{-1} and $\kappa_Y = 0.0033$ torr^{-1} In this case of identical linkage (competitive binding of the two ligands), the value of the derivative is everywhere negative.

2.8.2   Two Binding Sites: One for X and One for Y

Next, let us consider M to have two binding sites, one specifically for X and the other specifically for Y. Then the binding reactions are described as follows:

$$M + X \rightarrow MX, \qquad \kappa_X = \beta_X = \frac{[MX]}{[M]x}, \qquad (2.89)$$

$$M + Y \rightarrow MY, \qquad \kappa_Y = \beta_Y = \frac{[MX]}{[M]y}, \qquad (2.90)$$

$$M + X + Y \rightarrow MXY, \qquad \beta_{XY} = \frac{[MXY]}{[M]xy}, \qquad (2.91)$$

where subscripts x and y are used to denote the ligands involved in a particular binding process. We shall use the β constants, since they apply to the appropriate overall processes of both ligands. The amounts of X, Y, and the pair XY bound per total M are

$$\bar{X} = \frac{[MX] + [MXY]}{[M] + [MX] + [MY] + [MXY]} = \frac{\beta_X x + \beta_{XY} xy}{1 + \beta_X x + \beta_Y y + \beta_{XY} xy}, \qquad (2.92)$$

$$\bar{Y} = \frac{[MY] + [MXY]}{[M] + [MX] + [MY] + [MXY]} = \frac{\beta_Y y + \beta_{XY} xy}{1 + \beta_X x + \beta_Y y + \beta_{XY} xy}, \qquad (2.93)$$

$$\overline{XY} = \frac{[MXY]}{[M] + [MX] + [MY] + [MXY]} = \frac{\beta_{XY} xy}{1 + \beta_X x + \beta_Y y + \beta_{XY} xy}. \qquad (2.94)$$

Here the binding polynomial is now given as

$$P = 1 + \beta_X x + \beta_Y y + \beta_{XY} xy. \qquad (2.95)$$

The linkage relation (2.86) yields

$$\left(\frac{\partial \bar{X}}{\partial \ln y}\right)_x = y\left(\frac{\partial \bar{X}}{\partial y}\right)_x = \frac{\beta_{XY} xy}{P} - \frac{(\beta_X x + \beta_{XY} xy)(\beta_Y y + \beta_{XY} xy)}{(P)^2} \qquad (2.96)$$

or

$$\left(\frac{\partial \bar{X}}{\partial \ln y}\right)_x = \frac{\beta_{XY} xy - \beta_X \beta_Y xy}{(P)^2}. \qquad (2.97)$$

This differs from the identical-linkage situation [equation (2.87)] in that we have here an additional positive term that determines whether positive or negative heterotropic cooperativity occurs. The choice is dictated by the difference in binding constants, as is evident in equation (2.97). For the zero-cooperative case, this difference is zero, or $\beta_{XY} = \beta_X\beta_Y$; with this condition the binding polynomial equation (2.95) may be factored as

$$P_{zero-coop} = (1 + \beta_X x)(1 + \beta_Y y). \tag{2.98}$$

Application of the heterotropic linkage relation (2.86) to a binding polynomial that factors into a set of terms representing single-site binding will always give zero heterotropic cooperativity.

2.9   INDIVIDUAL-SITE BINDING ISOTHERMS

It is sometimes possible to examine the details of ligand binding to each individual site of macromolecule. Certain physical techniques lend themselves to this level of examination, such as NMR spectroscopy and DNA footprinting (Ackers *et al.*, 1983). A simple example of individual-site binding reactions is illustrated by the protonation of an amino acid with two ionizable groups (Edsall and Wyman, Ch. 9, 1958). For glycine, we have the diagram for the pertinent microscopic reactions shown in Figure 2-18.

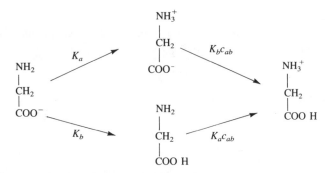

Figure 2-18.
Ionization scheme for glycine. The microscopic constants K_a and K_b are the protonation constants for the amino and carboxyl groups to the unprotonated form, and c_{ab} is a cooperativity factor indicating interaction between the two sites. Estimates for these parameters for glycine at 25°C are $K_a = 5 \times 10^9 \ M^{-1}$, $K_b = 2 \times 10^4 \ M^{-1}$, and $c_{ab} = 10^{-2}$. The small value of c_{ab} indicates a strong electrostatic repulsion between the sites.

The microscopic site binding constants, K_a and K_b for sites a and b, are related to the stoichiometric stepwise reaction constants K_1 and K_2 by $K_1 = K_a + K_b$ and $K_1 K_2 = K_a K_b c_{ab}$. We can see by equations (2.40) and (2.41) that the square-root term $[(K_a + K_b)^2 - 4K_a K_b c_{ab}]$ is positive if $c_{ab} < (K_a + K_b)^2/4K_a K_b$. This condition is valid for glycine, and shows that the overall

proton-binding polynomial factors into two terms that macroscopically describe two independent site reactions with reaction constants $\kappa_b = 2 \times 10^2$ M^{-1}
and $\kappa_a = 5 \times 10^9$ M^{-1}. The proton-binding curve for glycine is shown as a
function of pH in Figure 2-19a. In order to resolve the microscopic constants
of this system, one requires either some measure of the interaction coefficient
c_{ab} or a measure of one of the microscopic constants K_a or K_b. These might
be obtained from individual-site binding curves using NMR. However, for
glycine K_b was estimated from studies of a methyl ester of glycine, permitting
the evaluation of K_a and c_{ab} as given in the legend of Figure 2-19.

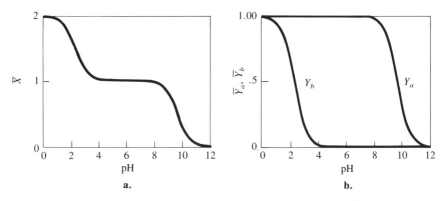

Figure 2-19.
(a) Proton binding to glycine as a function of pH. (b) Individual site-binding curves
for glycine with $\bar{Y}_a$ (amino) and $\bar{Y}_b$ (carboxyl).

We can calculate the individual-site binding isotherms for the amino (A) and
the carboxyl group (B), as $\bar{Y}_a$ and $\bar{Y}_b$, by

$$\bar{Y}_a = \frac{K_a x + K_a K_b c_{ab} x^2}{1 + (K_a + K_b)x + K_a K_b c_{ab} x^2}, \tag{2.99}$$

$$\bar{Y}_b = \frac{K_b x + K_a K_b c_{ab} x^2}{1 + (K_a + K_b)x + K_a K_b c_{ab} x^2}. \tag{2.100}$$

The use of these equations is illustrated for the example of glycine in Figure 2-19b.

This approach of single site binding isotherms has been applied to
repressor-binding operators in DNA by Ackers et al. (1982, 1983) and Shea
and Ackers (1985) by means of quantitative footprinting analysis.

2.10 SUMMARY

The preceding illustrations show how the cooperativity (both homotropic and heterotropic) depends upon the slope of a binding curve by the primary or secondary ligand activity. Negative homotropic cooperativity always results when a non-allosteric macromolecule has several independent sites with different affinities, or when a frozen allosteric system of molecules has independent sites with different affinities. Positive homotropic cooperativity occurs in two-site reactions when the binding of the second ligand is assisted by the presence of the first. The allosteric model provides a particularly simple mechanism for producing positive homotropic cooperativity.

We have seen how homotropic cooperativity may be defined by comparing the slope of the observed binding curve with that of a simple titration curve. The slope of the Hill plot gives a direct measurement of this ratio, and thus of the degree of homotropic cooperativity. If there are two different ligands, the heterotropic cooperativity may be expressed by the linkage derivative being negative, zero, or positive. For competitive single-site binding for X or Y, known as *identical linkage*, X competes with Y, and only negative heterotropic cooperativity is found. When X and Y can bind nonexclusively, then a range of heterotropic cooperativity, from negative to positive values, is possible. Microscopic binding constants can be evaluated from detailed knowledge of individual-site-binding isotherms. In later chapters we show how these ideas may be generalized to any number of sites, alike or different. Our goal in this chapter has been to develop several basic ideas by examining some simple special cases.

The Binding Polynomial 3
(Nonassociating Macromolecules)

The partition function for a macromolecular system (Wyman, 1964; Hess and Szabo, 1979; Hill, 1985) represents the sum of all the different macromolecular species within a system. Since each ligated species of the macromolecule is formed by a reaction between the unliganded macromolecule and appropriate quantities of ligand, we may use mass-law expressions to obtain the general sum of all species in terms of a polynomial in ligand activity. The degree of the polynomial is the same as the number of sites for the ligand, and each coefficient is the mass-law constant for the corresponding reaction. Examples of this procedure have been given in detail for some elementary situations in Chapter 2. In this chapter we wish to describe more general properties of ligand-binding partition functions, formulated as binding polynomials. Further relations between binding curves, binding polynomials, ligand-binding free energy, and the median ligand activity will be developed (Wyman, 1964; Gill, 1979), and formal mathematical properties of symmetry and factorability of the binding polynomial will be established (Wyman and Phillipson, 1974; Bardsley, 1977a, 1977b; Briggs, 1983). The concept of co-operativity for binding systems will be defined and explored in various ways: factorization, the slope of the binding curve, and the Hill plot. One purpose of this chapter is to show how these properties are related to the general idea of cooperativity. Starting from ligand binding involving a single species, we will then consider the form of binding polynomials for several ligands, and the linkage relations that necessarily follow, connecting the binding properties of one ligand with another. Our aim is to provide insight into how the equilibrium-functional properties of the macromolecule may be deduced from the binding polynomial.

3.1 SPECIFIC AND NONSPECIFIC BINDING

In discussing ligand binding it is important to distinguish between specific binding and nonspecific binding. Specific ligand binding can be described in terms of the chemical reactions to a macromolecule in accordance with the mass law. Nonspecific binding refers to the residual amount of ligand present in the solution that may interact with the macromolecule in a manner not described by the mass law. An example of the latter is dealt with in Debye-Hückel theory of electrolytes. In this chapter we shall be concerned with the portion of ligand that is specifically bound to a finite number of ligand-binding sites on the macromolecule. The activity of the ligand determines the fraction of occupation of sites, and at high activities essentially all sites are occupied, which means the binding curve ($\bar{X}$ versus $\ln x$) passes from a lower to an upper horizontal asymptote. This is a characteristic feature of specific binding.

Nonspecific binding falls outside the properties of mass-action laws. It has no characteristic saturation limit that would indicate a finite number of reaction sites. It therefore cannot be quantitatively described by simple reaction processes. Long-range electrostatic interaction between counterions and a polyelectrolyte macromolecule falls in the category of nonspecific binding.

Biological macromolecules can for the most part be studied only in the presence of solvent water. Even in a crystal many water molecules are present. The solvent water itself is a ligand, and deserves special attention. It certainly interacts with the macromolecule, and there might be many reaction sites that this solvent could occupy. However, the representation of these interactions cannot in general be expressed in terms of a mass law defining specific binding. There is also nonspecific binding, and for the solvent, separation of the two would require some experimental technique—e.g., one that distinguishes free from bound solvent—that is generally not available. Classical thermodynamic procedures, such as dialysis, fail to provide this type of discrimination. Spectroscopic techniques (NMR and X-ray) offer a way to characterize water interaction with the macromolecule. Lacking any exact mass-law formulation, we will introduce the concept of activity coefficients based on the laws of ideal solutions. (However, a possible mass-law formulation for solvent binding has been proposed by Tanford, 1969.)

The total amount of ligand X contained in a system per mole of macromolecule includes both nonspecific and specific bound ligand. There is no fundamental problem in calculating this quantity for the system. It is the total amount of X per mole of macromolecule (or moles of certain reaction sites) in the system. This is a problem of chemical analysis. The portion that we can regard as bound will then depend on whether we can discriminate between what is free and what is bound. Dialysis equilibrium can give a measure of this number. If specific spectroscopic changes are related to occupancy of certain sites, as oxygen in hemoglobins or hemocyanins, then the amount of specific binding can be measured.

In this chapter we wish to limit our concern to cases where the macromolecules are of a fixed molecular weight that does not change with concentration. This excludes situations where dissociation or aggregation occurs. These will be considered in Chapter 6 on polysteric effects. Chapter 3 represents a more searching and quantitative examination of the concepts of ligand binding introduced in Chapter 2. In order to provide a cohesive development of these ideas, we will repeat some basic equations from Chapter 2 at the beginning of several sections.

3.2 MASS-LAW DESCRIPTION OF THE BINDING OF A SINGLE LIGAND

3.2.1 The Adair Constants and the Binding Polynomial

As noted, the binding polynomial represents a normalized partition function in which each term in the sum is proportional to the concentration of a particular macromolecular species. The relation between the macromolecular species terms is established by use of the mass-action law. Adair (1925b) described the binding of oxygen to the four heme sites of hemoglobin in terms of mass-action laws, and his name has been customarily attached to this general procedure. There are two ways to describe the relevant reactions between ligands and macromolecule: as either overall or stepwise ligand-binding reactions. The overall reaction for adding i X ligands to any unligated macromolecule M containing t sites to produce the species MX_i is given by

$$M + iX \rightarrow MX_i, \qquad i = 1 \text{ to } t. \tag{3.1}$$

This reaction has an equilibrium constant, β_i, which describes the overall reaction, given as

$$\beta_i = \frac{[MX_i]}{[M]x^i}. \tag{3.2}$$

Here $[MX_i]$ and $[M]$ are the concentrations of MX_i and M in a solution at equilibrium, and x is the activity of X.*

Any overall reaction can be broken down into a sequence of stepwise reactions. This procedure gives the second way of describing the relevant reaction processes, as follows:

$$MX_{i-1} + X \rightarrow MX_i, \qquad i = 1 \text{ to } t. \tag{3.3}$$

The stepwise reaction equilibrium constant, K_i, is given as

$$K_i = \frac{[MX_i]}{[MX_{i-1}]x}. \tag{3.4}$$

---

* In writing this equation in terms of the ratio of concentrations, we are absorbing the activity coefficients of MX and M into the constant β_i.

Either of these formulations, overall or stepwise, describes the ligation reactions of the system. The overall (β_i) or stepwise (K_i) equilibrium constants are generally known as the *Adair constants*. The relation between the overall and stepwise constants is given as

$$\beta_i = K_1 K_2 K_3 \cdots K_i \tag{3.5}$$

or

$$K_i = \frac{\beta_i}{\beta_{i-1}}. \tag{3.6}$$

The concentration of any ligated species can be expressed in terms of the binding constants, the concentration of the unliganded form, and the ligand activity raised to a power denoting the ligated state of the macromolecule, as follows:

$$[MX_i] = \beta_i x^i [M] = K_1 K_2 \cdots K_i x^i [M]. \tag{3.7}$$

Since the binding partition function, Q, represents the sum of the species concentrations taken relative to a reference species (Wyman, 1948, 1964; Hill, 1960), chosen here as the unliganded form, we may write Q as

$$Q = \sum_{i=0}^{t} \frac{[MX_i]}{[M]} = 1 + \frac{[MX]}{[M]} + \frac{[MX_2]}{[M]} + \cdots + \frac{[MX_t]}{[M]}. \tag{3.8}$$

With the use of equation (3.7), this gives the binding partition function in the form of a polynomial expressed in terms of the overall reaction constants (β_i) and ligand activities raised to the *i*th power. This polynomial is called the binding polynomial and is denoted by P in terms of β's or K's:

$$P = \sum_{i=0}^{t} \beta_i x^i = 1 + \beta_1 x + \beta_2 x^2 + \cdots + \beta_t x^t$$

$$\tag{3.9}$$

$$P = \sum_{i=0}^{t} K_1 K_2 \cdots K_i x^i = 1 + K_1 x + K_1 K_2 x^2 + \cdots + K_1 K_2 \cdots K_t x^t.$$

Each term represents the relative concentration of the macromolecular species ligated with *i* ligands.

3.2.2   The Extent of Binding: The Bar Notation

A binding curve describes the relation between the amount of ligand bound and the ligand activity. We denote the amount of ligand X specifically bound per mole of macromolecule by $\bar{X}$. In terms of the various ligated macro-molecular species, it is given as the average of the various species weighted by the amount of ligand each carries:

$$\bar{X} = \frac{\sum\limits_{i=0}^{t} i[MX_i]}{\sum\limits_{i=0}^{t} [MX_i]} = \frac{[MX] + 2[MX_2] + \cdots + t[MX_t]}{[M] + [MX] + [MX_2] + \cdots + [MX_t]}. \tag{3.10}$$

Since the species concentrations are expressed in mass-law terms of ligand activity and unligated macromolecule concentration, we shall use the β forms of equation (3.7), with the result

$$\bar{X} = \frac{\sum\limits_{i=0}^{t} i\beta_i x^i}{\sum\limits_{i=0}^{t} \beta_i x^i} = \frac{\beta_1 x + 2\beta_2 x^2 + \cdots + t\beta_t x^t}{1 + \beta_1 x + \beta_2 x^2 + \cdots + \beta_t x^t}. \tag{3.11}$$

We've seen the simple cases of single- and double-site binding for this expression in Chapter 2. The denominator is the binding polynomial P. The numerator is x times the derivative of P with respect to x, provided the β_is are true constants, in other words, that the activity coefficients are independent of x. This enables us to write $\bar{X}$ as

$$\bar{X} = \frac{x}{P} \frac{dP}{dx} = \frac{d \ln P}{d \ln x}. \tag{3.12}$$

This result is general, and enables us to obtain the binding-curve equation from binding polynomials that describe various detailed models of particular binding processes for nonassociating macromolecules.

We first mentioned in Chapter 2 that the area under the binding curve, expressed as $\bar{X}$ versus $\ln x$, gives the binding polynomial, P. We now wish to show that the area above the binding curve gives another important property of the ligand-binding macromolecular system. The area under the binding curve up to a given value of x is given as

$$A_u = \int_{-\infty}^{\ln x} \bar{X} \, d \ln x. \tag{3.13}$$

Similarly the area above the binding curve, bounded by t, the number of binding sites, and integrated from $\ln x$ to the asymptotic limit of high ligand activity, is given as

$$A_a = \int_{\ln x}^{\infty} (t - \bar{X}) \, d \ln x. \tag{3.14}$$

The representation of these areas in relation to the binding curve is shown in Figure 3-1.

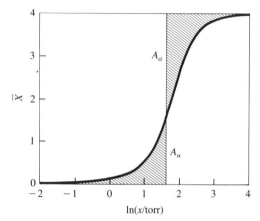

Figure 3-1.
Binding curve of oxygen to hemoglobin ($t = 4$) calculated from data at 25°C and pH 7.4 given by Imai and Yonetani (1975a). The areas defined above (A_a) and under (A_u) the binding curve are denoted by the crosshatch markings.

The areas A_u and A_a determine the fraction of macromolecules in the unligated or fully ligated form. We've seen this in Chapter 2 for the unligated situation, and the relation for the other extreme is easily developed. To see this, we recognize that the species fraction for the ith ligated species, MX_i, denoted by α_i, is defined as

$$\alpha_i = \frac{\beta_i x^i}{\sum\limits_{i=0}^{t} \beta_i x_i^{\,i}} = \frac{\beta_i x^i}{P}. \tag{3.15}$$

The unligated species fraction, α_0, is $1/P$, and the fully ligated species fraction, α_t, is $(\beta_t x^t/P)$. The difference $t - \bar{X}$ is given by the differentiation of $d\ln(\beta_t x^t/P)/d\ln x$. Thus the integral of equation (3.14) gives $-\ln(\beta_t x^t/P)$, which in turn is equal to $-\ln \alpha_t$. Thus the negative logarithmic values of the two limiting species fractions are given by the areas defined under and above the binding curve from equations (3.13) and (3.14), and the fractions themselves are then expressed by the exponentials of the negative values of the respective areas:

$$\alpha_0 = \exp\left(-\int \bar{X}\, d\ln x\right) = e^{-A_u} \tag{3.16}$$

and

$$\alpha_t = \exp\left(-\int (t - \bar{X}) d \ln x\right) = e^{-A_a}. \tag{3.17}$$

The areas that determine the species fractions, α_0 and α_t, are shown in Figure 3-1.

The ratio of the fractions α_t and α_0, along with the ligand activity x, determines the overall equilibrium constant β_t for the reaction $M + tX \rightarrow MX_t$, as follows:

$$\beta_t = \frac{\alpha_t}{\alpha_0 x^t}. \tag{3.18}$$

This expression applies to any value of ligand activity x, but the value of x when $\alpha_0 = \alpha_t$ is of special interest, since at this point the areas are equal. This is called the *median activity*, x_m, and the overall binding constant is determined by its value:

$$\beta_t = \frac{1}{(x_m)^t}. \tag{3.19}$$

Again, this is a perfectly general result for ligand binding to nondissociating or nonassociating macromolecules. We can find the median activity relatively easily by graphical or computer integration of the binding curve. For symmetric binding curves, the median activity is equivalent to the activity at half-saturation. Furthermore, since the overall binding constant determines the standard-state free-energy change for the corresponding reaction, we can find this free-energy change by simply knowing the value of the median activity. We shall develop these ideas more extensively in the next section.

3.2.3 The Median Activity and the Free Energy of Ligation

The work (or free energy) involved in adding an infinitesimal amount, δn_x, of ligand X drawn from a reservoir at standard-state condition (unit activity) to the macromolecule in equilibrium with ligand at activity x is given by

$$\delta G_X = (\mu_X - \mu_X^0) \delta n_x = (RT \ln x) \delta n_x, \tag{3.20}$$

where G_X is the free energy of ligand binding, μ_X is the chemical potential of ligand X, and μ_X^0 is the standard-state chemical potential of X. This concept of the work of adding ligand to a macromolecular system was originally developed by Wyman (1964). Considering one mole of macromolecule, the total work of ligation, ΔG_X, that arises from a state where there is no ligand in the system and leads finally to a state with $\bar{X}$ moles in the system is then given by the integral of the last equation,

$$\Delta G_X = RT \int_0^{\bar{X}} \ln x \, \delta \bar{X}, \qquad (3.21)$$

where $\delta n_x = \delta \bar{X}$, since one mole of macromolecule is considered. The ligation process described by this integral is represented by the areas shown in Figure 3-2.

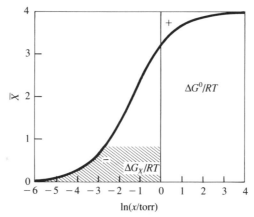

Figure 3-2.
This plot shows how the binding free energy to β_4 chains, isolated from hemoglobin (data from Tyuma *et al.*, 1971), is depicted by the areas between the standard-state ligand axis (ln 1 = 0) and the binding curve. Negative values (indicated by a minus sign) of the free energy of ligation occur when the binding curve is to the left of the reference line, and positive values (indicated by the plus sign) occur when the curve is to the right. The free energy of saturation ΔG_t^0 is given by the sum of both areas (with the proper sign) in the limits as $\ln x \to -\infty$ to $+\infty$.

The total work of saturation is given by the area involved in going from the bottom to the top asymptote. The work of saturation is equivalent to the standard free-energy change for converting the unligated macromolecule M to the fully liganded macromolecule MX_t described by the reaction process: $M + tX \to MX_t$. The standard free-energy change for the process ΔG_t^0 is thus also given by $-RT \ln \beta_t$. Furthermore, the total work of saturating the macromolecule is represented by the area between the binding curve and the standard-state axis multiplied by RT. This area is equivalent to a rectangle defined by the standard-state axis and the line drawn through the median activity x_m as shown in Figure 3-3. The shaded area is $RTt \ln x_m$. (The median line occurs where the areas under, A_u, and above, A_a, are seen to be equal.) As already noted, the same free-energy change is given by the $-RT \ln \beta_t$, which yields the relation of x_m and β_t given by equation (3.19). Clearly, the total free

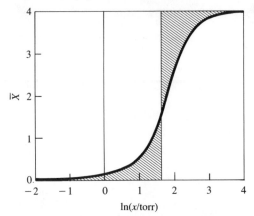

Figure 3-3.
Oxygen-binding curve of normal hemoglobin drawn from data of Imai (1982): 25°C, pH 7.4, 0.1 M Cl$^-$ (intrinsic binding constants $\kappa_1 = .0218$, $\kappa_2 = .062$, $\kappa_3 = .30$, $\kappa_4 = 3.45$ in torr^{-1}). The median ligand pressure, x_m (5.18 torr), is defined by the position of equal shaded areas (A_u and A_a) or by the equivalence of the rectangular area to the area between the binding curve and abscissa, at ln $x = 0$. $\bar{X}$ represents the moles of oxygen bound per tetramer.

energy of binding depends on the standard state chosen for the ligand X, since this state defines the areas to the binding curve.

The median rule and other relations involving the binding polynomial are obvious for a single-site molecule, where $t = 1$; here the binding curve is always symmetric, and the median activity is the same as the half-saturation activity, $x_{1/2}$, and is given by $1/\beta_1$.

A convenient choice of the standard state of the ligand, if we want to examine the symmetry of the binding curve, is to make it the same as the median, x_m. This is equivalent to changing the variable x to x' by the transformation $x = x_m x'$. The resulting normalized binding polynomial (Briggs, 1983), P_N, is then written as

$$P_N = 1 + \beta_1(x_m)x' + \beta_2(x_m)^2 x'^2 + \cdots + \beta_t(x_m)^t x'^t. \qquad (3.22)$$

By equation (3.19) the coefficient of the last term becomes unity:

$$P_N = 1 + \beta_1 x_m x' + \beta_2 x_m^2 x'^2 + \cdots + x'^t \qquad (3.23)$$

or

$$P_N = 1 + \beta_1' x' + \beta_2' x'^2 + \cdots + x'^t, \text{ where } \beta_i' = \beta_i x_m^i.$$

The relation between the internal coefficients will determine whether the binding curve is symmetric or not (see Section 3.2.5).

3.2.4 Properties of the Species Fractions

As we have seen, the ligand-binding properties of the macromolecule, represented by an experimental binding curve, are uniquely defined by the binding polynomial. Underlying these general results are the concentrations of the various ligated species and their functional dependence on ligand activity. In this section we wish to explore some of the properties and relationships between species concentrations. For convenience we shall express these concentrations as species fractions. They are then represented by the various terms in the binding polynomial, normalized by the polynomial itself, and as we have seen in Chapter 2 may be written as

$$\alpha_i = \frac{\beta_i x^i}{P}. \tag{3.24}$$

Since by this expression $\alpha_0 = 1/P$, we see that the various fractions are linearly related to each other through the factor $\beta_i x^i$ as

$$\alpha_i = \alpha_0 \beta_i x^i, \tag{3.25}$$

or in terms of the stepwise constants, K_i, we obtain from their definition the result

$$\alpha_i = \alpha_{i-1} K_i x. \tag{3.26}$$

The sum of all species fractions is, of course, equal to unity:

$$\sum \alpha_i = 1. \tag{3.27}$$

Each species fraction α_i, when plotted against $\bar{X}$, passes through a maximum at the point given by $\bar{X} = i$. To show this important result, differentiate the logarithm of α_i, given by equation (3.24), with respect to $\ln x$, as follows:

$$\frac{d \ln \alpha_i}{d \ln x} = \left(i - \frac{d \ln P}{d \ln x} \right) = (i - \bar{X}) \tag{3.28}$$

or

$$\frac{d \ln \alpha_i}{d \bar{X}} = \frac{i - \bar{X}}{\dfrac{d \bar{X}}{d \ln x}}. \tag{3.29}$$

The condition that α_i be a maximum is that $\bar{X} = i$. This condition holds for $i = 1, 2, \ldots, t - 1$. However, when $i = 0$ or t, corresponding to $\bar{X} = 0$ or t, the right side of equation (3.29) becomes indeterminate, because $d\bar{X}/d \ln x \to 0$.

The values of α_0 and α_t diminish monotonically from a maximum value of 1.

In order to evaluate the values of $\alpha_i(\text{max})$ for i from 0 to t it is necessary to know the values of the binding constants β_i. As an example, consider the simplest case of a macromolecule containing t independent and identical binding sites. Then the binding polynomial is

$$P = (1 + \kappa x)^t \qquad (3.30)$$

and

$$\beta_i = \binom{t}{i} \kappa^i \qquad (3.31)$$

where the parenthetical term is the binomial coefficient. Thus

$$\alpha_i = \frac{\binom{t}{i}(\kappa x)^i}{(1 + \kappa x)^t}. \qquad (3.32)$$

We know that α_i is a maximum for the value of $x = x_i(\text{max})$, where $\bar{X} = i$. The $\bar{X}$ is given from (3.30) by

$$\bar{X} = \frac{t\kappa x}{1 + \kappa x}. \qquad (3.33)$$

So setting $\bar{X} = i$, we obtain

$$\kappa x_i(\text{max}) = \frac{i}{t - i}, \qquad (3.34)$$

whence

$$\alpha_i(\text{max}) = \binom{t}{i} \left[\frac{i}{t}\right]^i \left[\frac{t - i}{t}\right]^{t-i}. \qquad (3.35)$$

Note that this result is independent of the intrinsic binding constant κ, and is symmetric with respect to $i \leftrightarrow t - i$. The more general expression for the dependence of α_i on $\bar{X}$ is also given from equations (3.32) and (3.33) as

$$\alpha_i = \binom{t}{i} \left[\frac{\bar{X}}{t}\right]^i \left[\frac{t - \bar{X}}{t}\right]^{t-1}. \qquad (3.36)$$

This expression is equivalent to the corresponding terms in the binomial expansion of $(p + q)^t$ where $\bar{X}/t = p$ and $(t - \bar{X})/t = q = 1 - p$. An example of the species fractions computed for this statistical situation is shown in Figure 3-4.

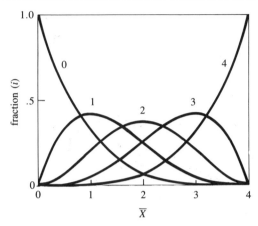

Figure 3-4.
Species fractions for a macromolecule such as β_4 hemoglobin with four equivalent binding sites as a function of $\bar{X}$.

An example that illustrates the general theorem that the maximum value of the species fraction α_i occurs when $\bar{X} = i$ is shown in Figure 3-5, using data for the binding of oxygen to human hemoglobin (Chu et al., 1984). The maximum value of α_1 is seen to be reached at $\bar{X} = 1$, and the fractions α_2 and α_3, which are so small that they can hardly be discerned, must have their maxima at 2 and 3, respectively.

General statistical properties of the distribution of ligated species that determine the binding curve are described by moments of the species distribution (Gill et al., 1978). In principle, if we knew all the moments, we could evaluate all the binding constants. Generally this is not possible, but other useful properties are described by relations involving the moments of lower degrees, and we shall outline some of these results.

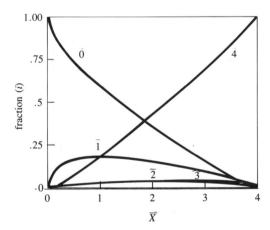

Figure 3-5.
Species fraction plot (α_i) versus degree of oxygen saturation ($\bar{X}$) for human hemoglobin (pH 7.4) using binding constants established by Chu et al. (1984).

The qth moment of the species fractions is given by weighting each species fraction by the number of ligands it contains, by the factor i^q, and summing over all species. The zeroth moment is just the sum of unity-weighted α's, which is equal to one. The first moment is the same as $\bar{X}$, and higher moments are defined accordingly. These results are shown as follows:

zeroth moment,
$$\sum_{i=0}^{t} i^0 \alpha_i = \frac{\sum \beta_i x^i}{\sum \beta_i x^i} = 1; \tag{3.37}$$

first moment,
$$\sum_{i=0}^{t} i^1 \alpha_i = \frac{\sum i \beta_i x^i}{\sum \beta_i x^i} = \bar{X}; \tag{3.38}$$

second moment,
$$\sum_{i=0}^{t} i^2 \alpha_i = \frac{\sum i^2 \beta_i x^i}{\sum \beta_i x^i} = \overline{X^2}; \tag{3.39}$$

qth moment,
$$\sum_{i=0}^{t} i^q \alpha_i = \frac{\sum i^q \beta_i x^i}{\sum \beta_i x^i} = \overline{X^q}. \tag{3.40}$$

The moments are related to various derivatives of the binding curve expressed as $\bar{X}$ versus $\ln x$. This may be illustrated by formulating the derivative of $d\bar{X}/d\ln x$ from $\bar{X}$ given by equation (3.38) as follows:

$$\frac{d\bar{X}}{d\ln x} = \frac{x \, d\bar{X}}{dx} = \frac{\sum i^2 \beta_i x^i}{\sum \beta_i x^i} - \left(\frac{\sum i \beta_i x^i}{\sum \beta_i x^i}\right)^2. \tag{3.41)*}$$

From equations (3.38) and (3.39) we thus obtain the result

$$\frac{d\bar{X}}{d\ln x} = \overline{X^2} - (\bar{X})^2, \tag{3.42}$$

which shows that the slope of any titration curve at a given point is equal to the difference between the two kinds of averages, the mean of the square and the square of the mean. Higher derivatives can be found by extending this process (Gill *et al.*, 1978). The first derivative given by equation (3.41) is a measure of the buffering power or the binding capacity of a system. A large value of the binding capacity means the system can accept or deliver large quantities of X for relatively small changes in ligand activity x. In other words, the binding capacity is simply a measure of cooperativity, namely, the steepness of the binding curve (Di Cera *et al.*, 1988b).

We have encountered various linear equations (3.18, 3.25, 3.26, 3.27, 3.37, etc.) involving the species fractions. These are related to various equilibrium

---

* K. Linderstrøm-Lang had given this derivation at a lecture at Harvard in 1939. He was then cut off from communication by the war, and Cohn and Edsall gave the derivation in their 1943 book with acknowledgement to him.

constants, areas defined above and below the binding curve, and to derivatives of the binding curve through their moments. These equations are summarized in a convenient linear form as follows:

$$\left(\frac{x}{x_m}\right)^t \quad \alpha_0 \qquad\qquad - \quad \alpha_t = 0;$$

$$(K_1x) \quad \alpha_0 - \alpha_1 \qquad\qquad\qquad = 0;$$

$$(K_t x)\alpha_{t-1} - \quad \alpha_t = 0; \qquad (3.43)$$

$$\alpha_0 + \alpha_1 + \quad \alpha_2 + \cdots + \quad \alpha_{t-1} + \quad \alpha_t = 1;$$

$$\alpha_1 + \quad 2\alpha_2 + \cdots + \quad (t-1)\alpha_{t-1} + \quad t\alpha_t = \bar{X};$$

$$\alpha_1 + 2^2\alpha_2 + \cdots + (t-1)^2\alpha_{t-1} + t^2\alpha_t = \overline{X^2};$$

etc.

If the binding curve is symmetric, there are additional constraints in the form of symmetrically placed species fractions (see below). Consequently a body of information is available for finding the values of the species fractions as a function of the ligand activity x. Such values are useful for, e.g., evaluating the equilibrium constants. In order to solve for the $t + 1$ species fractions, we need at least $t + 1$ equations. The main practical problem is the evaluation of the experimental parameters $(x_m, K_1, K_t, \bar{X}, \bar{X}^2,$ etc.).* Details of this procedure will be outlined in Appendix 3.3.

3.2.5 Symmetry

When a binding curve ($\bar{X}$ versus $\ln x$) is obtained for a multisite macromolecule, the curve will in general have a shape that is different as the two ends are approached; i.e., the curve is nonsymmetric. A special situation arises when the curve is symmetric, and we wish to describe what properties of the binding polynomial create this symmetry.

The mathematical requirement for a symmetric binding curve is that a graph of $\bar{X}$ versus $\ln x$ has a twofold axis perpendicular to its plane at the point $x = x_m$ (Wyman, 1948, 1978). In other words, the point at x_m, where $\bar{X} = t/2$, is a center of symmetry. This situation is illustrated for a four-site macromolecule in Figure 3-6. As seen in this figure, any two areas, defined by vertical sides situated at equal distances from $\ln x_m$, and indicated by shaded areas shown in the figure, will be equal when the curve is symmetric. Examination of the features that determine these areas will show us what conditions on the equilibrium constants within the binding polynomial are necessary and sufficient for symmetry.

* The Hill plot provides information about K_1, K_t, and $\overline{X^2}$. Thus one may solve for species fractions in situations where $t < 5$.

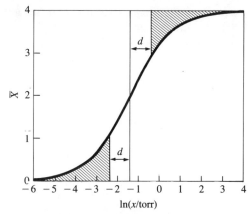

Figure 3-6.
Binding curve for a four-site macromolecule (see Figure 3-2). The asymptotic areas under and above the binding curve are defined by vertical boundaries at equal distances (d) from $\ln x_m$.

We first transform the binding curve so that the zero axis, or reference state, is shifted to its median activity value, i.e., to $\ln x_m$. This is achieved by normalizing the values of the activity x by the median in order to define a normalized activity x' as $x' = x/x_m$. We have already seen that this transformation gives the normalized binding polynomial [equation (3.23)] in terms of the median-normalized activity x'. The shape of the binding curve is invariant under this transformation. The result of making this median transformation on the binding curve of Figure 3-6, which then becomes $\bar{X}$ versus $\ln x'$, is shown in Figure 3-7. As we see in this figure, the zero reference

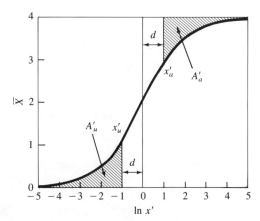

Figure 3-7.
Median normalized binding curve to a four-site macromolecule (see Figure 3-6) where $x' = x/x_m$. Note that the reference-state axis becomes the median line. The vertical lines defining the asymptotic areas $(A'_a$ and $A'_u)$ are at activities x'_u and x'_a, where $\ln x'_a = -\ln x'_u = d$.

axis is indeed the same as the median. Also shown in this figure are the areas A_u' and A_a', which are here defined at two arbitrary points x_u' and x_a'. For the binding curve to be symmetric, these areas must be equal when the distances $-\ln x_u' = \ln x_a'$, or $x_a' = 1/x_u'$. We can evaluate these areas from equations (3.13) and (3.14) in terms of x_a':

$$A_u' = \ln P_N(x_u') = \ln P_N\left(\frac{1}{x_a'}\right), \tag{3.44}$$

$$A_a' = \ln \frac{P_N(x_a')}{x_a'^t}. \tag{3.45}$$

Thus for symmetry:

$$\frac{P_N(x_a')}{x_a'^t} = P_N\left(\frac{1}{x_a'}\right). \tag{3.46}$$

Substitution yields

$$\frac{1 + \beta_1 x_m x_a' + \beta_2 x_m^2 x_a'^2 + \cdots + \beta_t x_m^t x_a'^t}{x_a'^t}$$

$$= 1 + \beta_1 x_m \frac{1}{x_a'} + \beta_2 x_m^2 \left(\frac{1}{x_a'}\right)^2 + \cdots + \frac{\beta_t x_m^t}{x_a'^t}. \tag{3.47}$$

Remembering that $\beta_t x_m^t = 1$, we then identify terms of equal powers in $1/x_a'$. These results determine necessary conditions for symmetry* given as

$$\beta_{t-i} x_m^{t-i} = \beta_i x_m^i. \tag{3.48}$$

Furthermore, this result shows that within the normalized form of the binding polynomial given by equation (3.23), the coefficients of the $t - i$ and i species are equal. Thus when the normalized binding polynomial is symmetric, it gives rise to a symmetric binding curve. Furthermore, this result shows that the species fractions α_i and α_{t-i} must be equal to each other at the value of the median activity x_m. An example of this situation is shown in Figure 3-8. Note the reflective symmetry for conjugate species pairs. Indeed, we can prove,

---

* This condition was first given by Wyman (1948) employing a somewhat different method. When formulated in terms of stepwise constants, K_i, the symmetry conditions [equation (3.48)] may be found also from

$$(K_1 K_2 \cdots K_{t-i})(K_1 K_2 \cdots K_{t-i})^i = (K_1 K_2 \cdots K_i)(K_1 K_2 \cdots K_t).$$

For example when $t = 4$, one finds $K_1 K_4 = K_2 K_3$. Note: it makes no difference whether stoichiometric Ks or intrinsic κs are used in these expressions, since in the latter situation the statistical factors cancel to unity in the expressions.

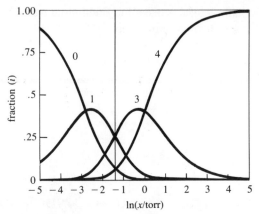

Figure 3-8.
For a four-site molecule the symmetric species fractions α_i and α_{4-i} follow curves that have reflection symmetry about the median activity, x_m, when plotted versus $\ln x$ (data from Figure 3-2, $\ln x_m = -1.38$).

following arguments similar to equations (3.44) to (3.47), that the species fractions α_i and α_{t-i} at x' and $1/x'$, respectively, are equal when the general symmetry conditions of equation (3.48) hold. Also, since $\bar{X}$ versus $\ln x$ is symmetric under these conditions, the fractions α_i and α_{t-i} will be symmetric with respect to $t/2$ when plotted against $\bar{X}$. An example of this is seen in Figure 3-4.

The effect of symmetry is also manifested in the relation between symmetrically related fractions α_i and α_{t-i} when equations (3.48) and (3.25) are combined to yield the linear forms

$$\alpha_i = \alpha_{t-i} \frac{x_m^{t-i}}{x_m^{i}} \frac{x^i}{x^{t-i}} \tag{3.49}$$

or

$$\alpha_i = \alpha_{t-i} \frac{(x')^i}{(x')^{t-i}}. \tag{3.50}$$

When symmetry is then detected for a binding curve, this additional set of relations may be added to the general linear equations given by (3.43).

Symmetry conditions will necessarily occur for single- and double-site binding situations, in which the normalized binding polynomial is always symmetric. If symmetry can be detected experimentally by the shape of the binding curve, or the dependence of species fractions on ligand activity, then the mathematical relations given above will apply. Finally, various hypothetical models for macromolecular binding processes will always yield binding polynomials that can be subjected to the median normalization procedure and then examined in terms of their symmetric or nonsymmetric properties.

An important example of a nonsymmetric binding curve is found for oxygen binding to human hemoglobin. Weber (1982) and Peller (1982) pointed out that the curve displays higher cooperativity at high degrees of oxygen saturation than at complementary low degrees of saturation. This is also indicated by the fact that $K_1 K_4 \ll K_2 K_3$, or even more directly by the recent observation that the triply oxygenated species has a markedly lower population than the singly oxygenated species (Gill et al., 1987). Weber and Peller point out that this situation confers a physiological advantage for efficient transfer of oxygen under the usual conditions where the blood is saturated between 50 and 100 percent.

3.3 THE BINDING POLYNOMIAL FOR INDEPENDENT MULTI-SITE MOLECULES

As noted in Chapter 2, the simplest binding of a single ligand by a multi-site macromolecule occurs when the sites are all independent. This situation provides an important reference case, and its general properties can be described with the concepts that have been developed. Each site has its own binding polynomial, namely, $1 + \kappa x$. Since they are independent, the binding polynomial for the macromolecule will then be the product of t such terms. When all the sites are identical, the result is

$$P(\text{identical sites}) = (1 + \kappa x)^t. \tag{3.51}$$

The binding curve, found by taking the logarithmic derivative with respect to $\ln x$, is

$$\bar{X} = \frac{t\kappa x}{1 + \kappa x}. \tag{3.52}$$

As may be seen by inspection, the binding curve is symmetric and the median $x_m = 1/\kappa$. This may be proven more systematically by expansion of equation (3.51) and noting that $\beta_t = \kappa^t$, and thus by equation (3.19) we find $x_m = 1/\kappa$. The slope $d\bar{X}/d\ln x$ may also be found from equation (3.52) to be t times the slope given by the one of the single-site curves:

$$\frac{d\bar{X}}{d\ln x} = \frac{t\kappa x}{1 + \kappa x} - \frac{t\kappa^2 x^2}{(1 + \kappa x)^2}, \tag{3.53}$$

$$\frac{d\bar{X}}{d\ln x} = \bar{X} - \frac{1}{t}(\bar{X})^2 = \bar{X}\left(1 - \frac{1}{t}\bar{X}\right). \tag{3.54}$$

The slope or binding capacity has a maximum value of $t/4$ when $\bar{X} = t/2$. The binding capacity is also given by the general result of equation (3.42) and thus $\overline{X^2}$ is given in terms of $\bar{X}$ as

$$\overline{X^2} = \bar{X} + (\bar{X})^2 - \frac{1}{t}(\bar{X})^2. \tag{3.55}$$

The normalized form of the binding polynomial is given by substitution into (3.51) as follows:

$$x = x_m x' = (1/\kappa)x'$$

$$P_N(\text{identical sites}) = (1 + x')^t. \tag{3.56}$$

When expanded, this gives by the binomial expansion

$$P_N(\text{identical}) = 1 + tx' + \frac{t(t-1)}{2!}x'^2 + \cdots + \frac{t!}{(t-i)!i!}x'^i + \cdots + x'^t. \tag{3.57}$$

The coefficients of the binomial expansion are symmetric (recall the Pascal triangle rule for the binomial coefficients). In terms of the Adair coefficients, we find that

$$\beta_i = \frac{t!}{(t-i)!i!}\kappa^i \tag{3.58}$$

and

$$K_i = \frac{\beta_i}{\beta_{i-1}} = \frac{t!}{(t-i)!i!}\frac{(t-i+1)!(i-1)!}{(t)!}\kappa = \frac{t-i+1}{i}\kappa. \tag{3.59}$$

The coefficients preceding the site-binding constants in these equations are termed the *statistical factors* (Edsall and Wyman, 1958), and serve to define the intrinsic binding constants κ_i in terms of the stepwise binding constants even for nonidentical binding sites:

intrinsic constants: $$\kappa_i = \frac{i}{t-i+1}K_i. \tag{3.60}$$

In general, the overall Adair constants are defined in terms of stepwise intrinsic constants as

$$\beta_i = \frac{t!}{(t-i)!i!}\kappa_1\kappa_2\cdots\kappa_i. \tag{3.61}$$

For independent but nonidentical binding sites, the state of each site is specified by its own binding polynomial, namely, $1 + \kappa_i x$, for the ith site. The binding polynomial for the macromolecule is then

$$P(\text{independent sites}) = \prod_{i=1}^{t}(1 + \kappa_i x). \tag{3.62}$$

The binding curve is given as

$$\bar{X} = \frac{d \ln P}{d \ln x} = \frac{\kappa_1 x}{1 + \kappa_1 x} + \frac{\kappa_2 x}{1 + \kappa_2 x} + \cdots + \frac{\kappa_t x}{1 + \kappa_t x}, \tag{3.63}$$

which shows the additive contribution of each site. The median may be found from the last term in the expansion of equation (3.62):

$$\kappa_1 \kappa_2 \cdots \kappa_t = \beta_t = 1/x_m{}^t, \tag{3.64}$$

$$x_m = (\kappa_1 \kappa_2 \cdots \kappa_t)^{-1/t}. \tag{3.65}$$

The overall standard free energy of binding, $-RT \ln \beta_t$, may be readily seen from equation (3.64) to consist of the sum of free energies of binding to the individual independent sites. Finally, the binding polynomial and thus the binding curve will always be symmetric for $t = 2$ or $t = 1$. For $t > 2$, symmetry will depend on particular values of the binding constants.

3.4 THE BINDING POLYNOMIAL FOR A FROZEN MIXTURE

We noted in Chapter 2 that the binding polynomial for a mixture of macromolecules with single binding sites of different affinities is found by raising the binding polynomials of each type of macromolecule by a power equal to the mole fraction of that species. For a more general system, where there is a mixture of macromolecules A and B, with mole fractions α_A and α_B, the binding polynomial is then

$$P = P_A{}^{\alpha_A} P_B{}^{\alpha_B}, \tag{3.66}$$

where P_A and P_B are the binding polynomials of each type of macromolecule. The X binding curve is then

$$\bar{X} = \alpha_A \bar{X}_A + \alpha_B \bar{X}_B, \tag{3.67}$$

where $\bar{X}_A$ and $\bar{X}_B$ are the binding curves for A and B.

The median activity x_m for the overall binding curve is related to terminal Adair constants for each of the binding polynomials as follows. Let P_A be of degree r, P_B be of degree s, and $t = \alpha_A r + \alpha_B s$. Then the median activities for A

and B are x_{mA} and x_{mB} respectively. These median activities are determined by the terminal Adair constants, β_{rA} and β_{sB}, as follows:

$$\beta_{rA} = \frac{1}{x_{mA}{}^r}, \qquad \beta_{sB} = \frac{1}{x_{mB}{}^s}. \tag{3.68}$$

The terminal Adair constant for the expansion of equation (3.66) is β_t and is related to β_{rA} and β_{sB} as

$$\beta_{rA}{}^{\alpha_A}\beta_{sB}{}^{\alpha_B} = \beta_t. \tag{3.69}$$

Thus the medians are related to each other as

$$\left(\frac{1}{x_{mA}}\right)^{r\alpha_A}\left(\frac{1}{x_{mB}}\right)^{s\alpha_B} = \left(\frac{1}{x_m}\right)^t. \tag{3.70}$$

The free energy of complete ligation from the standard state is then

$$\Delta G_X^0 = -RT(\alpha_A \ln \beta_{rA} + \alpha_B \ln \beta_{sB}). \tag{3.71}$$

These results can easily be extended to mixtures of more than two components.

3.5 FACTORABILITY OF BINDING POLYNOMIALS

As we have now seen in some detail, the ligand-binding curve of a non-dissociating macromolecule of t sites is determined by a set of t mass-action law reactions that relate the concentration of unligated (M) to various ligated species (MX$_i$) through equilibrium constants (β_i). The sum of all macromolecular species determines the partition function of the system, which can be described as a power series in ligand activity x, and is called the binding polynomial. Each term represents the relative concentration of the macromolecular species with iX ligands bound, i.e., MX$_i$, and as we have seen, the binding polynomial P is given by $1 + \beta_1 x + \beta_2 x^2 + \cdots + \beta_t x^t$. Experimental binding curves, provided they are accurate enough, allow evaluation of the β's.

The problem we now wish to solve is this: given a specific binding polynomial, do the binding sites interact cooperatively? In particular, could the binding events be described by sites that bind independently, or not? This question is answered by considering how the polynomial factors into linear, quadratic, etc., subpolynomials with positive coefficients. The coefficients of all binding polynomials represent equilibrium constants, i.e., ratios of molecular concentrations, and only positive values have physical significance. The conditions of factorability of P into positive coefficient polynomials are a mathematical problem. Two groups, Bardsley, Woolfson, and Woods in Manchester, and Briggs in Boulder, have examined various aspects of this problem, and here we summarize some of their findings. (For more details, see Bardsley *et al.*, 1977a, 1977b, 1980a, 1980b; and Briggs, 1983, 1984, 1985a, 1985b.)

If the binding polynomial is completely factorable into linear terms of the form $1 + \kappa_i x$, we can interpret this to mean that all the sites behave independently. For this situation successive overall Adair constants have been found to satisfy the following rule (Wyman and Phillipson, 1974):

$$\frac{\left[\beta_j \Big/ \binom{t}{j}\right]^{1/j}}{\left[\beta_{j-1} \Big/ \binom{t}{j-1}\right]^{1/(j-1)}} \leqq 1. \tag{3.72}$$

However, this relation by itself does not guarantee complete factorability into linear terms; it is a necessary but not a sufficient condition for complete factorability. If some of the ratios (3.72) are greater than 1, then complete factorization to linear terms is not possible, and there must be some interaction between sites.

From a practical point of view, we can always calculate the roots of the binding polynomial by computer methods. When the roots are all real and negative, this corresponds to linear binding factors where the roots (r_i) determine the independent binding constants as $-1/\kappa_i$. Another situation occurs when the roots are all complex, occurring in pairs of complex conjugates. This corresponds to site-site interactions. Whenever the binding polynomial gives complex roots, we may be sure the system contains some positively interacting sites, and we may define positive site-site interaction by the presence of complex roots. In terms of the Hill plot, a slope greater than 1 at any given point tells us that the binding polynomial is not completely factorable into positive linear terms, and there must be interaction between at least some of the sites. When the Hill slope is everywhere less than 1, we can decide whether positive site-site interaction exists only by exploring the roots of the binding polynomial. If any are complex, then there are some site-site interactions. This analysis of site-site interactions says nothing about the nature of the mechanism which produces them. However, it gives an overall guidance for developing a mechanistic model.

As we have seen before, the binding curve and its derivative are determined by the nature of the binding polynomial. Thus when the binding polynomial is factorable, then the various factors contribute additively to the binding curve and to the slope of the binding curve. For binding polynomials that factor as $P = P_r P_s$, the binding curve $\bar{X}$ is given as

$$\bar{X} = \bar{X}_r + \bar{X}_s, \tag{3.73}$$

where $\bar{X}_r$ and $\bar{X}_s$ are the sub-binding curves for the binding polynomial P_r and P_s. The degree of P_r is r, and the degree of P_s is such that $r + s = t$. The overall slope of the binding curve is also seen to be the sum of the slopes of sub-binding curves:

$$\frac{d\bar{X}}{d \ln x} = \frac{d\bar{X}_r}{d \ln x} + \frac{d\bar{X}_s}{d \ln x}. \tag{3.74}$$

For two single-site polynomials, $r = s = 1$, and we see that the overall slope will be greatest when P_r and P_s are identical; otherwise each contributes out of synchrony, and the slope is always less than if the two sites are identical. We shall see how this result always leads to a Hill slope of less than one and is a mark of negative cooperativity. For the general case, the Hill slope cannot be greater than the larger of r and s.

A graphical representation of the root patterns and the cooperativity of the Hill slope is depicted by the possible root locations on the complex plane. For a dimer, $P_N = 1 + \alpha x' + x'^2$, which has the real roots $-r$ and $-1/r$ when $\alpha > 2$, and has nonreal roots, given by $\cos \theta \pm i \sin \theta$ when $\alpha < 2$. The possible root patterns are then located along the negative real axis, or on the unit circle on the negative real side, as shown in Figure 3-9a. The Hill coefficient n_H for the median activity x' takes on values determined by $4/(\alpha + 2)$, with a maximum value of 2 when $\alpha = 0$ or $\theta = \pi/2$, going to a value of 1 when $\alpha = 2$ or $r = 1$, and decreasing further as α exceeds 2. In the more general situation shown in Figure 3-9b, for the symmetric case with t binding sites, possible root locations are extended into the positive half-plane, with a limit defined by the angle π/t. If a root occurs at this angle, then $n_H = t$. If all roots are

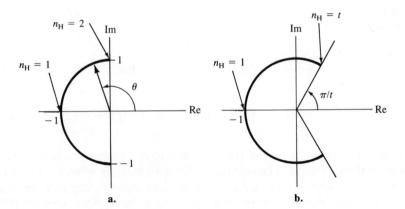

Figure 3-9.
Root locations and limiting Hill coefficient values (n_H) for two-site binding (a) and for t-site binding (b). (From Briggs, 1985b.)

equal (-1), then $n_\mathrm{H} = 1$. For a Hill slope greater than 1, some combination of nonreal and real roots is required. Hill slopes less than one must occur with all negative real roots, and may occur with certain combinations of negative real roots and nonreal roots. For the four-site molecule hemoglobin, an analysis of roots reveals a variety of site-interaction patterns under different conditions (Connelly *et al.*, 1986). Further mathematical details concerning factorization are given in Appendix 3.4.

3.6 HILL PLOTS

The Hill plot (Hill, 1910; see Chapter 2) displays information about site-site interaction in a broad sense. The plot is made by $\log[\bar{X}/(t - \bar{X})]$ versus $\log x$. It is also given in terms of the fractional saturation $\theta = \bar{X}/t$ as $\log[\theta/(1 - \theta)]$ versus $\log x$. The parameters of the Hill plot in terms of overall Adair constants are given as follows:

$$\frac{\theta}{1 - \theta} = \frac{\bar{X}}{t - \bar{X}} = \frac{\sum i\beta_i x^i}{t\sum \beta_i x^i - \sum i\beta_i x^i}. \tag{3.75}$$

These parameters behave in the asymptotic regions where x is small and $\theta \to 0$, and where x is large and $\theta \to 1$, as follows:

$$\text{as } \theta \to 0, \quad \theta/(1 - \theta) = (\beta_1 x)/t + \cdots;$$

$$\text{as } \theta \to 1, \quad \theta/(1 - \theta) = t[\beta_t/\beta_{t-1}]x + \cdots. \tag{3.76}$$

Since $\beta_1 = K_1$ (the first step equilibrium constant) and $\beta_t/\beta_{t-1} = K_t$ (the last step equilibrium constant), we can assess how the Hill plot will behave in these limiting regions:

$$\text{as } \theta \to 0, \quad \log\frac{\theta}{1 - \theta} = \log\frac{K_1}{t} + \log x + \cdots; \tag{3.77}$$

$$\text{as } \theta \to 1, \quad \log\frac{\theta}{1 - \theta} = \log tK_t + \log x + \cdots. \tag{3.78}$$

In these limiting regions the Hill plot will have linear asymptotes with a positive slope of unity. The intercepts of the asymptotes when $\log x = 0$ are $\log(K_1/t)$ and $\log(tK_t)$. Since the initial and final intrinsic step constants are $\kappa_1 = K_1/t$ and $\kappa_t = tK_t$, these intercepts give these intrinsic constants directly. This is shown for human hemoglobin in Figure 3-10. Note that these asymptotes are experimentally defined by measurements at very low and very high saturations that are generally difficult to make accurately.

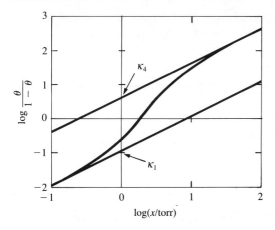

Figure 3-10.
Hill plot of oxygen binding to hemoglobin A at 25° in 0.05 M bis-tris (pH 7.4) (Imai, 1973). Asymptotes intercept the reference-state axis at intrinsic constants κ_1 and κ_4 ($\kappa_1 = 0.114$, $\kappa_2 = 0.165$, $\kappa_3 = 1.17$, $\kappa_4 = 4.04$ torr^{-1}).

3.6.1 Hill Plot and Cooperativity

The slope of the binding curve can indicate the cooperativity or interaction of binding between sites (Bardsley and Wyman, 1978). We compare the slope of a binding curve with the slope of a reference curve for a system with the same number of sites. The reference system is chosen to be one of t identical binding sites, and its slope is given by $\bar{X}(1 - \bar{X}/t)$. The coefficient of cooperativity n_H is then defined by the ratio of the slopes of the two curves:

$$n_H = \frac{\dfrac{d\bar{X}}{d \ln x}}{\bar{X}(1 - \bar{X}/t)} = \frac{\dfrac{d\theta}{d \ln x}}{\theta(1 - \theta)}, \tag{3.79}$$

where we have also noted that $\bar{X}/t = \theta$. From equation (3.42) we find that n_H defines the second moment of the binding curve, $\overline{X^2}$, as

$$\overline{X^2} = n_H \bar{X}\left(1 - \frac{\bar{X}}{t}\right) + (\bar{X})^2. \tag{3.80}$$

For hemoglobin ($t = 4$), at half-saturation, where the Hill coefficient is denoted by $n_{1/2}$, we see that the second moment is $n_{1/2} + 4$.

The slope of the Hill plot gives n_H directly as may be seen from

$$n_H = \frac{d \ln \dfrac{\theta}{1 - \theta}}{d \ln x} = \frac{d \ln \theta}{d \ln x} - \frac{d \ln(1 - \theta)}{d \ln x}$$

$$= \left(\frac{1}{\theta} + \frac{1}{1 - \theta}\right)\frac{d\theta}{d \ln x} \tag{3.81}$$

$$= \frac{1}{\theta(1 - \theta)}\frac{d\theta}{d \ln x},$$

where the last expression is the same as (3.79). The maximum value of n_H cannot exceed t, the number of binding sites on the macromolecule.

The binding polynomial, when there are only two species M and MX_t in the system, represents the situation of maximum cooperativity. This is given by $1 + x^t$ in normalized form. The slope of this binding curve is $t\bar{X}(1 - \bar{X}/t)$ and thus $n_H = t$, corresponding to a t-order reaction.

General expressions relating the Hill slope to the binding polynomial and its derivatives are developed in Appendix 3.2. An application using Hill-plot information for hemoglobin and making use of the linear equations described in (3.43) is described in Appendix 3.3.

3.7 BINDING POLYNOMIAL FOR SEVERAL LIGANDS

Up to this point our concern has been to formulate the effects of binding a single ligand to a multisite macromolecule. The relationships between reaction constants, the factorability of the binding polynomial, and the idea of cooperativity reflect homotropic interactions between binding sites. We now turn to the general situation, in which any number of different ligands may bind. In any practical situation we are faced with the problem that many different ligands bind to the macromolecule, and we must examine their influence upon each other. The binding polynomial for a given ligand has coefficients that will in general depend on the activity of other ligands, including the solvent, and thus are apparent binding constants. In this section we consider the formulation of the binding polynomial for two ligands, X and Y, and show how this polynomial describes the effects of one ligand on the binding of another. As indicated in Chapter 1, these are called *heterotropic effects*.

3.7.1 The Adair Form of the Binding Partition Function

The general binding polynomial is a mixed function of the activities of the several ligands. Consider a macromolecule M which binds both X and Y ligands. Suppose there are t X-binding sites and s Y-binding sites. Then we can form a variety of XY-ligated macromolecular species. These are shown in Figure 3-11 in the form of an array. The reactions in the array are described by

$$M + iX + jY \rightarrow MX_iY_j, \tag{3.82}$$

with an equilibrium constant β_{ij} given as

$$\beta_{ij} = \frac{[MX_iY_j]}{[M]x^iy^j}. \tag{3.83}$$

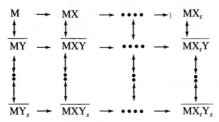

Figure 3-11.
Macromolecular species array for molecule with t X-binding sites
and s Y-binding sites.

Here x and y represent the ligand activities. As we have seen for a single ligand,
the binding partition function Q is just the sum of all the concentrations of all
species in the system, normalized to the concentration of a reference species,
here the unligated species:

$$Q = \sum_{j=0}^{s} \sum_{i=0}^{t} [MX_i Y_j]/[M]. \qquad (3.84)$$

The binding polynomial is then obtained by introducing the equilibrium
constant relations, and the result follows:

$$P = \sum_{j=0}^{s} \sum_{i=0}^{t} \beta_{ij} x^i y^j, \qquad (3.85)$$

where the lead term is unity. This is the Adair form of the equilibrium reactions
that describe the system, and represents an extension of the original Adair
scheme, which is applied to a single ligand. The macromolecule is nondissociating, and a specific number of X and Y binding sites exists. The binding
curves, namely, $\bar{X}$ versus $\ln x$ and $\bar{Y}$ versus $\ln y$, can be formulated in terms of
the appropriately weighted species concentrations in the species array as
follows:

$$\bar{X} = \frac{\sum_{j} \sum_{i} i[MX_i Y_j]}{\sum_{j} \sum_{i} [MX_i Y_j]}, \qquad (3.86)$$

$$\bar{Y} = \frac{\sum_{j} \sum_{i} j[MX_i Y_j]}{\sum_{j} \sum_{i} [MX_i Y_j]}. \qquad (3.87)$$

These definitions may be expressed in terms of the Adair reactions in the array,
and then even more succinctly by the use of the partial derivative operation as

follows:

$$\bar{X} = \frac{\sum\sum i\beta_{ij}x^iy^j}{P} = \left(\frac{\partial \ln P}{\partial \ln x}\right)_y, \tag{3.88}$$

$$\bar{Y} = \frac{\sum\sum j\beta_{ij}x^iy^j}{P} = \left(\frac{\partial \ln P}{\partial \ln y}\right)_x. \tag{3.89}$$

The expression ln P describes the species state of the macromolecule, and as such it may be regarded as a function of state. Indeed, we have seen that the binding polynomial P is equivalent to the partition function of the macromolecule; so we may draw on the general relations of statistical thermodynamics connecting the partition function and the thermodynamic properties of macromolecular systems. That fundamental foundation is described in detail by Hill (1960, 1985). We will also see in a later chapter that the value ln P determines the chemical potential of the macromolecule in the presence of its ligands (Wyman, 1965; Schellman, 1975). Thus recognizing that ln P is a function of the state, and that its differential is exact (see equation (2.82)), we may equate the cross partial derivatives:

$$\frac{\partial^2 \ln P}{\partial \ln x\, \partial \ln y} = \frac{\partial^2 \ln P}{\partial \ln y\, \partial \ln x}. \tag{3.90}$$

Insertion of equations (3.88) and (3.89) gives the first general linkage relation of different ligand activities on the binding curves:

$$\left(\frac{\partial \bar{X}}{\partial \ln y}\right)_x = \left(\frac{\partial \bar{Y}}{\partial \ln x}\right)_y. \tag{3.91}$$

This result is similar to the Maxwell relations found for the variables S, T, V, and p for simple thermodynamic systems. By Legendre transformations we obtain the three other linkage relations:*

$$\left(\frac{\partial \bar{X}}{\partial \bar{\bar{Y}}}\right)_x = -\left(\frac{\partial \ln y}{\partial \ln x}\right)_{\bar{Y}}, \tag{3.92}$$

$$\left(\frac{\partial \bar{Y}}{\partial \bar{\bar{X}}}\right)_y = -\left(\frac{\partial \ln x}{\partial \ln y}\right)_{\bar{X}}, \tag{3.93}$$

$$\left(\frac{\partial \ln y}{\partial \bar{X}}\right)_{\bar{Y}} = \left(\frac{\partial \ln x}{\partial \bar{Y}}\right)_{\bar{X}}. \tag{3.94}$$

---

* The Legendre transformation may be illustrated here by passing to a new function, ln $P - \bar{X}$ ln x, which when differentiated gives $d(\ln P - \bar{X} \ln x) = -\ln x\, d\bar{X} + \bar{Y}\, d\ln y$. Since this function is exact, we may equate the cross partial derivatives to obtain

$$-\left(\frac{\partial \ln x}{\partial \ln y}\right)_{\bar{X}} = \left(\frac{\partial \bar{Y}}{\partial \bar{X}}\right)_y.$$

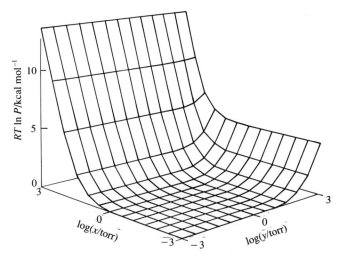

Figure 3-12.
Binding potential $(RT \ln P)$ of lobster hemocyanin as a function of O_2 and CO partial pressure as calculated by Robert *et al.* (1987) from data of Richey and Gill (1985). Note this system is an example of identical linkage discussed in Section 3.7.2.

We also note from equations (3.88) and (3.89) that $\ln P$ may be obtained by graphical integration of the observed binding curves, $\bar{X}$ and $\bar{Y}$ [see equation (2.84)]. Thus the full determination of $\ln P$ is given by the areas under the $\bar{X}$ and $\bar{Y}$ binding curves. When $\ln P$ is plotted versus $\ln x$ and $\ln y$, the result is a three-dimensional surface from which $\bar{X}$ and $\bar{Y}$ may be obtained. In Figure 3-12 we show such a surface, representing the binding properties of lobster hemocyanin, where the variables are oxygen and carbon monoxide.

An explicit formulation of heterotropic linkage can be developed by combining specific reactions involving columns or rows of the array of species in Figure 3-11. Consider the reaction of adding iX ligands to the macromolecule that is unligated in X but has various Y-ligated species. This is a reaction between species represented in the first column to species in the ith column. We let P_{0Y} and P_{iY} represent the Y-binding polynomials for the first column and ith column of species. The sum of all species in the respective columns is $[M]P_{0Y}$ and $[MX_i]P_{iY}$. The overall X-binding constant β_i is thus

$$\beta_i = \frac{[MX_i]P_{iY}}{[M]P_{0Y}x^i}. \tag{3.95}$$

Then with $\beta_{i0} = [MX_i]/([M]x^i)$ we obtain

$$\beta_i = \beta_{i0}\frac{P_{iY}}{P_{0Y}}. \tag{3.96}$$

In terms of stepwise X-binding constants between adjacent columns of species, we have

$$K_i = \frac{\beta_i}{\beta_{i-1}} = K_{i0} \frac{P_{iY}}{P_{i-1Y}}. \tag{3.97}$$

These equations show how the apparent X-binding constants depend on the Y ligand activity. Only when the Y-binding polynomials are different from one another will any Y activity affect the X-binding constants.

An alternative way (Wyman, 1948) of obtaining the same results is to normalize the binding polynomial given by equation (3.85) with the first-column Y-binding polynomial, i.e., (P/P_{0Y}). The lead term is unity, and the coefficients of the x activity are indicated as

$$\frac{P}{P_{0Y}} = 1 + \beta_{10} \frac{P_{1Y}}{P_{0Y}} x + \beta_{20} \frac{P_{2Y}}{P_{0Y}} x^2 + \cdots + \beta_{t0} \frac{P_{tY}}{P_{0Y}} x^t. \tag{3.98}$$

The Adair constant for the iX-binding reaction is then seen to be

$$\beta_i = \beta_{i0} \frac{P_{iY}}{P_{0Y}}. \tag{3.99}$$

This procedure is simply using another choice for the reference set of concentrations, namely, the set of Y-ligated species without any X.

The effect of a second ligand on the equilibrium constant of the first ligand, namely, β_i or K_i, provides direct information about the amount of Y ligand that is displaced for a specific X-binding reaction. The pertinent equation is found by taking the logarithm of equation (3.99) and differentiating partially (holding x activity fixed) with respect to $\ln y$:

$$\frac{\partial \ln \beta_i}{\partial \ln y} = \frac{\partial \ln P_{iY}}{\partial \ln y} - \frac{\partial \ln P_{0Y}}{\partial \ln y}. \tag{3.100}$$

The derivatives of the Y-binding polynomials give the amount of Y bound, $\bar{Y}_i$ and $\bar{Y}_0$, for the macromolecular species containing i and zero X ligands. We thus obtain

$$\frac{\partial \ln \beta_i}{\partial \ln y} = \bar{Y}_i - \bar{Y}_0. \tag{3.101}$$

The difference $\bar{Y}_i - \bar{Y}_0$ represents the change in Y ligands bound upon X ligation from the X-unligated to the iX-ligated state of the macromolecule. Similarly, the dependence of y on the stepwise constants K_i is given as

$$\frac{\partial \ln K_i}{\partial \ln y} = \bar{Y}_i - \bar{Y}_{i-1}. \tag{3.102}$$

A particularly important situation is that of β_t, which relates the first column of species to the last, and as we have seen is determined by the median activity x_m (note: $\beta_t x_m{}^t = 1$):

$$\frac{\partial \ln \beta_t}{\partial \ln y} = -t\frac{\partial \ln x_m}{\partial \ln y} = \bar{Y}_t - \bar{Y}_0. \qquad (3.103)$$

Thus the dependence of the median of X-binding curves on the Y activity immediately tells us about the difference in the amount of Y bound in going from the unligated X state to the fully ligated X state. Examples of this relation are discussed in Sections 3.7.3 and 3.7.4.

In terms of factorability, heterotropic linkage exists when P cannot be factored into two sets of binding polynomials, each of which is solely a function of a given ligand. Linkage exists even though the polynomials (for Y) for each column are completely factorable, provided they contain at least one linear factor that is different between columns.

3.7.2 Identical Linkage

As already noted, when X-Y binding is mutually exclusive, we have a situation which is called *identical linkage* (Wyman, 1948). This situation occurs when oxygen and carbon monoxide bind to heme in hemoglobin or myoglobin, or bind to the binding sites composed of copper in hemocyanin. Suppose there is just one binding site, and that it can bind either X or Y, but not both. Then the only species in the system are M, MX, and MY, and these are defined by the simple triangle in the upper left corner of the array in Figure 3-11. In the more general case, the array of possible species is given by a triangle with an equal number of t binding sites for X and Y. The array is limited by the diagonal, where the sum of X- and Y-filled sites is t.

The identically linked species when $t = 4$ are shown by an isosceles triangle in Figure 3-13. As can be seen in this array, the Y-binding polynomials are of different degree for each column, and linkage is thus mandatory. The binding polynomials may be formulated for this situation as already described. The case of a one-site identical linkage reaction has been elaborated in Chapter 2 [see equation (2.79)].

M	MX	MX$_2$	MX$_3$	MX$_4$
MY	MXY	MX$_2$Y	MX$_3$Y	
MY$_2$	MXY$_2$	MX$_2$Y$_2$		
MY$_3$	MXY$_3$			
MY$_4$				

Figure 3-13.
The elements of this triangle describe the species array for identical linked sites for X and Y binding ($t = 4$).

An experimental study of oxygen and carbon monoxide binding to hemoglobin under saturation conditions has been made by Wyman *et al.* (1982). The relevant macromolecular species in that work correspond to those of the diagonal of Figure 3-13. The binding polynomial for this situation can be formulated by taking MX_4 as the reference species, and writing the reactions $MX_4 + iY \rightarrow MX_{4-i}Y_i + iX$ with equilibrium constants β_i^*. The saturation binding polynomial is then given as $P^* = \sum \beta_i^*(x/y)^i$. The amount of oxygen or carbon monoxide bound is then given by the appropriate partial differentiation. A Hill plot of the fraction of carbon monoxide bound under different oxygen and carbon monoxide partial pressures is shown in Figure 3-14. These results show that this replacement binding process is non-

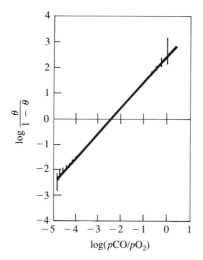

Figure 3-14.
The Hill plot of $\log[\theta/(1-\theta)]$ versus $\log(pCO/pO_2)$ for carbon monoxide binding to hemoglobin in the presence of oxygen. The data was taken under conditions where all four sites of hemoglobin are fully saturated by oxygen or carbon monoxide (Wyman *et al.*, 1982).

cooperative, and describable by a single constant binding polynomial:

$$P^* = (1 + \kappa x/y)^4.$$

Although the measurement of carbon monoxide binding to hemoglobin presents special problems because of its high affinity, Di Cera *et al.* (1987b) have found experimental conditions (pH 7, 10 mM IHP (inositolhexaphosphate)) where both oxygen and carbon monoxide binding curves can be evaluated on the same sample of human hemoglobin HbA_0. The results permit a full evaluation of the Adair constants β_{ij} for the reaction ($M + iX + jY \rightarrow MX_iY_j$) depicted in Figure 3-13. The binding partition function for this case is given as

$$Q = \sum_{i=0}^{4} \sum_{j=0}^{4-i} \beta_{ij}x^iy^j, \tag{3.104}$$

Table 3.1
Overall Adair constants (β_{ij}) for reaction $M + iO_2 + jCO \rightarrow M(O_2)_i(CO)_j$[a]

$\beta_{10} = .016 \pm .002$ torr^{-1}	$\beta_{04} = 231 \pm 15.4$ torr^{-4}
$\beta_{20} = .00031 \pm .00003$ torr^{-2}	$\beta_{31} = 7.1 \times 10^{-5} \pm 5.0 \times 10^{-6}$ torr^{-4}
$\beta_{30} = 0 \pm 2.4 \times 10^{-8}$ torr^{-3}	$\beta_{22} = .020 \pm .002$ torr^{-4}
$\beta_{40} = 4.8 \times 10^{-8} \pm 3.8 \times 10^{-9}$ torr^{-4}	$\beta_{13} = 3.80 \pm .28$ torr^{-4}
$\beta_{01} = 2.72 \pm .48$ torr^{-1}	$\beta_{21} = 0 \pm 6.0 \times 10^{-6}$ torr^{-3}
$\beta_{02} = 7.23 \pm .61$ torr^{-2}	$\beta_{12} = 0 \pm .002$ torr^{-3}
$\beta_{03} = 0 \pm 4.1$ torr^{-3}	$\beta_{11} = .12 \pm .02$ torr^{-2}
$m_1 = \beta_{01}/\beta_{10} = 170 \pm 37$	$m_2 = (\beta_{02}/\beta_{20})^{.5} = 153 \pm 20$
$m_4 = (\beta_{04}/\beta_{40})^{.25} = 263 \pm 27$	

[a] The partition coefficient m_k is the equilibrium constant for the reaction $CO + \frac{1}{k}M(O_2)_k \rightarrow O_2 + \frac{1}{k}M(CO)_k$. The errors on the parameters are twice the actual errors estimated in the fit.

where x and y denote the activities (or partial pressures) for oxygen and carbon monoxide. The binding functions $\bar{X}$ and $\bar{Y}$ are then given by appropriate partial differentiation of $\ln Q$ with respect to $\ln x$ or $\ln y$. The best-fitted values for the parameters β_{ij} are summarized in Table 3.1.

A feature of these results when expressed as binding curves or their derivatives (shown in Figure 3-15 for pure O_2 and CO) is a difference in the shape of the curves. This means that Haldane's first law (Haldane and Smith, 1897) is not valid. This law assumed a constant value for the partition coefficient m, defined as

$$m = \frac{\theta_y}{\theta_x} \frac{x}{y}. \tag{3.105}$$

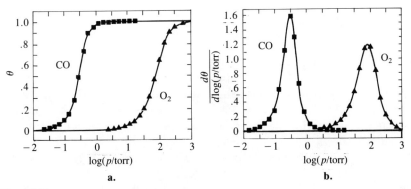

Figure 3-15.
Carbon monoxide and oxygen binding curves (a) and derivative curves (b) for HbA, at pH 7, mM IHP, and 25°C (Di Cera et al., 1987b).

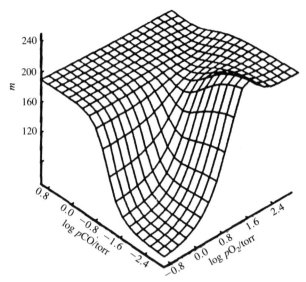

Figure 3-16.
Haldane partition coefficient, m, as a function of O_2 and CO partial pressures for human hemoglobin HbA_0 (Di Cera *et al.*, 1987b).

Values of m calculated from the experimental results described above are shown in Figure 3-16 as a function of θ for oxygen and carbon monoxide. A variation of nearly a factor of two exists between low and high saturation. Values of m have been determined for pure α and β chains from HbA_0 (Wyman *et al.*, 1982). The similarity of the values for the α chain and the initial value of the partition coefficient for the $\alpha_2\beta_2$ tetramer suggests that initial binding occurs to the α chains in HbA_0.

3.7.3 The Bohr Effect

The Bohr effect (Bohr *et al.*, 1904) is the classic example of interaction between two different ligands, oxygen and protons, in hemoglobin. It provides an excellent example for illustrating the concepts and analysis of heterotropic linkage. The dependence of the median activity (approximated by $p_{1/2}$) on the pH is shown in Figure 3-17 at various temperatures. The experimentally measured amount of protons displaced per mole of oxygen bound is shown in Figure 3-18.

Alternatively, the number of protons displaced upon oxygen saturation may be calculated from the dependence of β_4 on the pH. We write this dependence in terms of the proton-binding polynomials ($Y = H^+$) as follows:

$$\beta_4 = \beta_4{}^o \frac{P_{4H^+}}{P_{OH^+}}. \tag{3.106}$$

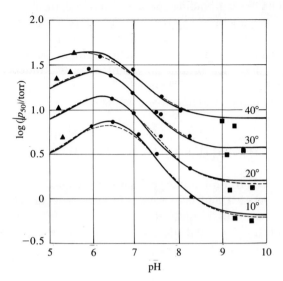

Figure 3-17.
The plot of $\log p_{50}$ versus pH for oxygen binding to hemoglobin as measured at four temperatures. Points show experimental values of $\log p_{50}$, read from the oxygen equilibrium curves: ●, in 0.15 M phosphate buffer; ▲, in 0.4 M acetate buffer; ■, in 2 percent borate buffer. Dashed lines are calculated by graphical integration of titration curves, and solid lines are results of calculations with assumed proton-linked binding constants and heats of reaction (see Antonini *et al.*, 1965).

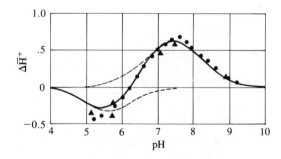

Figure 3-18.
Proton release per mole of O_2 binding to hemoglobin at 20°C as measured by titration (Antonini *et al.*, 1965). The solid theoretical line has been calculated by assuming two oxygen-linked proton-binding sites per heme, and is drawn using defined constants and equation (3.111).

If we assume the oxygen-binding curve is symmetric, then the median activity is given by $p_{1/2}$. Thus $\beta_4 = (1/p_{1/2})^4$, $\beta_4^o = (1/p_{1/2}^o)^4$, where $p_{1/2}^o$ is the reference $p_{1/2}$ at high pH. The proton-binding polynomials, P_{4H^+} and P_{OH^+}, are for the fully oxygenated and deoxygenated hemoglobin species. Antonini *et al.* (1965) assumed that each proton polynomial has two independent linked proton-binding terms *per heme*. The ratio of binding polynomials then has the following surviving (other unlinked-site factors cancel) linear terms:

$$\frac{P_{4H^+}}{P_{OH^+}} = \left[\frac{(1 + \lambda_{4a}[H^+])(1 + \lambda_{4b}[H^+])}{(1 + \lambda_{0a}[H^+])(1 + \lambda_{0b}[H^+])}\right]^4. \tag{3.107}$$

The oxygen-linked proton-binding constants are denoted by $\lambda_{4a}, \lambda_{4b}, \lambda_{0a}$, and λ_{0b} for the oxygenated and deoxygenated states. The values at 20°C that represent the experimental results, if we define $\lambda_{ij} = 10^{pK_{ij}}$, are $pK_{0a} = 5.46$, $pK_{4a} = 6.26$, $pK_{0b} = 7.85$, and $pK_{4b} = 6.45$. The influence of pH on $p_{1/2}$ is derived from (3.106) as

$$\log p_{1/2} = \log p_{1/2}^o - \frac{1}{4}\log\frac{P_{4H^+}}{P_{OH^+}}. \tag{3.108}$$

Insertion of the proposed proton-binding polynomial ratio, along with the preceding values for the constants, gives the theoretical curves shown in Figure 3-17.

The linkage between the oxygen-binding process and the proton activity, namely, the dependence of $\log p_{1/2}$ on pH, reflects the change in the number of bound protons for the overall process of oxygenation per heme binding site. Application of equation (3.103) with $x_m \cong p_{1/2}$ gives

$$\bar{H}_4^+ - \bar{H}_0^+ = \frac{\partial \ln \beta_4}{\ln [H^+]} = -4\frac{\partial \ln x_m}{\partial \ln [H^+]} \cong +4\frac{\partial \log p_{1/2}}{\partial pH}. \tag{3.109}$$

With equation (3.106) the proton change per mole of macromolecule is given in terms of the proton-binding polynomial ratio:

$$\bar{H}_4^+ - \bar{H}_0^+ = \frac{\partial \ln\left(\dfrac{P_{4H^+}}{P_{OH^+}}\right)}{\partial \ln [H^+]}. \tag{3.110}$$

For the specific situation denoted by equation (3.107) we find

$$\bar{H}_4^+ - \bar{H}_0^+ = 4\left[\frac{\lambda_{4a}[H^+]}{1 + \lambda_{4a}[H^+]} + \frac{\lambda_{4b}[H^+]}{1 + \lambda_{4b}[H^+]}\right.$$
$$\left. - \frac{\lambda_{0a}[H^+]}{1 + \lambda_{0a}[H^+]} - \frac{\lambda_{0b}[H^+]}{1 + \lambda_{0b}[H^+]}\right]. \tag{3.111}$$

As shown in Figure 3-18, the difference in bound protons $(\bar{H}_4^+ - \bar{H}_0^+)/4$ per heme has been measured directly by titration procedures, and compared to values calculated from the slope of the $\log p_{1/2}$ versus pH curve. The preceding analysis in terms of two oxygen-linked proton-binding sites per heme is the simplest possible one that represents the positive and reverse Bohr effect. Recent NMR (Russo *et al.*, 1982) and electrostatic considerations (Matthews *et al.*, 1981) show that even more linked binding sites are certainly involved; but these combine to give the same result. Imai (1982) has summarized his pH-dependent oxygen-binding studies of the Bohr effect, and finds that the stepwise oxygen-binding reactions have distinct pH dependence. This is indicated by the results (Imai and Yonetani, 1975b) shown in Figure 3-19 for the amount of protons released in each of the successive stepwise oxygen reactions as a function of pH. The distinct nature of these curves shows that

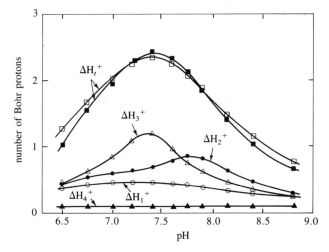

Figure 3-19.
Bohr protons released per mole of oxygen bound to hemoglobin as a function of pH for stepwise reactions (Imai and Yonetani, 1975b).

different proton-binding polynomials must exist for each of the proton-species array columns of Figure 3-11.

A recent study (Di Cera *et al.*, 1988a) of the pH dependence of oxygen binding to concentrated HbA$_0$ (1 mM heme), where dissociation effects to $\alpha\beta$ dimers are found negligible, has enabled construction of a series of linkage graphs (Wyman, 1984) from the binding polynomial, thus allowing a further description of the O$_2$-proton linkage. Figure 3-20 shows the experimental data and fitted binding curves as a function of pH from these studies. The proton has little influence on the shape of the O$_2$ binding curve, in nice agreement with the early prediction of Wyman (1948) and the recent study of Chu *et al.* (1984). Figure 3-21 shows the number of protons bound per hemoglobin molecule as a function of the number of bound oxygens at several fixed pHs.

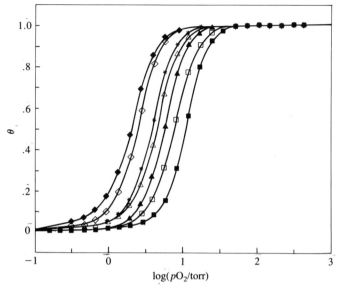

Figure 3-20.
Oxygen-binding curve of HbA, at various pH values. Data were obtained from differential changes in optical density, and are depicted here as binding curves. The pH values are: 6.95 (■), 7.27 (□), 7.51 (▲), 7.71 (△), 7.91 (◆), 8.50 (◇), and 9.10 (*). The theoretical curves were drawn using fitted parameters from an allosteric model discussed by Di Cera *et al.* (1987a).

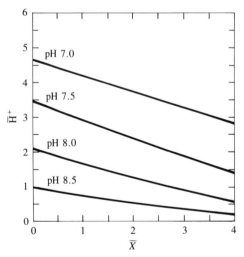

Figure 3-21.
Number of protons bound ($\bar{H}^+$) per hemoglobin molecule at different fixed pH (shown in the figure), as a function of the number of O_2 molecules bound ($\bar{X}$). (Di Cera *et al.*, 1988a). The curves were drawn with the model binding polynomial described in Di Cera *et al.* (1987a).

The plots in Figure 3-21 are related by the familiar linkage equation (Wyman, 1964)

$$\left(\frac{\partial \bar{H}^+}{\partial \bar{X}}\right)_{pH} = -\left(\frac{\partial \ln x}{\partial \ln h}\right)_{\bar{x}}, \tag{3.112}$$

where $\bar{H}^+$ and $\bar{X}$ are the number of protons and oxygens bound per molecule of hemoglobin and h is the proton activity. The linearity observed in the plots of Figure 3-22 is a graphical demonstration that the derivative on the left of equation (3.112) is equal to a constant throughout the entire range of $\bar{X}$. Thus, the derivative shown on the right is equal to a constant for all values of $\bar{X}$ as well, and indicates that proton release is linearly related to O_2 uptake.

Figure 3-22 displays the linkage relationship between the number of oxygens bound and the number of protons bound, at several fixed O_2 activities.

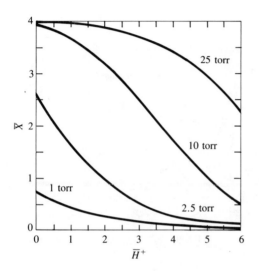

Figure 3-22.
Number of O_2 molecules bound ($\bar{X}$) per hemoglobin molecule at various fixed O_2 partial pressures, as a function of the number of protons bound ($\bar{H}^+$). The curves were drawn with the model binding polynomial described in Di Cera *et al.* (1988a).

As can be seen, the plots are not linear, in contrast to the converse effect plotted in Figure 3-21. Consequently the shape of the proton-binding curve must change at different activities of O_2 as shown in Figure 3-23.

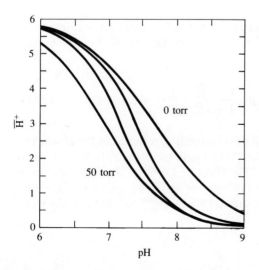

Figure 3-23.
Titration of the O_2-linked proton-binding sites at various fixed O_2 partial pressures, as calculated from the model binding polynomial discussed in Di Cera *et al.* (1988a). The O_2 partial pressures of the intermediate curves are 5 and 10 torr.

3.7.4   The DPG Effect on Hemoglobin

The heterotropic effect of 2,3-diphosphoglycerate (DPG) on oxygen binding to hemoglobin is another important example of linkage (Chanutin and Curnish, 1967; Benesch and Benesch, 1967). In this case there is only one DPG binding site on the hemoglobin molecule with four oxygen-binding sites. The exact location of the site has been found from X-ray structural studies on deoxyhemoglobin–DPG crystals by Arnone (1972). As seen in Figure 3-24,

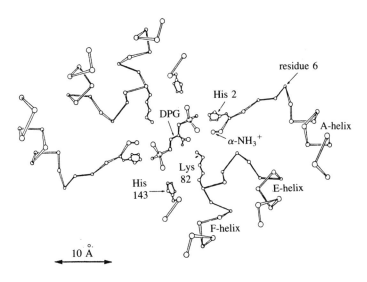

Figure 3-24.
Binding site of DPG to deoxyhemoglobin (Arnone, 1972).

the contacting amino-acid groups contribute positive charges to neutralize the highly negative charge carried by the DPG molecule. The effect on the median oxygen activity is then given as

$$\beta_4 = \frac{1}{x_m^4} = \beta_{40}\frac{1 + \kappa_{HbO_2}^{DPG}[DPG]}{1 + \kappa_{Hb}^{DPG}[DPG]},\qquad(3.113)$$

where $\beta_{40} = (1/x_m^o)^4$ is the overall oxygen-binding constant in the absence of DPG, and $\kappa_{HbO_2}^{DPG}$ and κ_{Hb}^{DPG} are the DPG binding constants to fully oxygen-ligated or unligated hemoglobin. The effect of DPG on the p_{50} is shown in Figure 3-25. Szabo and Karplus (1976) have analyzed this data, assuming $x_m \cong p_{50}$, and find $\kappa_{Hb}^{DPG} = 8.5 \times 10^4\,M^{-1}$ and $\kappa_{HbO_2}^{DPG} = 330\,M^{-1}$ for these conditions.

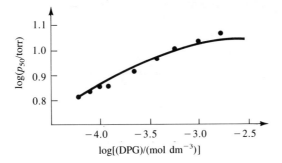

Figure 3-25.
Oxygen binding p_{50} values plotted as a function of DPG concentration (Benesch and Benesch, 1974)).

3.7.5   The Chloride Effect on Hemoglobin

Another example of heterotropic linkage to hemoglobin is found in the chloride linkage studies of Haire and Hedlund (1977) shown in Figure 3-26. As there is with protons, there is here a reversed-chloride Bohr effect, which calls for at least two chloride-binding sites. The existence of such sites has been established by NMR studies (Chiancone *et al.*, 1975).

A detailed analysis of these results may be given as follows using the laws of mass action. (This analysis neglects possible changes in water activity

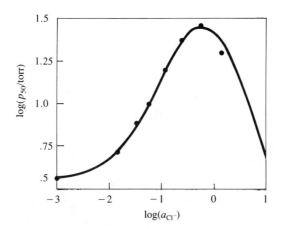

Figure 3-26.
Dependence of p_{50} (O_2) on the activity of sodium chloride for hemoglobin, as calculated from data of Haire and Hedlund (1977). Least-square fit parameters found for the theoretical curve are $\kappa_a = 28 \pm 3$ M^{-1} $n_a = 2.3 \pm 3$, $\kappa_b = 1.7 \pm .5$ M^{-1}, $n_b = 4 \pm .4$. See text for definitions.

produced by higher concentrations of sodium chloride.) We consider the chloride linkage on the overall oxygen-binding reaction $Hb + 4O_2 \rightarrow Hb(O_2)_4$. The oxygen-binding constant, β_4, for the reaction is linked through the chloride-binding polynomials, P_{0Cl^-} and P_{4Cl^-}, to the deoxy and oxy hemoglobin species, by $\beta_4 = \beta_{40}(P_{4Cl^-}/P_{0Cl^-})$, where β_{40} is the oxygen-binding constant in the absence of chloride. The half-saturation oxygen pressure, $p_{1/2}$, equals $(\beta_4)^{-1/4}$. This enables us to write in logarithmic form the relation between the half-saturation pressure and the chloride-binding polynomials:

$$\log p_{1/2} = \log p_{1/2}{}^o + 1/4 \log \frac{P_{4Cl^-}}{P_{0Cl^-}}. \tag{3.114}$$

We find the simplest form of binding polynomials by considering independent sites of equal intrinsic affinity. If there are n_a of these for the deoxygenated form, then $P_{0Cl^-} = (1 + \kappa_a a_{Cl^-})^{n_a}$, where κ_a is the intrinsic binding constant of chloride to the form. Likewise, if there are n_b sites with the binding constant κ_b on the fully oxygenated form, then $P_{4Cl^-} = (1 + \kappa_b a_{Cl^-})^{n_b}$. As we've already noted, only sites with different binding properties on the two forms under consideration will survive when we take the ratio of binding polynomials. By nonlinear least-square optimization of the parameters, we find two relatively strong ($\kappa_a = 30\,M^{-1}$) chloride-binding sites on the deoxygenated form, which are linked to four relatively weak chloride-binding sites ($\kappa_b = 2\,M^{-1}$) on the oxygenated form. The theoretical fit to the data is shown in Figure 3-26. The difference in the amount of chloride bound per mole of oxygen bound is given by differentiation of (3.114) to give

$$\overline{\Delta Cl^-} = 1/4\left(\frac{n_a \kappa_a a_{Cl^-}}{1 + \kappa_a a_{Cl^-}} - \frac{n_b \kappa_b a_{Cl^-}}{1 + \kappa_b a_{Cl^-}}\right). \tag{3.115}$$

This expression will be zero at the maxima of Figure 3-26, which requires that $n_b > n_a$. The left portion of the curve is regarded by Haire and Hedlund (1977) as due to specific (or mass law) binding of chloride, and they interpret the effect of very high concentrations in terms of nonspecific effects on water activity. This interpretation cannot be ruled out with present evidence.

3.8   THE BINDING OF LIGAND X IN THE PRESENCE OF A FIXED AMOUNT OF Y

We now turn to the very practical problem of studying binding processes in situations where the *amount* of a second ligand is fixed. In this case, the activity of the second ligand changes in the course of ligation of the primary ligand. We wish to show in this section how such problems may be formulated along the lines given by Robert *et al.* (1988a, 1988b). Initial work concerning this problem was done by Imai and Tyuma (1973) and Herzfeld and Stanley (1974).

As we saw in Section 3.7.1, the binding polynomial P may be written in terms of the Y-binding polynomials for each column i of the species array, P_{iY}, as

$$P = P_{0Y} + \beta_{10}P_{1Y}x + \cdots + \beta_{t0}P_{tY}x^t. \tag{3.116}$$

For a single Y-binding site on the macromolecule, $P_{iY} = 1 + M_i y$, where M_i is the Y-binding constant to the macromolecule with iX bound. In general P_{iY} will be a polynomial in y of order of the number of Y-binding sites.

The X- and Y-binding curves at given x and y activities are obtained by differentiation:

$$\bar{X} = \left(\frac{\partial \ln P}{\partial \ln x}\right)_y = \frac{\beta_{10}P_{1Y}x + 2\beta_{20}P_{2Y}x^2 + \cdots + t\beta_{t0}P_{tY}x^t}{P}, \tag{3.117}$$

$$\bar{Y} = \left(\frac{\partial \ln P}{\partial \ln y}\right)_x = \frac{P'_{0Y} + \beta_{10}P'_{iY}x + \cdots + \beta_{t0}P'_{tY}x^t}{P}, \tag{3.118}$$

where P'_{iY} is given by the derivative

$$P'_{iY} = \left(\frac{\partial P_{iY}}{\partial \ln y}\right)_x. \tag{3.119}$$

The concentration of free ligand Y, i.e., y, is determined by the total concentration of Y, y_t, minus the amount of Y ligand that is bound. The concentration of bound ligand is $\bar{Y}m$, where m is the macromolecular concentration. Thus we write this mass-balance condition as

$$y = y_t - \bar{Y}m \tag{3.120}$$

or

$$\bar{Y} = \frac{y_t - y}{m}. \tag{3.121}$$

Equating this expression to the form given by (3.118) sets the stage for evaluating y for a set of specific conditions of binding parameters and values of y_t and m. If the P_{iy} binding polynomials are linear or quadratic, then we can solve for y directly, and substitution of y into the appropriate terms of (3.117) yields the desired $\bar{X}$ binding curve. For higher-degree P_{iY} polynomials, we would resort to computer solution to obtain y.

Consider the case of single Y-site binding ($P_{iY} = 1 + M_i y$):

$$\frac{y_t - y}{m} = \frac{(M_0 + \beta_{10}M_1 x + \cdots + \beta_{t0}M_t x^t)y}{1 + \beta_{10}x + \cdots + \beta_{t0}x^t + (M_0 + \beta_{10}M_1 x + \cdots + \beta_{t0}M_t x^t)y}, \tag{3.122}$$

and with the following definition of the X-binding polynomials for the first and second row of the species array,

$$P_{0X} = 1 + \beta_{10}x + \cdots + \beta_{t0}x^t, \tag{3.123}$$

$$P_{1X} = \frac{1}{M_0}[M_0 + \beta_1 M_1 x + \cdots + \beta_{t0} M_t x^t], \tag{3.124}$$

we obtain the quadratic expression

$$M_0 P_{1X} y^2 - (M_0 P_{1X} y_t - M_0 P_{1X} m - P_{0X})y - P_{0X} y_t = 0. \tag{3.125}$$

We then substitute the solution of y, namely,

$$y = \frac{M_0 P_{1X} y_t - M_0 P_{1X} m - P_{0X} + [(M_0 P_{1X} y_t - M_0 P_{1X} m - P_{0X})^2 + 4 M_0 P_{1X} P_{0X} y_t]^{1/2}}{2 M_0 P_{1X}}$$

$$\tag{3.126}$$

into (3.117) to obtain the binding curve of X, written for the single-site binding of Y as

$$\bar{X} = \frac{\beta_{10}(1 + M_0 y)x + 2\beta_{20}(1 + M_1 y)x^2 + \cdots + t\beta_{t0}(1 + M_t y)x^t}{1 + M_0 y + \beta_{10}(1 + M_1 y)x + \cdots + \beta_{t0}(1 + M_t y)x^t}. \tag{3.127}$$

We next turn our attention to the effect of a fixed quantity of secondary ligand on the median properties of the binding curve. The problem is to examine what happens to the median of X, x_m, when there is a fixed amount of Y. Ackers (1979) has shown how the median of oxygen binding to hemoglobin is determined by Y-binding (in particular, DPG-binding) polynomials P_{0Y} and P_{tY}. We shall develop a somewhat different derivation that yields equivalent results.

We start by noting the definition of the median by the equality of areas above and below the binding curve:

$$\int_{x=0}^{x=x_m} \bar{X}\, d\ln x = \int_{x=x_m}^{x=\infty} (t - \bar{X})\, d\ln x. \tag{3.128}$$

$\bar{X}$ is obtained from equation (3.117), and integration of (3.128) is facilitated by the following expression in terms of total derivatives:

$$\bar{X} = \frac{d\ln P}{d\ln x} - \bar{Y}\frac{d\ln y}{d\ln x}. \tag{3.129}$$

Substitution into (3.128) and integration give

$$\ln P \Bigg]_{x=0}^{x=x_m} - \int_{y(x=0)}^{y(x=x_m)} \bar{Y} \, d \ln y = t \ln x \Bigg]_{x=x_m}^{x=\infty} - \ln P \Bigg]_{x=x_m}^{x=\infty} + \int_{y(x=x_m)}^{y(x=\infty)} \bar{Y} \, d \ln y$$

$$(3.130)$$

or

$$\ln P \Bigg]_{x=0}^{x=\infty} - t \ln (x = \infty) + t \ln x_m = \int_{y(x=0)}^{y(x=\infty)} \bar{Y} \, d \ln y. \qquad (3.131)$$

The $\bar{Y}$ integral may be evaluated using (3.121) between limits y_0 and y_∞, i.e., $y(x = 0)$ and $y(x = \infty)$, as follows:

$$\int_{y_0}^{y_\infty} \bar{Y} \, d \ln y = \int_{y_0}^{y_\infty} \frac{y_t}{m} \, d \ln y - \int_{y_0}^{y_\infty} \frac{1}{m} \frac{dy}{} \qquad (3.132)$$

$$= \frac{y_t}{m} \ln \frac{y_\infty}{y_0} - \left(\frac{y_\infty - y_0}{m} \right). \qquad (3.133)$$

Equation (3.131) can then be evaluated in these terms as

$$t \ln x_m = \ln \left[\frac{P_{0Y}(y_0)}{\beta_t P_{tY}(y_\infty)} \right] + \frac{y_t}{m} \ln \frac{y_\infty}{y_0} - \left(\frac{y_\infty - y_0}{m} \right). \qquad (3.134)$$

We note that $\ln 1/\beta_t = t \ln x_m{}^o$, where $x_m{}^o$ is the median when $y = 0$. An equivalent form using (3.121) to express y_0 and y_∞ in terms of $\bar{Y}_0$ and $\bar{Y}_\infty$ is

$$t \ln x_m = t \ln x_m{}^o + \ln \frac{P_{0Y}(y_0)}{P_{tY}(y_\infty)} + \frac{y_t}{m} \ln \frac{y_t - \bar{Y}_\infty m}{y_t - \bar{Y}_0 m} + (\bar{Y}_\infty - \bar{Y}_0). \quad (3.135)$$

From equation (3.118) we may evaluate $\bar{Y}_\infty$ and $\bar{Y}_0$ in terms of the Y-binding polynomials and their logarithmic derivatives

$$\bar{Y}_\infty = \frac{P'_{tY}(y_\infty)}{P_{tY}(y_\infty)}, \qquad (3.136)$$

$$\bar{Y}_0 = \frac{P'_{0Y}(y_0)}{P_{0Y}(y_0)}. \qquad (3.137)$$

These expressions are quite general. For single-site Y-binding they become

$$\bar{Y}_\infty = \frac{M_t y_\infty}{1 + M_t y_\infty} \quad \text{and} \quad \bar{Y}_0 = \frac{M_0 y_0}{1 + M_0 y_0}, \qquad (3.138)$$

which, when equated to the mass-balance expression (3.120), yields two quadratics in either y_0 or y_∞. The solutions are

$$y_0 = \frac{-(M_0 m + 1 - M_0 y_t) + [(M_0 m + 1 - M_0 y_t)^2 + 4y_t M_0]^{1/2}}{2M_0}, \quad (3.139)$$

$$y_\infty = \frac{-(M_t m + 1 - M_t y_t) + [(M_t m + 1 - M_t y_t)^2 + 4y_t M_t]^{1/2}}{2M_t}. \quad (3.140)$$

The median dependence for this single Y-site example is then found by substituting these expressions for y_0 and y_∞ into

$$t \ln x_m = t \ln x_m^{\,o} + \ln \frac{1 + M_0 y_0}{1 + M_t y_\infty} + \frac{y_t}{m} \ln \frac{y_\infty}{y_0} - \left(\frac{y_\infty - y_0}{m}\right). \quad (3.141)$$

An example of the use of this expression is shown in Figure 3-27, where the

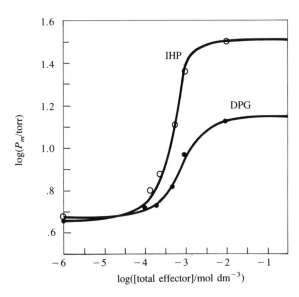

Figure 3-27.
Dependence of the median of the oxygen-binding curve on the total concentration of IHP (open circles) and 2,3 diphosphoglycerate (DPG, filled circles), for same concentration condition given in Figure 3-28 for Hb, IHP, and DPG.

value of x_m is plotted against y_t for the influence of inositolhexaphosphate (IHP) on the oxygen binding of hemoglobin. This plot was made from data obtained by Robert et al. (1988b) shown in Figure 3-28, in which the oxygen-binding curves are plotted for different total amounts of IHP. Note how the shape of the binding curves becomes quite complex when there is a fixed amount of IHP concentration, since there is a large change in free activity of IHP as oxygen binds to the hemoglobin molecule.

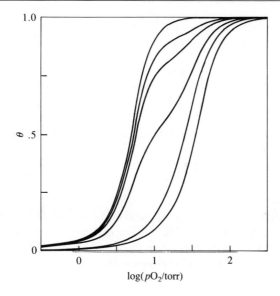

Figure 3-28.
Oxygen binding curves at a series of fixed total amounts of the effector inositol hexaphosphate (IHP) as determined from fitting differential binding data (Robert *et al*, 1988b). Total Hb tetramer concentration is 1 mM; total IHP concentrations are, from left, 0, 1.3, 2.4, 5.5, 1.05, and 10.5 mM.

3.9 ELECTRON-BINDING POLYNOMIALS

Electron-binding phenomena can be treated in a manner like that developed for chemical ligands, and the binding of electrons to sites on an initially oxidized macromolecule can be supposed to proceed by stepwise reduction of the macromolecule. We need only establish the general equation for the measurement of the electron activity, a_{e^-}, to show how this ligand fits into the general picture. The electron activity may be defined with reference to a standard electrode. The standard electrode has conventionally been chosen to be the hydrogen electrode operating at unit atmosphere (strictly, fugacity) of hydrogen gas in contact with a platinum electrode immersed in a solution of acid at unit activity of hydrogen ion. The voltage E which is generated between the standard electrode and the electrode immersed into the solution of the electron-binding system, with suitable liquid junctions between the solutions about each electrode, defines the electron activity as

$$RT \ln a_{e^-} = -FE. \qquad (3.142)$$

This equation reflects the equilibrium condition that holds for electrons at the operating electrode and in the contiguous solution. The measurement of a_{e^-} is therefore conditioned upon the reversibility of such electrodes.

The formal equations for electron binding can be written exactly like those of any ligand:

$$M + e^- \rightarrow M^-,$$

$$M + 2e^- \rightarrow M^{2-}, \tag{3.143}$$

$$M + ie^- \rightarrow M^{i-},$$

and the equilibrium constant for such overall reactions will be β_i given as

$$\beta_i = \frac{[M^{i-}]}{[M]a_{e^-}{}^i}, \tag{3.144}$$

where again, for convenience of presentation, activity coefficients of the reaction species have been absorbed in β_i. The binding curve is also obtained by the same operations we have seen applied to chemical ligands using the binding polynomial or partition function for electron binding

$$Q_e = \sum \beta_i a_{e^-}{}^i. \tag{3.145}$$

The convention in electrochemistry is to express electron equilibrium constants in terms of standard electron voltages, E_i^o. This voltage describes the condition where $[M^{i-}] = [M]$, and from (3.144) we see using $a_{e^-} = e^{-FE/RT}$ that

$$\beta_i = \exp\left(\frac{iFE_i^o}{RT}\right). \tag{3.146}$$

The electron-binding partition function is then given as

$$Q_e = \sum \exp[iF(E_i^o - E)/(RT)]. \tag{3.147}$$

The electron-binding curve, which describes experimental results of moles of electrons bound per mole of macromolecule $(\overline{e^-})$, is readily obtained from differentiation of Q_e as

$$\overline{e^-} = \frac{d\ln Q_e}{d\ln a_e} = -\frac{RT}{F}\frac{d\ln Q_e}{dE}. \tag{3.148}$$

Binding curves of $\overline{e^-}$ versus E may be depicted in the form of a Hill plot as shown in Figure 3-29 for oxidation to the four heme sites of hemoglobin (Antonini et al., 1964). Note the positive cooperativity found in this situation.

All the properties we have described about chemical ligand-binding curves obviously apply to such electron-binding curves: areas, species fractions, median rule, symmetry, etc. The construction of the Hill plot and the assessment of cooperativity, whether positive or negative, follow directly.

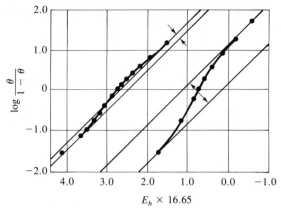

Figure 3-29.
Hill plots of electron-binding curves to reduced hemoglobin at pH 6.3 (left) and
pH 8.6 (right) (Antonini *et al.*, 1964).

A study of electron binding to ferritin, which is a large, 24-subunit protein
with a crystalline polymeric iron core accommodating as many as 4,500 iron
atoms, has shown that the reduction from Fe^{3+} to Fe^{2+} is noncooperative
and accompanied by the uptake of two protons (Watt *et al.*, 1985). The extent
of coulometric reduction as a function of imposed voltage under different pH
conditions is shown in Figure 3-30.

Evaluating linkage effects as seen in the cases of ferritin and hemoglobin
between electron binding and chemical binding follows the same rules already
developed. The electron activity is expressed through the voltage by equation (3.142). We can thus obtain the number of protons released per mole

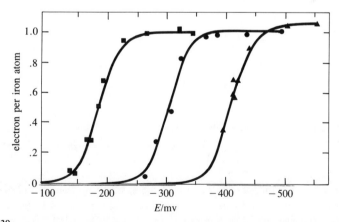

Figure 3-30.
Coulometric reduction of ferritin as a function of electrochemical potential (relative
to the normal hydrogen electrode under various pH conditions: ■, pH 7.0; ●,
pH 8.0; and ▲, pH 9.0 (Watt *et al.*, 1985).

of electron absorbed per mole of hemoglobin through studies of electron-binding curves at various pH values just as we observed the proton Bohr effect due to oxygen binding. The electron-linkage effects are also describable in terms of ratios of chemical ligand-binding polynomials that apply to any specific electron-binding process given by equations (3.143). An example of this type of analysis may be shown using data for the effect of pH on the half-saturation electron potential. The median (or half-saturation potential E_m) for the two-site macromolecule, cytochrome c', is shown as a function of pH in Figure 3-31. It may be concluded directly that the final slope of -1 is due

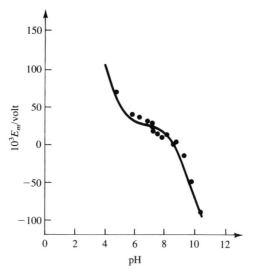

Figure 3-31.
Effect of pH on E_m for cytochrome c' (Barakat and Strekas, 1982).

to the elimination of a proton-binding site upon heme reduction, and the more complex dependence at intermediate pH values reflects differences in other parts of the proton-binding polynomials between fully reduced and oxidized forms.

Many of these concepts were realized by Wyman and Ingalls (1941) some years ago. However, electron binding-curve analysis has not yet been fully exploited. Interesting and important effects could be observed particularly in biological macromolecules, where free-energy transduction occurs through oxidation-reduction.

APPENDIX 3.1   BINDING CURVE AREAS AND INTERMEDIATE SPECIES CONCENTRATIONS

In order to see how the value of α_i diminishes from its maximum value, $\alpha_i(\text{max})$, as x moves away from its maximizing value, namely, $x_i(\text{max})$, we consider the areas defined under and above the binding curve with a new reference line drawn horizontally at $\bar{X} = i$. These areas, A_{u_i} and A_{a_i}, are shown specifically for the case $i = 3$ in Figure A3-1.

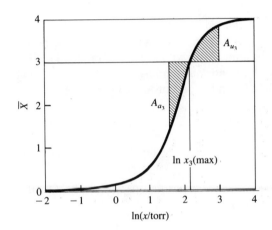

Figure A3-1.
Areas above and below the binding curve defined with reference to the state of ligation i. In this figure, representing hemoglobin, are shown the areas A_{u_3} and A_{a_3} determined by $\bar{X} = 3$. Data from Figure 3-3.

These areas are defined as positive quantities by the following expressions

$$A_{u_i} = \int_{\ln x_i(\text{max})}^{\ln x} (\bar{X} - i)\, d\ln x \qquad (A3.1)$$

and similarly,

$$A_{a_i} = \int_{\ln x}^{\ln x_i(\text{max})} (i - \bar{X})\, d\ln x. \qquad (A3.2)$$

Now, by use of equation (3.24), we obtain equivalent expressions

$$A_{u_i} = -\int \frac{d\ln \alpha_i}{d\ln x}\, d\ln x = \ln \frac{\alpha_i(\text{max})}{\alpha_i} \qquad (A3.3)$$

and

$$A_{a_i} = \int \frac{d\ln \alpha_i}{d\ln x}\, d\ln x = \ln \frac{\alpha_i(\text{max})}{\alpha_i}.$$

From the first of these expressions it follows that the area under the whole binding curve, A_u as denoted previously (A_{u_0} here), up to the point x gives the value of $\ln(1/\alpha_0)$ at that point. Likewise, the area above the whole binding curve, i.e., A_a (or A_{a_t} here), gives the value $\ln(1/\alpha_t)$. This is just what we deduced earlier.

APPENDIX 3.2   HILL SLOPE FROM BINDING POLYNOMIAL DERIVATIVES

The slope of the Hill plot can be calculated in a general form by the derivative relation given in this chapter. We shall develop a general result at this point, and then examine special situations that occur with the MWC model. The Hill slope, n, is given by the slope of the normal binding curve ($\bar{X}$ versus $\ln x$) weighted by the amount of ligand bound, $\bar{X}$, according to the expression

$$n_H = \frac{\dfrac{d\bar{X}}{d\ln x}}{\bar{X}(1 - \bar{X}/t)}. \tag{A3.4}$$

The amount of ligand bound per mole of macromolecule, $\bar{X}$, obtained by the logarithmic derivative, will be written as

$$\bar{X} = \frac{d\ln P}{d\ln x} = \frac{1}{P}\frac{dP}{d\ln x} = \frac{P'}{P}, \tag{A3.5}$$

where P' is the derivative of P with respect to $\ln x$. The derivative of $\bar{X}$ is then obtained as

$$\frac{d\bar{X}}{d\ln x} = \frac{-1}{P^2}\left(\frac{dP}{d\ln x}\right)^2 + \frac{1}{P}\frac{d^2P}{(d\ln x)^2} = -\frac{1}{P^2}(P')^2 + \frac{1}{P}P'', \tag{A3.6}$$

where the second derivative of P with respect to $\ln x$ is denoted by P''. The denominator of the Hill coefficient can then be expressed in these terms as

$$\bar{X}(1 - \bar{X}/t) = \frac{P'}{tP^2}(tP - P'). \tag{A3.7}$$

The slope of the Hill plot is thus given by the following combination of derivatives of the binding polynomial:

$$n = t\frac{PP'' - (P')^2}{P'(tP - P')}. \tag{A3.8}$$

This result is quite general, and applies to any situation where the binding polynomial describes the properties of a t-site macromolecule. It is especially convenient, when examining features of cooperativity, to arrange the last expression into a form where a comparison with unit Hill slope can be made. The result is

$$n = 1 + \frac{\{t[PP'' - (P')^2] - P'(tP - P')\}}{P'(tP - P')}. \tag{A3.9}$$

Since the term $P'(tP - P')$ must be a positive quantity [see equation (A3.7)], the sign of the term in curly brackets controls whether the Hill slope is greater or smaller than unity.*

APPENDIX 3.3   EVALUATION OF K_1 AND K_2 FROM HILL PLOTS FOR HEMOGLOBIN

One application of the linear equations given in (3.43) is to use the midpoint and asymptotic features of a Hill plot (Gill *et al.*, 1978; Di Cera *et al.*, 1988d) to evaluate intermediate stepwise constants (K_2 and K_3) for hemoglobin ($t = 4$). To illustrate this idea, we recognize that the asymptotes determine K_1 and K_4. Furthermore, the Hill coefficient at half-saturation ($x_{1/2}$) given as $n_{1/2}$ determines $\bar{X}^2$. The five linear equations needed from equation (3.43) are

$$K_1 x_{1/2} \alpha_0 - \alpha_1 = 0, \tag{A3.10}$$

$$K_4 x_{1/2} \alpha_3 - \alpha_4 = 0, \tag{A3.11}$$

$$\alpha_0 + \alpha_1 + \alpha_2 + \alpha_3 + \alpha_4 = 1, \tag{A3.12}$$

$$\alpha_1 + 2\alpha_2 + 3\alpha_3 + 4\alpha_4 = \bar{X} = 2, \tag{A3.13}$$

$$\alpha_1 + 4\alpha_2 + 9\alpha_3 + 16\alpha_4 = \bar{X}^2 = n_{1/2} + 4, \tag{A3.14}$$

which may be solved to give at mid-saturation:

$$\alpha_1 = (1/2 + K_4 x_{1/2})/D, \tag{A3.15}$$

$$\alpha_2 = \{[1 + 3/(K_1 x_{1/2}) + 3K_4 x_{1/2} + 8K_4/K_1]$$
$$- [1 + 3/(2K_1 x_{1/2}) + 3K_4 x_{1/2}/2 + 2K_4/K_1]\} n_{50}/D, \tag{A3.16}$$

$$\alpha_3 = [1/2 + 1/(K_1 x_{1/2}) n_{1/2}]/D, \tag{A3.17}$$

where

$$D = 1 + 3/(K_1 x_{1/2}) + 3K_4 x_{1/2} + 8K_4/K_1. \tag{A3.18}$$

---

* Bardsley (1978) has pointed out that the bracketed term is proportional to the algebraic form called the *Hessian* of the polynomial. The signs and zeros of the Hessian control Hill-slope properties.

The values of K_2 and K_3 can then be expressed in terms of the experimental parameters using

$$K_2 = \frac{\alpha_2}{\alpha_1 x_{1/2}}, \tag{A3.19}$$

$$K_3 = \frac{\alpha_3}{\alpha_2 x_{1/2}}. \tag{A3.20}$$

These equations permit all four Adair constants for hemoglobin ligation to be evaluated directly from a Hill plot whenever K_1 and K_4 either are known beforehand or can be obtained by extrapolating the Hill plot to its asymptotes. Table A3.1 shows two examples from the hemoglobin literature. We compare our calculated values of K_2 and K_3 with values for these constants to those obtained from the hemoglobin saturation isotherm.

Taking different $n_{1/2}$ values has a marked effect on values of K_2 and K_3, largely through the influence on the fraction α_2. This same effect is, of course, also noted in the error estimate for K_2 and K_3 given by Roughton and Lyster (1965). The influence of the choice of $x_{1/2}$ is less marked.

Table A3.1
Comparison of K_2 and K_3 values from Hill plot data with literature values[a]

Parameters	Literature		Hill plot	
HbA (pH 7.4, 25°C)[b]				
$n_{1/2}$	(2.530)	2.6	2.5	
$x_{1/2}$(mmHg O_2)	(1.929)	1.8	1.8	
K_1(mmHg O_2)$^{-1}$	0.316	0.32	0.32	
K_2(mmHg O_2)$^{-1}$	0.443	(0.37)	(0.50)	
K_3(mmHg O_2)$^{-1}$	0.500	(0.81)	(0.60)	
K_4(mmHg O_2)$^{-1}$	1.088	1.00	1.00	
HbA (pH 6.96, 19°C)[c]				
$n_{1/2}$	(2.967)	3.0	2.9	2.9
$x_{1/2}$(mmHg O_2)	(9.158)	9.2	9.5	9.2
K_1(mmHg O_2)$^{-1}$	0.0493 ± 7%	0.047	0.047	0.047
K_2(mmHg O_2)$^{-1}$	0.0427 ± 7%	(0.037)	(0.035)	(0.063)
K_3(mmHg O_2)$^{-1}$	0.221 ± 78%	(0.27)	(0.25)	(0.16)
K_4(mmHg O_2)$^{-1}$	1.320 ± 21%	0.31	0.31	0.31

[a] The various data columns listed under "Hill plot" result from reading from the original Hill plots alternative values for one or more of the graph parameters. In any column calculated parameters are enclosed in parentheses.
[b] Tyuma et al. (1971) note values were evaluated from reported intrinsic κ_i values; i.e., $K_1 = 4\kappa_1$, $K_2 = 3/2 \, \kappa_2$, $K_3 = 2/3 \, \kappa_3$, $K_4 = 1/4 \, \kappa_4$.
[c] Roughton and Lyster (1965).

This method provides a way to obtain a full set of Adair constants for hemoglobin directly from available Hill plots. However, practical experience shows that the best method for obtaining these constants is to use nonlinear least-square analysis of binding-curve data.

APPENDIX 3.4 FACTORIZATION OF BINDING POLYNOMIALS

Briggs (1983) has summarized many of the properties of the roots of normalized polynomials. In order to maintain close correspondence with his notation, we note that his normalized binding polynomial is denoted by $N(x') = P_N$. Thus the roots of such polynomials with real coefficients have the following properties.

1. If $a + bi$ is a root, then so is its complex conjugate $a - bi$.
2. The total number of roots of a polynomial of degree t is t. The number of non-real roots must be even.
3. Since the coefficients of $N(x')$ are all positive, then any real root is negative.
4. If $N(x')$ is symmetric ($\beta_i' = \beta_{t-i}'$), and if the complex number z is a root, then $1/z$ is also a root.
5. If the roots of $N(x')$ are $z_1, \ldots, z_t$, then $P_N = (x' - z_1)(x' - z_2) \cdots (x' - z_t)$. The product of the roots is $(-1)^t$, their sum taken one at a time is $-\beta_{t-1}'$, and their sum of this product taken i at a time is $(-1)^i \beta_{t-1}'$.
6. The roots expressed in the form $r(\cos \theta + i \sin \theta)$, with $-\pi < \theta < \pi$, cannot lie in the region $|\theta| < \pi/t$; θ is the angle from the positive real axis.

These results have a relation to Hurwitz polynomials, which are positive polynomials whose zeros all lie in the left half-plane, $\text{Re } z < 0$. They arise in stable solutions of linear differential equations describing physical systems. Routh in 1875 and Hurwitz in 1895 developed algorithms called the Routh-Hurwitz Criterion for finding the distribution of zeros of a polynomial in the right and left half-planes of the complex plane.

All positive polynomials of degree two are Hurwitzian:

$$P_N = 1 + \alpha x' + x'^2 \text{ where } \alpha \geq 0. \tag{A3.21}$$

The roots are real if $\alpha \geq 2$, and by (4) the real roots are given as $-r$ and $-1/r$, and if they are nonreal as $\cos \theta \pm i \sin \theta$.

Positive polynomials of higher degree, to be factorable into positive polynomials, must meet special criteria depending on their degree. By definition, irreducible polynomials cannot be factored into polynomials having nonnegative coefficients. If the polynomial is Hurwitzian, then it can be factored uniquely into positive linear and quadratic factors. The real problem is to discover the factorization of non-Hurwitzian cases. We shall briefly summarize some of Briggs' results for these cases.

For the cubic case $t = 3$, we consider

$$P_N = 1 + \beta'_1 x' + \beta'_2 x'^2 + x'^3, \tag{A3.22}$$

and by the Routh-Hurwitz Criterion, this is Hurwitzian if $\beta'_1 \beta'_2 > 1$. In this case, P_N can be factored into either three linear factors or a linear factor and a positive quadratic factor. If $\beta'_1 \beta'_2 = 1$, then

$$P_N = (x' + \beta'_2)(x'^2 + \beta'_1). \tag{A3.23}$$

To find the location of the roots of an irreducible cubic P_N, assume them to be $-r$ and $\alpha \pm \beta i$, with $r > 0$ and $\alpha > 0$. Then

$$
\begin{aligned}
P_N(x') &= (x' + r)(x' - \alpha + \beta i)(x' - \alpha - \beta i) \\
&= (x' + r)(x'^2 - 2\alpha x' + \alpha^2 + \beta^2) \\
&= x'^3 + (r - 2\alpha)x'^2 + (\alpha^2 + \beta^2 - 2\alpha r)x' + r(\alpha^2 + \beta^2).
\end{aligned} \tag{A3.24}
$$

Since $N(x')$ is a positive polynomial, we have either

$$r - 2\alpha > 0, \ \alpha^2 + \beta^2 - 2\alpha r > 0, \text{ and } r(\alpha^2 + \beta^2) = 1$$

or

$$0 < \alpha \leqq r/2 \text{ and } (\alpha - r)^2 + \beta^2 \geqq r^2. \tag{A3.25}$$

Briggs has shown that the region of roots for these conditions may be depicted as in Figure A3-2.

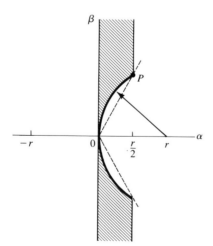

Figure A3-2.
Shaded region indicates allowable complex root location for an irreducible cubic polynomial (Briggs, 1985b).

The conditions of factorization of a positive quartic can be analyzed by similar arguments. The polynomial is Hurwitzian if $\beta'_1 \beta'_2 \beta'_3 \geq \beta'^2_3 + \beta'^2_1$. In that case, it can be factored into linear and quadratic factors. The equality condition gives a factor of the form $(x'^2 + a)$. If the polynomial is non-Hurwitzian and has no real roots, then these roots may be described at $-r \pm si$ and $\alpha \pm \beta i$, with $r > 0$ and $\alpha > 0$. Briggs has shown that the location of the roots for this situation is controlled by the situation shown in Figure A3-3 for the case where $r > s$. For an irreducible quartic, the roots involving α and β must fall in the cross-hatched region. The conditions of root

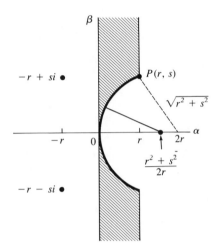

Figure A3-3.
Shaded region gives complex root location for quartic non-Hurwitzian irreducible polynomial with no real zeros (Briggs, 1985b).

location when $s < r$ and for the non-Hurwitzian quartic case of two real and two nonreal roots have been given by Briggs (1985b). In the non-Hurwitzian case, the quartic is irreducible, and the binding sites can be regarded as cooperatively linked in a set of four. It is also possible to have a quartic with two real and two nonreal zeros that is non-Hurwitzian but reducible to cubic and linear factors.

In general, we see that the root patterns determine the factorization that is possible for a given polynomial. Let $L(x)$ represent linear factors, $Q(x)$ quadratic, $C(x)$ cubic, and $T(x)$ quartic irreducible terms. Then various possible root patterns for a quartic polynomial are shown in the complex plane in Figure A3-4.

In order to illustrate how these mathematical results apply to a real situation where binding constants have been determined for the four-site macromolecule, we examine the properties of oxygen binding to hemoglobin. Oxygen-binding constants for human hemoglobin at pH 7.4 by Imai and Yonetani (1975b) are found as $\beta_1 = 0.1168$ torr^{-1}, $\beta_2 = 0.01069$ torr^{-2}, $\beta_3 = 0.00114$ torr^{-3}, and $\beta_4 = 0.002115$ torr^{-4}. The normalized constants are

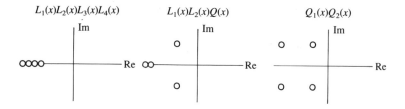

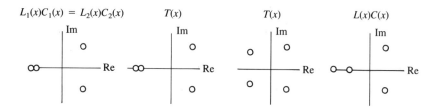

Figure A3-4.
Schematic representation of root patterns in the complex plane for a quartic binding polynomial with resulting factorization into positive subpolynomials indicated by L(linear), Q(quadratic), C(cubic), and T(quartic). Details of regional conditions are given by Briggs (1985a). Top three zero patterns are Hurwitzian, whereas bottom four are non-Hurwitzian.

given as

$$\beta'_1 = \beta_1 \beta_4^{-1/4} = 0.5446;$$

$$\beta'_2 = \beta_2 \beta_4^{-2/4} = 0.2324; \qquad \text{(A3.26)}$$

$$\beta'_3 = \beta_3 \beta_4^{-3/4} = 0.1156.$$

The roots are then found to be $0.6412 \pm 0.8724i$ and $-0.6990 \pm 0.6038i$, so that $P_N(x')$ is non-Hurwitzian and irreducible. Thus all four sites interact together by this mathematical criterion.

The condition of symmetric binding polynomials imposes particular root properties and factorization conditions on the polynomial (Briggs, 1984). For the normalized quartic case $[P_N(\text{sym}) = 1 + rx' + sx'^2 + rx'^3 + x'^4]$ the nature of the zeros is described by Figure A3-5. The nature of the Hill slope has been explored in detail by Briggs also for this case. An interesting situation can occur where the Hill slope is everywhere less than unity, but the binding polynomial still cannot be factored into linear terms.

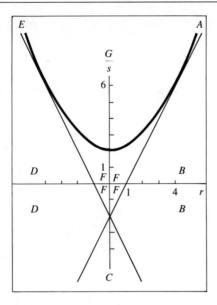

Figure A3-5.
Zeros of a symmetric quartic: $1 + rx' + sx'^2 + rx'^3 + x'^4$. The equation of the parabola is $\Delta = r - 4s + 8 = 0$, and the equations of the lines are $2r - s = 2$, and $2r + s = -2$. Zeros in designated regions are: (A) four negative zeros, (B) two negative zeros and two nonreal zeros on $|x'| = 1$, (C) two positive and two negative zeros, (D) two positive zeros and two nonreal zeros on $|x'| = 1$, (E) four positive zeros, (F) four nonreal zeros on $|x'| = 1$, (G) four nonreal zeros not on $|x'| = 1$ which are conjugate in pairs and reciprocal in pairs (Briggs, 1984). The cases (C), (D), and (E), which contain negative values for the coefficients of the quartic, do not correspond to any real binding polynomial.

Allosteric Systems 4

In Chapter 3 we took a purely phenomenological approach to a mass-law binding of ligands by a macromolecule having a finite number of sites. This approach leads to the concept of a binding polynomial of degree equal to the number of sites available for each ligand. In this chapter we will interpret these phenomena in terms of molecular mechanisms applicable to the macromolecule. In doing this we shall limit ourselves to a molecule that neither associates nor disassociates during its reaction with its ligands. In Chapter 6 we consider molecules that dissociate.

The origin of the allosteric mechanism lay in the phenomena of homotropic cooperativity shown in the binding of a single ligand by a multisite macromolecule exemplified by hemoglobin. At the time little was known about the structure of hemoglobin, beyond the fact that it had four sites for oxygen binding (Adair, 1925a). The idea that conformational changes controlled by the ligand could explain these phenomena first took clear shape in the late 1940s (Wyman, 1948) and early 1950s (Wyman and Allen, 1951). It was supported by the earlier observation of Haurowitz (1938) of the transformation of monoclinic oxy hemoglobin crystals to hexagonal deoxy crystals, and the subsequent X-ray structural observations of Perutz *et al.* (1960), who found significant differences in the diffraction patterns of hemoglobin crystals that depended on their state of ligation. Additional physical evidence has confirmed this general picture.

We first wish to outline the background that led to the allosteric idea, and then to formulate the concept in general terms, before we describe some simplifying assumptions that have yielded the operational models for interpreting experimental results.

4.1 HISTORICAL BACKGROUND

The effect that the binding of one ligand has on the binding of another was first quantified by careful studies of oxygen and hemoglobin. In the early 1900s Christian Bohr, K. A. Hasselbalch, and August Krogh (1904) reported the first accurate results on oxygen binding to dog blood. The oxygen-binding curve did not follow the expected curve of simple binding to a single site, namely, a rectangular hyperbola, but traced an S-shaped curve that rose slowly at low pressures, became steeper at intermediate pressures, and leveled off at saturation pressures. The S-shaped curve has since been recognized as indicative of positive cooperativity, where the presence of the first added oxygen assists the binding of subsequent molecules.* As mentioned before, the influence of one ligand on itself has been called homotropic interaction (Monod *et al.*, 1965), whereas the effect of a second ligand is termed heterotropic interaction. The presence of CO_2, also studied by Bohr, decreases the binding of oxygen at a given oxygen partial pressure, and this is described as a *negative heterotropic effect*.

It is not surprising that hemoglobin played a key role in the development of our ideas about cooperativity. A great deal was already known about hemoglobin at the time of Bohr's work. It had been crystallized in 1840. Iron was known to be the site of oxygen binding, and accurate analysis of the iron content by Zinoffsky (1886) had led to a minimum molecular weight of about 17,000. However, the actual molecular weight of hemoglobin was not well-established. An early osmotic pressure study by Hüfner and Gansser (1907) gave an erroneous result of 16,700. This led to the false conclusion that hemoglobin contained a single oxygen-binding site. Hill (1910, 1913) proposed that hemoglobin monomers must associate to aggregates with an average size of *n* monomers. Furthermore, he suggested that cooperative binding then occurred by binding *n* oxygens with each aggregate molecule. This proposal indeed gave the required S-shaped binding curve, but the suggested aggregation was not in agreement with the then-available molecular-weight studies. This situation changed with the work of Adair (1925a), who performed accurate osmotic pressure measurements, and analyzed his results by the thermodynamic concepts of Willard Gibbs. Adair found a molecular weight four times as large as the minimum molecular weight. The result was soon confirmed by Svedberg by application of ultracentrifuge measurements (Svedberg and Fahreus, 1926). Adair (1925b) formally described the oxygen binding to the four sites of hemoglobin by four successive stoichiometric reactions, and these equations have since been called the Adair equations. These are purely thermodynamic expressions of the successive reaction steps, and do not address the intriguing problem of the mechanism of cooperativity.

---

* John Edsall has traced the historical origins of the concept of allosterism (Edsall, 1980) and has gathered many details of the history of the properties of blood and hemoglobin (Edsall, 1972). For a historical account of the ideas leading to the allosteric concept, see also Claude Debru (1983, 1987).

What is the molecular basis of the cooperativity observed in hemoglobin? Pauling (1935) proposed a diagramatic scheme in which the hemes are arranged at the corners of a "square," and the interactions along the sides of the square changed upon oxygenation of the hemes. Such a scheme gives an equation which approximately describes the binding-curve data, but leaves the nature of the interaction unexplained. Since tetrameric molecules of the hemoglobin could be split into dimers, Allen *et al.* (1950) suggested substituting a rectangular form of interactions in place of the "square," but again without addressing the question of the nature of the interactions. This approach was purely formal, because the physical nature of the interactions was not understood. Indeed, even now a molecular description of the details that form the basis of cooperativity still remains in a relatively simplified state.

An important observation was made by Felix Haurowitz (1938), though at the time its significance was not understood. He found that deoxygenated crystals when exposed to oxygen shattered. Some ten years later Wyman (1948) proposed that ligand-linked structural changes could explain the cooperative binding properties found by Bohr and his colleagues. The full connection was developed a few years later by Wyman and Allen (1951). They argued that the Bohr effect could be explained by a change in the pKs of various proton-ionizable groups caused by the oxygen-induced conformational change of the hemoglobin structure. In a similar way the cooperativity of the oxygen binding itself could be explained by the shift in the equilibria of the structural forms upon oxygenation.

At the same time, the oxygen-linked structural change in hemoglobin was being studied in unprecedented detail by Perutz and his collaborators (1960) by means of X-ray structural measurements. Their work would eventually provide exact pictures of the state of the hemoglobin molecule in its unligated and ligated state. Some of the first results (Boyes-Watson *et al.*, 1947) showed that oxidation of the iron could produce large changes in the structure, although it took another ten years, along with the development of the method of isomorphous replacement, before a precise picture of the structural change accompanying oxygenation could be presented. Continued efforts along these lines have provided an unparalleled view of the structural change that occurs in hemoglobin crystals (Perutz, 1976). Thus the initial simple observation of Haurowitz has acquired great significance in giving a general picture of how structural changes of large biological macromolecules can be regulated by ligand binding.

The term *allosteric* was originally introduced by Monod and Jacob (1961) to describe the long-range effect of binding an activator upon the reactivity of an enzyme substrate bound at a distant site. This implied some structural change, but no precise picture of how this occurred was given. A more precise meaning of the term was elaborated (Monod *et al.*, 1963) with the idea that the binding ligand induced conformation changes. These are described as *allosteric transitions*. Upon removal of the bound ligand, the original conformation state was restored.

Wyman recognized that the allosteric terminology proposed by the Institut Pasteur group was an apt expression for the concept of ligand-linked conformational changes that he had introduced some fifteen years before (Wyman, 1948). Wyman then proposed (1963) a broader use of the term *allosteric*, to include the earlier ideas of equilibria between macromolecular forms and the influence of ligand activity upon these equilibria. The equations, called *linkage equations*, which describe the effect of ligand concentration on the ratio of different conformations, were first formulated by Wyman and Allen (1951). A general review of the thermodynamic concepts of linkage and reciprocal effects demonstrated how the quantitative aspects of these ideas could be used to understand many different properties of respiratory proteins (Wyman, 1964).

An important consolidation of the allosteric concept came with the outline of a very specific model by Monod, Wyman, and Changeux. This MWC model (Monod *et al.*, 1965), based on the equilibria between two macromolecular forms (*R* and *T*), contained the essence of how function could be expressed in terms of structural change. Intrinsically, it is a thermodynamic model based on mass-law principles. The "interactions" of the early Pauling model are replaced by the different energetic properties of the proposed structures that the macromolecule can assume. This is both a source of great strength and a limitation. The MWC model does not address the nature of differences between the thermodynamic properties of allosteric forms, any more than the interaction "bond" model addresses the origin of "bond" interaction energies. The real importance of the MWC approach is that it is based on structural changes that have been observed in detailed structural studies. The Pauling model was essentially based on the concept of the macromolecule as a generalized space-interaction model, with specific rules that determined the effects of binding on the interaction bonds between sites. The original suggestion of Pauling was further elaborated in a series of models, sometimes termed the *induced fit model* or *KNF model*, by Koshland *et al.* (1966). They formulated site-site interactions by considering binding to the site only in a specific form, and included changes of interactions of specifically ligand-occupied states by geometric contact rules between subunits. In this sense they obtained a distinct allosteric form for each state of ligation. Thus from the broad view we can now see that the MWC and KNF models both originated from the idea that different macromolecular structures show different binding and energetic properties. Wyman (1972) pointed out how the KNF model could, like the MWC model, be regarded as a special case of a more general allosteric model.

In the last fifteen years there has been strong effort to use the detailed structural knowledge gained from X-ray crystallography and spectroscopic studies in order to describe the thermodynamic properties of hemoglobin. Perutz (1970, 1976, 1979) proposed a mechanism of cooperativity based on structural information, and this has led to the incorporation of such features into statistical thermodynamic models developed by Szabo and Karplus (1972), and Johnson and Ackers (1982). Extensive binding studies have been conducted, in particular by Imai (1982 and references therein) and by Ackers (e.g., Mills *et al.*, 1976; Chu *et al.*, 1984; Gill *et al.*, 1987; Di Cera *et al.*, 1987b; Robert *et al.*, 1988b). Especially detailed functional studies by Smith and Ackers (1985) have uncovered a challenging twist to hemoglobin's function in terms of differences in the order of oxidation, which might be linked to oxygen ligation, to the α and β subunits. Not surprisingly, the simple allosteric models are not able to explain such observations in detail. However, extension of the simple picture to include nested hierarchies of allosteric processes (Wyman, 1984; Decker *et al.*, 1986; Robert *et al.*, 1987; Brunori *et al.*, 1986) accounts for many of the complexities observed.

Although the study of hemoglobin and other respiratory proteins remains a major focus and source of structural and functional information, the success of even the simple allosteric models for biological regulation processes is widespread in macromolecular systems. In this chapter we wish to examine the general properties of the allosteric concept. We will describe a basic framework that facilitates the translation step between a specific model and observed properties of a macromolecular system.

4.2 THE GENERAL ALLOSTERIC MODEL

We introduced in Chapter 2 the ideas of ligand binding to two allosteric forms of a macromolecule. The central idea is that structure determines ligand-binding properties, and ligand activities will in turn determine the populations of different structures. For example, in the presence of arabinose, the crystal structure of the arabinose-binding protein (ABP) is found in a tightly packed conformation surrounding the sugar molecule (Gilliland and Quiocho, 1981), whereas in the absence of arabinose (Mao *et al.*, 1982), calculations indicate the protein assumes an open cleft form (see Figure 4-1).

The allosteric concept may be extended to cover the more general case where the macromolecule has $q + 1$ conformers, which we designate by an h subscript having values of 0, 1, 2, q. Each allosteric form h can bind a maximum number of t_h ligands. Thus the zeroth form has t_0 binding sites, etc. We identify an hth conformer with iX ligands bound by $M_h X_i$. The general array of all species is depicted in Figure 4-2. The horizontal arrows denote allosteric reactions, and the vertical arrows denote ligand-binding reactions. A column in the array describes the successive reactions for addition of the X ligand to a given allosteric form. Note that the columns need not contain the same number of species; i.e., there may be a different number of binding sites for each form.

The entire system of species is considered to be in equilibrium with ligand X at a given activity x. The reactions within the array are described by appropriate mass-action laws. The general reaction from the M_{00} reference species involves the addition of iX ligands and a change to the hth molecular conformation as follows:

$$M_{00} + iX \rightarrow M_h X_i. \tag{4.1}$$

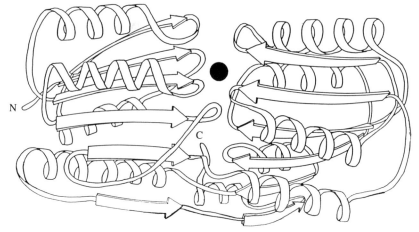

Figure 4-1.
Ribbon structure of arabinose binding protein showing arabinose binding site in cleft between two lobes of the protein. Drawing provided by F. Quioche, Rice University. The structure in the absence of arabinose ligand is thought to be in an open hinged form (Mao *et al.*, 1982).

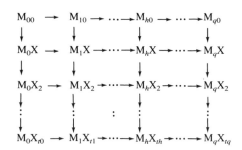

Figure 4-2.
Allosteric species array of $q + 1$ forms binding various amounts of X ligands.

The equilibrium constant for such a reaction is denoted by β_{hi}. The concentration of $M_h X_i$ is given then as

$$[M_h X_i] = \beta_{hi}[M_{00}]x^i. \tag{4.2}$$

The binding partition function, Q, is obtained by taking the sum of all concentrations relative to the concentration of the reference form M_{00}. This leads with the use of equation (4.2) to

$$Q = \sum_{h=0}^{q} \sum_{i=0}^{t_h} \beta_{hi}x^i. \tag{4.3}$$

The partition function is a polynomial in powers of x activity, and is equivalent to the binding polynomial (P) we saw in Chapter 3. However, here, various allosteric forms have been included.

Traditionally the symbol L is used to describe the equilibrium constant between different allosteric forms, i.e., between the species in different columns with respect to the zeroth-form column. The designation L_{h0} denotes the equilibrium constant for the unligated conformational change in the first row of the array:

$$M_{00} \rightarrow M_{h0}, \qquad L_{h0} = \frac{[M_{h0}]}{[M_{00}]}. \tag{4.4}$$

It is especially convenient to describe the sum of species in a given column relative to the top member of the column by the *sub-binding* polynomial P_h, one for each conformation:

$$P_h = \sum_{i=0}^{th} \frac{[M_h X_i]}{[M_{h0}]}. \tag{4.5}$$

With equation (4.2) and the definition of L_{h0} in (4.4), the first summation in equation (4.3), i.e., sum of species in the hth column, is seen as

$$P_h = \frac{\sum_{i=0}^{th} \beta_{hi} x^i}{L_{h0}}. \tag{4.6}$$

In these terms the binding partition function, equation (4.3), is given by the sum of all columns:

$$Q = \sum_{h=0}^{q} (L_{h0})(P_h). \tag{4.7}$$

This expression is based on the top left corner (or M_{00}) reference state. Other reference conditions may also be chosen, depending on the problem being addressed. For example, if the starting or reference condition is that of all unligated species, then one would normalize Q to this sum, i.e., $\sum L_{h0}$, and obtain a normalized binding polynomial written as P:

$$P = \frac{\sum_h (L_{h0})(P_h)}{\sum_h (L_{h0})}. \tag{4.8}$$

with a leading term of 1.

The fraction of a given allosteric form out of all the macromolecules in the system is an important characterizing parameter of the system. The unligated fraction of the hth form will be denoted by α_{h0}, and in terms of L_{h0} is given as

$$\alpha_{h0} = \frac{L_{h0}}{\sum_h (L_{h0})}. \tag{4.9}$$

The binding polynomial [equation (4.8)] is thus the appropriately weighted sum of all sub-binding polynomials, and may be written in these terms as

$$P = \sum_h \alpha_{h0} P_h. \tag{4.10}$$

The binding curve, $\bar{X}$, obtained by the logarithmic derivative $d \ln x$ is

$$\bar{X} = \frac{d \ln P}{d \ln x} = \frac{1}{P} \sum \alpha_{h0} P_h \frac{d \ln P_h}{d \ln x}. \tag{4.11}$$

This expression can be interpreted by making use of (1) the fraction of all species that are in the h allosteric form, defined by α_h,

$$\alpha_h = \frac{\alpha_{h0} P_h}{P} = \frac{\alpha_{h0} P_h}{\sum \alpha_{h0} P_h}, \tag{4.12}$$

and (2) the binding curve for a given allosteric form h, defined by $\bar{X}_h$,

$$\bar{X}_h = \frac{d \ln P_h}{d \ln x}. \tag{4.13}$$

Then it follows that the total binding curve [equation (4.11)] is just

$$\bar{X} = \sum \alpha_h \bar{X}_h. \tag{4.14}$$

As seen, the overall binding curve is the fractionally weighted sum of the individual allosteric form binding curves. However, the fractions α_h are functions of the ligand activity, and thus change during the course of ligation. It is this feature that distinguishes the allosteric model from a mixture of molecules held in their original proportions, i.e. "frozen," as ligation proceeds.

4.3   SPECIFIC CASES OF THE ALLOSTERIC MODEL

As might be imagined, given the preceding description of the allosteric model, a great many special cases can be envisioned, depending on the number of allosteric forms $(q + 1)$ and the form of each conformation binding polynomial (P_h). So far the general formalism will necessarily accommodate any stoichiometric binding data, and it provides no new insights until it is simplified. In order to explore some particular situations, we will consider some of the simplest sub-binding polynomials. In this spirit of simplification, we shall also assume they all have the same number of binding sites, although in general this need not be so. Formally, we can always treat the system as if the ts in each conformation are equal to the maximum, and then set certain binding constants equal to 0.

If the sub-binding polynomials describe independent site binding, then they have the form

$$P_h = (1 + \kappa_{h1}x)(1 + \kappa_{h2}x)\cdots(1 + \kappa_{ht}x), \tag{4.15}$$

where κ_{hi} is the single site-binding constant for the ith binding site on the hth allosteric form. If all the sites are identical in binding affinity for the hth form, then

$$P_h = (1 + \kappa_h x)^t. \tag{4.16}$$

This special case, one of the many that could be imagined, has received the most attention within the framework of the allosteric model. The binding polynomial P is then given from equations (4.8) and (4.10) as

$$P = \sum_h \alpha_{h0}(1 + \kappa_h x)^t = \frac{\sum L_h(1 + \kappa_h x)^t}{\sum L_h}, \tag{4.17}$$

and the binding curve is then

$$\bar{X} = \frac{1}{P}\sum \alpha_{h0} t \kappa_h x (1 + \kappa_h x)^{t-1}, \tag{4.18}$$

$$\bar{X} = \frac{\sum L_h t \kappa_h x (1 + \kappa_h x)^{t-1}}{\sum L_h (1 + \kappa_h x)^t}. \tag{4.19}$$

For the situation of an allosteric molecule with just a single binding site ($t = 1$), the binding polynomial is then

$$P = \sum \alpha_{h0}(1 + \kappa_h x) = 1 + \left(\sum \alpha_{h0}\kappa_h\right)x. \tag{4.20}$$

From this expression we see that the Adair constant β_1 is just the average value of κ_h:

$$\beta_1 = \sum \alpha_{h0}\kappa_h. \tag{4.21}$$

Furthermore, for a macromolecule with a single binding site, equation (4.20) yields a simple single-site binding curve with the form

$$\bar{X} = \frac{\sum \alpha_{h0}\kappa_h x}{1 + \sum \alpha_{h0}\kappa_h x}. \tag{4.22}$$

We therefore cannot tell from the shape of such a curve that allosteric transitions are occurring. This, of course, could be applied to oxygen binding to myoglobin, but not to proton binding, where there are many binding sites.

The standard free energy of saturating an allosteric macromolecule is always less than for a macromolecule that does not respond to allosteric changes. As we have seen in Chapter 3, the coefficient of the last term of the binding polynomial determines this free-energy change. From equation (4.17) this coefficient is

$$\beta_t = \frac{\sum L_h \kappa_h^{\,t}}{\sum L_h} = \sum \alpha_{h0} \kappa_h^{\,t}, \tag{4.23}$$

and the standard free energy of saturation is thus

$$\Delta G_x^{\,\circ}(\text{allosteric}) = -RT \ln \sum \alpha_{h0} \kappa_h^{\,t}. \tag{4.24}$$

In contrast, if the system had been frozen in the initial distribution, so that allosteric equilibrium is forbidden, then the saturating free energy is the mole-fraction-weighted sum of each form, and as seen from equation (3.71)

$$\Delta G_x^{\,\circ}(\text{frozen}) = -RT \sum \alpha_{h0} \ln \kappa_h^{\,t}. \tag{4.25}$$

The free-energy change of the frozen situation is always greater than that of the allosteric equilibrium situation (Wyman, 1967). This means that the binding curve for the allosteric case defines a smaller area to the standard-state line, and will always be steeper than the frozen situation. This leads to a general conclusion: any system that can respond by an equilibrium reaction between forms, or between various aggregated species, will have a lower free energy of binding than corresponding systems that are frozen into their initial conformer state. This might be thought of as the seduction of a susceptible macromolecule by the ligand. In broad terms, allosteric systems show positive cooperativity when compared to frozen systems. The binding curve for a two-conformer four-site situation ($t = 4$, $\alpha_{10} = .5$), either frozen or in allosteric equilibrium, is shown in Figure 4-3.

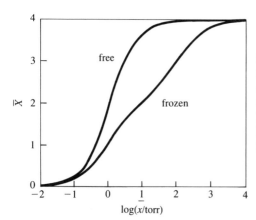

Figure 4-3.
Binding curve under free and frozen conditions of an allosteric molecule with four binding sites and two forms ($\alpha_{10} = 0.5$, $\kappa_R = 1$, $\kappa_T = .01$). Note that the curve for the frozen form has a lesser slope than that for the freely equilibrating case.

4.3.1 The MWC Model: Two Allosteric Forms

The MWC model, formulated by Monod *et al.* (1965), is the simplest form of the general allosteric model. Only two allosteric forms are considered, and the ligand binding to each form is assumed to take place at independent and identical sites whose affinity is determined solely by the particular form. Many properties of allosteric systems can be illustrated by this simple model, and we shall thus develop this case in greater detail than was given in Chapter 2.

The two allosteric forms are denoted by T and R, with R the reference form. The equilibrium constant for the unligated state reaction,

$$R_0 \rightarrow T_0, \tag{4.26}$$

is denoted by L_0:

$$L_0 = \frac{[T_0]}{[R_0]}. \tag{4.27}$$

The macromolecular species when X ligand is present are represented by a two-column array,

$$
\begin{array}{ccc}
R_0 & \rightarrow & T_0 \\
\downarrow & & \downarrow \\
RX & \rightarrow & TX \\
\downarrow & & \downarrow \\
RX_2 & \rightarrow & TX_2 \\
\downarrow & & \downarrow \\
\vdots & & \vdots \\
\downarrow & & \downarrow \\
RX_t & \rightarrow & TX_t.
\end{array}
$$

The intrinsic site-binding constants for the R and T forms are designated by κ_R and κ_T, and the sub-binding polynomials to each form are given as

$$P_R = (1 + \kappa_R x)^t, \tag{4.28}$$

$$P_T = (1 + \kappa_T x)^t. \tag{4.29}$$

The binding partition function, Q, with the R_0 form serving as the reference species, is then

$$Q = P_R + L_0 P_T, \tag{4.30}$$

or in terms of allosteric form-binding polynomials for R and T,

$$Q = (1 + \kappa_R x)^t + L_0 (1 + \kappa_T x)^t. \tag{4.31}$$

For ligand-binding purposes we "normalize" the binding polynomial* to the sum of all unligated species, i.e., $1 + L_0$, and

$$P = \frac{1}{1 + L_0}(1 + \kappa_R x)^t + \frac{L_0}{1 + L_0}(1 + \kappa_T x)^t. \tag{4.32}$$

In this form the fractions of initially unligated R or T forms are

$$\alpha_{R_0} = \frac{1}{1 + L_0}; \quad \alpha_{T_0} = \frac{L_0}{1 + L_0}. \tag{4.33}$$

Expansion of the binding polynomial, P, and collection of terms with the same power of x yield the Adair binding constants; i.e., the overall stoichiometric coefficient, β_i, follows

$$\beta_i = \binom{t}{i}\frac{\kappa_R^i + L_0\kappa_T^i}{1 + L_0} = \binom{t}{i}K_R^i\left(\frac{1 + L_0 c^i}{1 + L_0}\right), \tag{4.34}$$

where

$$\binom{t}{i} = \frac{t!}{(t - i)!i!}$$

and the stepwise constants, $K_i = (\beta_i)/(\beta_{i-1})$, are then obtained as

$$K_i = \left(\frac{t - i + 1}{i}\right)\frac{\kappa_R^i + L_0\kappa_T^i}{\kappa_R^{i-1} + L_0\kappa_T^{i-1}} = \left(\frac{t - i + 1}{i}\right)\kappa_R^i\left(\frac{1 + L_0 c^i}{1 + L_0 c^{i-1}}\right), \tag{4.35}$$

where $c = \kappa_R/\kappa_T$.

The intrinsic stepwise constants, κ_i, are the K_is without the statistical factors. The ratio κ_i/κ_{i-1} determines the cooperativity of the system, and from the defining terms in equation (4.35) can be shown to be always greater than unity, i.e., positively cooperative, provided c is not equal to unity.

Various features of the MWC model are indicated by the specific properties of the binding curve. For example, the median activity (see Chapter 3) is computed from equation (4.34) for $i = t$. With $\beta_t x_m^t = 1$, one obtains

$$\beta_t = \left(\frac{1}{x_m}\right)^t = \alpha_{R_0}\kappa_R^t + \alpha_{T_0}\kappa_T^t, \tag{4.36}$$

---

* A frequently used form of the MWC binding polynomial is to refer the ligand activity to the R-state affinity by letting $\alpha = \kappa_R x$, and defining the relative affinities by $c = \kappa_T/\kappa_R$. The binding polynomial is then

$$P = (1 + L_0)^{-1}[(1 + \alpha)^t + L_0(1 + c\alpha)^t].$$

$$\left(\frac{1}{x_m}\right)^t = \alpha_{R_0}\left(\frac{1}{x_{Rm}}\right)^t + \alpha_{T_0}\left(\frac{1}{x_{Tm}}\right)^t, \tag{4.37}$$

where x_{Rm} and x_{Tm} are the median activities of the R and T form, i.e., $(\kappa_R)^{-1}$ and $(\kappa_T)^{-1}$. The binding curve is given from equation (4.32) as

$$\bar{X} = \frac{t\kappa_R x(1 + \kappa_R x)^{t-1} + tL_0\kappa_T x(1 + \kappa_T x)^{t-1}}{(1 + \kappa_R x)^t + L_0(1 + \kappa_T x)^t}. \tag{4.38}$$

This expression may also be written as

$$\bar{X} = \alpha_R \bar{X}_R + \alpha_T \bar{X}_T, \tag{4.39}$$

where α_R and α_T are the conformer fractions [see equation (4.12)].

(a) *The Hill plot of the MWC model.* We have seen that the Hill plot provides a general way for visualizing the cooperative nature of ligand-binding processes. The low and high ligand-activity asymptotes with unit slope intercept the vertical axis at the standard state ($x = 1$) at K_1/t and tK_t respectively, i.e.,

$$\kappa_1 = \frac{K_1}{t} = \left[\frac{\kappa_R + L_0\kappa_T}{1 + L_0}\right], \tag{4.40}$$

$$\kappa_t = tK_t = t\left[\frac{\kappa_R{}^t + L_0\kappa_T{}^t}{\kappa_R{}^{t-1} + L_0\kappa_T{}^{t-1}}\right]. \tag{4.41}$$

We shall use the binding polynomial with affinities (α) referred to the R-state affinity constant (see last footnote). The first and second derivatives of P with respect to $\ln \alpha$, i.e., P' and P'', can be expressed from P as

$$P = (1 + L_0)^{-1}[(1 + \alpha)^t + L_0(1 + c\alpha)^t], \tag{4.42}$$

$$P' = \frac{dP}{d\ln \alpha} = (1 + L_0)^{-1}[t\alpha(1 + \alpha)^{t-1} + tL_0c\alpha(1 + c\alpha)^{t-1}], \tag{4.43}$$

$$P'' = P' + (1 + L_0)^{-1}t(t-1)[\alpha^2(1 + \alpha)^{t-2} + L_0c^2\alpha^2(1 + c\alpha)^{t-2}]. \tag{4.44}$$

The Hill slope is given by equation (A3.9). With a bit of algebraic manipulation we find the bracketed term, the *Hessian* (see Appendix 3.4 in Chapter 3), in (A3.9) as

$$t[PP'' - (P')^2 - P(tP - P')] = t^2(t-1)\alpha^2 L_0 c(1 + \alpha)^{t-1}(1 + c\alpha)^{t-1}. \tag{4.45}$$

By inspection we see that this must always be positive. Thus the Hill coefficient for the simple MWC model is always greater than or equal to one. The explicit dependence of the Hill coefficient on the ligand activity (α) is a complicated

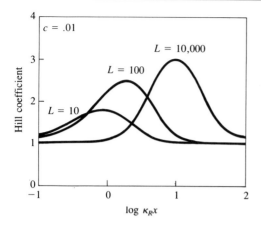

Figure 4-4.
Hill coefficient curves for the MWC model
($t = 4$) as a function of relative ligand activity
($\alpha = \kappa_R x$) for various values of L_0 with
$c = 0.01$ ($c = \kappa_T/\kappa_R$). Note that only for one
choice of L_0 and c is the Hill coefficient
curve symmetric.

expression formed by substitution of the relations for P, P', and P'' into equation (A3.9). There will be a maximum value of the Hill coefficient at some intermediate ligand activity, determined by c, L_0, and t. Of course, the asymptotic values of n at high and low ligand activity are unity. Some representative Hill coefficient plots of n versus $\ln \alpha$ are illustrated in Figure 4-4 for $t = 4$. As noted in this figure, all values of n are greater than unity. Furthermore, the dependence of n on the logarithm of the activity is in general nonsymmetric; only one curve, with specifically selected values of L and c, shows symmetry. The conditions for a symmetric binding curve for the MWC model are developed in Section 4.3.1(d).

(b) *The "switchover point."* As ligation proceeds within the scheme of the MWC model, we have the interesting possibility of starting with a low-affinity dominant form in the unligated state (suppose this is T) and converting the dominant form by ligation to a high-affinity R form at high ligand activity. The population of allosteric forms is thus changed by ligand activity. The point at which an equal amount of each form is present has been termed by Hopfield *et al.* (1971) the *switchover point.* We can find this point by considering the factors that determine the concentration of the two allosteric forms. If the ratio of all T species to R species is denoted by L, then from the MWC binding polynomial we write

$$L = \frac{[T \text{ species}]}{[R \text{ species}]} = L_0 \frac{(1 + c\alpha)^t}{(1 + \alpha)^t}. \tag{4.46}$$

The switchover point occurs when $L = 1$ and $\alpha = \alpha_s$. This condition determines the switchover activity α_s as

$$\alpha_s = \frac{1 - \left(\dfrac{1}{L_0}\right)^{1/t}}{\left(\dfrac{1}{L_0}\right)^{1/t} - c}. \tag{4.47}$$

Assuming $L_0 > 1$, then we see that a switchover point occurs only if

$$c < \left(\frac{1}{L_0}\right)^{1/t}. \tag{4.48}$$

A free-energy or chemical-potential diagram of the standard-state values for the RX_i and TX_i forms for a case $(t = 4)$ where switchover can occur is shown in Figure 4-5. The free-energy difference from the R_0 state is determined

$$
\begin{array}{ll}
0 \text{ ——— } R_0 & \\
& T_0 \text{ ——— } -RT(\ln L_0) \\
-RT(\ln \kappa_R + \ln 4) \text{ ——— } RX & \\
& TX_1 \text{ ——— } -RT(\ln L_0 + \ln \kappa_T + \ln 4) \\
& TX_2 \text{ ——— } -RT(\ln L_0 + 2\ln \kappa_T + \ln 6) \\
-RT(2\ln \kappa_R + \ln 6) \text{ ——— } RX_2 & \\
& TX_3 \text{ ——— } -RT(\ln L_0 + 3\ln \kappa_T + \ln 4) \\
-RT(3\ln \kappa_R + \ln 4) \text{ ——— } RX_3 & \\
& TX_4 \text{ ——— } -RT(\ln L_0 + 4\ln \kappa_T + \ln 1) \\
-RT(4\ln \kappa_R + \ln 1) \text{ ——— } RX_4 & \\
\end{array}
$$

Figure 4-5.
Free-energy diagrams of various ligated states of the RT conformers for $t = 4$. This specific situation illustrated is for $L_0 > 1$, $c = \kappa_T/\kappa_R < 1$, and shows that the manifold of T state lies within that for the R states for $t = 4$.

by the equilibrium constants for the reaction $R_0 + iX \rightarrow RX_i$ given by $\binom{t}{i}\kappa_R^i$ for the R column or $R_0 + iX \rightarrow TX_i$ given by $L_0\binom{t}{i}\kappa_T^i$ for the T column. If the manifold of state does not overlap in such a manner that the free energy of one form is contained within the extreme of the other, then switchover (defined as a change in the dominant species) will not occur. Note that the existence of a switchover point depends on the particular values of the allosteric parameters. Not all allosteric systems will show such special behavior, and this may have little to do with their functional properties.

(c) **Ligand control of allosteric forms: MWC model.** As we have seen, the fraction of a given allosteric form, irrespective of its state of ligation, will be determined by the ligand activity. In terms of the MWC model, this fraction, defined by the terms of the binding polynomial, is given for the R and T forms by α_R and α_T, respectively:

$$\alpha_R = \frac{(1 + \alpha)^t}{(1 + \alpha)^t + L_0(1 + c\alpha)^t}, \tag{4.49}$$

$$\alpha_T = \frac{L_0(1 + c\alpha)^t}{(1 + \alpha)^t + L_0(1 + c\alpha)^t}. \tag{4.50}$$

Note in these equations that the α alone denotes the relative activity given by $\kappa_R x$ and $c = \kappa_T/\kappa_R$. Let us examine the R fraction in a little more detail. By dividing numerator and denominator by $(1 + \alpha)^t$, we have

$$\alpha_R = \frac{1}{1 + L_0\left(\dfrac{1 + c\alpha}{1 + \alpha}\right)^t}. \tag{4.51}$$

Similarly the fraction of T is

$$\alpha_T = \frac{1}{\dfrac{1}{L_0}\left(\dfrac{1 + \alpha}{1 + c\alpha}\right)^t + 1}. \tag{4.52}$$

In the limiting cases of low and high ligand activity,

$$\alpha \to 0, \qquad \alpha^0{}_R = \frac{1}{1 + L_0}, \qquad \alpha^0{}_T = \frac{1}{\dfrac{1}{L_0} + 1}, \tag{4.53}$$

$$\alpha \to \infty, \qquad \alpha^\infty{}_R = \frac{1}{1 + L_0 c^t}, \qquad \alpha^\infty{}_T = \frac{1}{\dfrac{1}{L_0}\dfrac{1}{c^t} + 1}. \tag{4.54}$$

Thus, depending on the values of L_0, c, and t, we can cause α_R to increase or decrease as the activity of a ligand increases. The effect of increasing t is to make the change due to ligand activity more pronounced. This is seen in Figure 4-6.

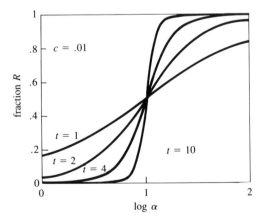

Figure 4-6.
The effect of the number of sites t on the fraction of the R form (α_R) versus the logarithm of the relative ligand activity α for $t = 1, 4, 10, 100$. $L_0 = 10$, $L_0 c^t = 0.1$. These last conditions assure symmetry for these curves.

(d) Symmetry condition: MWC model. There is one special situation where the α_R and α_T curves are symmetric with respect to each other (see Colosimo *et al.*, 1974): when $\alpha^0{}_R = \alpha^\infty{}_T$ or $\alpha^\infty{}_R = \alpha^0{}_T$. From equations (4.53) and (4.54), the symmetry condition is found by solving the equation

$$\frac{1}{\dfrac{1}{L_0} + 1} = \frac{1}{1 + L_0 c^t}. \tag{4.55}$$

We find

$$L_0{}^2 c^t = 1, \, t > 2. \tag{4.56}$$

Thus, when $L_0 = c^{-t/2}$, a symmetric fraction curve is obtained.

For this symmetric situation, the median activity, α_{ms}, will determine where $\alpha_R = \alpha_T = 1/2$. As we shall see, the median activity is controlled by the values of the intrinsic affinities to the R and T forms. From equation (4.51) we write

$$\frac{1}{2} = \frac{1}{1 + L_0 \left(\dfrac{1 + c\alpha_{ms}}{1 + \alpha_{ms}}\right)^t}, \tag{4.57}$$

which on rearrangement gives

$$\frac{1 - \left(\dfrac{1}{L_0}\right)^{1/t}}{\left(\dfrac{1}{L_0}\right)^{1/t} - c} = \alpha_{ms}. \tag{4.58}$$

Inserting the symmetry condition given by equation (4.56), we find

$$\alpha_{ms} = c^{-1/2}. \tag{4.59}$$

In terms of ligand activity x (note $\alpha = \kappa_R x$), the symmetric median x_{ms} and L_0 are given for the symmetric case as

$$x_{ms} = \left(\frac{1}{\kappa_T \kappa_R}\right)^{1/2} \text{ and } L_0 = \left(\frac{\kappa_R}{\kappa_T}\right)^{t/2}. \tag{4.60}$$

As was seen in Figure 4-6, the slope of the α_R versus $\ln \alpha$ curve is determined by t, c, L_0, and the ligand activity α. For the symmetric case we can easily evaluate the maximum slope, since by inspection this occurs at the median activity α_{ms}. Starting with equation (4.49), taking the logarithm, and differentiating with respect to $\ln \alpha$, we obtain

$$\frac{d \ln \alpha_R}{d \ln \alpha} = \frac{t\alpha}{1 + \alpha} - \bar{X}. \tag{4.61}$$

Now by imposing the symmetry condition $\alpha = \alpha_{ms} = c^{-1/2}$, and recognizing that at this activity $\alpha_R = 1/2$ and $\bar{X} = t/2$, we obtain

$$\left(\frac{d\alpha_R}{d \ln \alpha}\right)_{median} = \frac{1}{4} t \frac{c^{-1/2} - 1}{c^{-1/2} + 1} = \frac{1}{4} t \frac{1 - c^{1/2}}{1 + c^{1/2}}. \tag{4.62}$$

It should be noted that by imposing the condition of symmetry, we reduce the number of parameters (for a given t) from 2 (c and L_0) to just 1 (c). This result shows that when $c \to 0$, the slope becomes $t/4$. Thus an increase in binding sites will enable the fraction of allosteric forms to be controlled more sharply with ligand activity. The slope given by equation (4.62) is shown as a function of $\log c$ in Figure 4-7.

The Hill slope at the median (n_{ms}) for symmetric conditions is found to be given from equations (4.42–4.45):

$$n_{ms} = 2[1 + (t - 1)(1 + c)/(1 + c^{1/2})^2] - t. \tag{4.63}$$

This expression has the expected limits: as $c \to 0$, then $n_{ms} \to t$; and as $c \to \infty$, $n_{ms} \to t$. Of course, when $c = 1$, then $n_{ms} = 1$.

An illustration of the use of the Hill-slope expression for symmetric binding curves is found in the interpretation of oxygen-binding curves in the large,

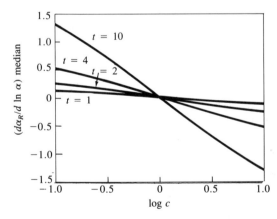

Figure 4-7.
The slope of the fractional change of the R state with a change in the logarithm of relative ligand activity ($d\alpha_R/d \ln \alpha$) at the median point as a function of c for various values of t.

multisite, respiratory protein hemocyanin from the snail *Helix pomatia*.
Under some pH and ion conditions, the binding curves are closely symmetric. The Hill slope at the median n_{ms} is characterized by the function given by
equation (4.63), and this is illustrated for selected values of c, the affinity constant ratio, in Figure 4-8.

Binding curves of hemocyanin *Helix pomatia* are shown in Figure 1-12c
(Zolla *et al.*, 1978). From the curve at pH 8.00 we can see that the spacing of the
asymptotes gives $c \sim 0.01$, and that the Hill slope at the midpoint of the curve
is about 6. Thus from the $c = 0.01$ curve in Figure 4-8, we see that $t \sim 8$. This

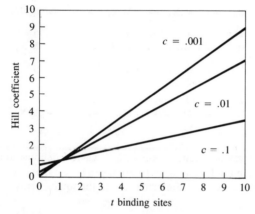

Figure 4-8.
Hill slope at the median for a symmetric MWC binding curve
as a function of t for selected values of $c = \kappa_T/\kappa_R$.

value of t effectively determines an allosteric constellation unit size imbedded
within the aggregate, assuming, of course, that the unit functions like an MWC
model. We see here one of the strengths of the MWC model: it can provide a
first-order representation of binding processes in complex aggregated forms
of proteins.

4.3.2   The Allosteric Square "Parent" Model

The MWC model is, as we have seen, a highly simplified special case of the
general allosteric model outlined in Figure 4-2. Clearly, many other possi-
bilities can be imagined, both in terms of the number of different allosteric
forms and in terms of sub-binding polynomials to each form. A special model,
called the *allosteric square "parent" model*, was formulated by Wyman (1972)
to show how the MWC model and the induced-fit models (KNF) of Koshland
et al. (1966) can be obtained as special cases of this parent allosteric model. The
parent model is similar in form to the general allosteric model (Figure 4-2),

except that it is restricted to a square array, such that the number of allosteric forms $(t + 1)$ equals the number of binding species in a given column,
including the unligated species, $(t + 1)$. This leads to a square array, shown in
Figure 4-9. In the array, each allosteric form of the macromolecule is labeled

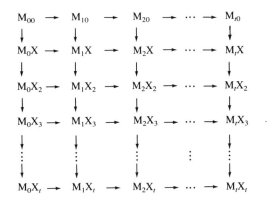

Figure 4-9.
Allosteric square array of reaction species M_hX_i where h denotes conformation and
i denotes X ligands bound. Each conformation can bind a maximum number of
t X ligands, and there are $t + 1$ conformations in the square array.

by a particular numerical subscript. The MWC two-state model occurs when
the two extreme allosteric forms are the dominant forms. The KNF model
results when the species along the diagonal dominate.

We shall need to specify some additional properties of the species in the
array in order to make these comparisons. Suppose the macromolecule is
composed of a set of q identical subunits. Each of these subunits has a single
site for a given ligand, and each one can exist in only one or the other of two
different states (or conformations) R and T, with binding constants κ_R and κ_T.
The macromolecule itself exists in a number of conformations M_h which are
uniquely determined by the state of the subunits: one for R_t, one for $R_{t-1}T$,
etc., to T_t. Thus in general $M_h = R_{t-h}T_h$. All subunits within a given conformation M_h are assumed independent of one another in their reaction with
ligands, and the whole system is in equilibrium. The sub-binding polynomial
for each column h is P_h or

$$P_h = (1 + \kappa_R x)^{t-h}(1 + \kappa_T x)^h. \tag{4.64}$$

The full binding-partition function is then obtained by summing over the
columns relative to the M_{00} form by use of the unligated equilibrium constant

L_h for ($M_{00} \rightarrow M_{h0}$), as follows:

$$Q(\text{square}) = \sum_{h=0}^{t} L_h(1 + \kappa_R x)^{t-h}(1 + \kappa_T x)^h. \qquad (4.65)$$

We consider several special cases of this model:

(a) ***The two-state MWC model.*** We note that $L_0 = 1$, and we observe that if only L_t of all L_h has a significant value (i.e., the intermediate columns of the species array are negligible), then we have the usual two-state MWC model.

(b) ***The KNF case, or the induced-fit model.*** This situation results by another choice of constraints on the allosteric equilibrium constants, L_h, and the binding constants κ_R and κ_T. This model assumes that only the concentration of macromolecules M_hX_h in a given column or row is significant. Binding h X ligands is assumed to occur to just one (the hth) allosteric form, and this match gives rise to the term "induced fit." This situation occurs when two conditions are imposed on the reaction constants that describe the square array. First, the affinity of subunit T is assumed to be negligible compared to that of subunit R. Then we obtain by expansion of equation (4.65) the concentrations of the various forms shown by the array in Table 4.1.

Table 4.1
Species concentrations

X ligation	Allosteric form (h): 0	1...	$t-3$	$t-2$	$t-1$	t
0	1	$L_1 \ldots$	L_{t-3}	L_{t-2}	L_{t-1}	L_t
1	$\binom{t}{1}\kappa_R x$	$L_1\binom{t-1}{1}(\kappa_R x)\ldots$	$L_{t-3}3\kappa_R x$	$L_{t-2}2\kappa_R x$	$L_{t-1}\kappa_R x$	0
2	$\binom{t}{2}(\kappa_R x)^2$	$L_1\binom{t-1}{2}(\kappa_R x)^2\ldots$	$L_{t-3}3(\kappa_R x)^2$	$L_{t-2}(\kappa_R x)^2$	0	0
3	$\binom{t}{3}(\kappa_R x)^3$	$L_1\binom{t-1}{3}(\kappa_R x)^3\ldots$	$L_{t-3}(L_R x)^3$	0	0	0
4	$\binom{t}{4}(\kappa_R x)^4$	$L_1\binom{t-1}{4}(\kappa_R x)^4\ldots$	0	0	0	0

The terms above the diagonal can be made as small as we desire by choosing values of L_h so that the last term in any row always dominates (Wyman, 1972). This requires that $L_t > L_{t-1} > \cdots > L_1 > 1$, and the sum of the remaining diagonal terms normalized by L_t gives

$$P(\text{KNF}) = 1 + \frac{L_{t-1}\kappa_R x}{L_t} + \frac{L_{t-2}(\kappa_R x)^2}{L_t} + \cdots + \frac{1}{L_t}(\kappa_R x)^t. \qquad (4.66)$$

A wide variety of choices can be made in terms of the t allosteric constants and one intrinsic binding constant κ_R for this model. Choices based on different geometric considerations of site-site interactions lead to various constraint rules between the various allosteric forms (Koshland *et al.*, 1966).

In accordance with this model the macromolecule changes from one allosteric form to another as each ligand is added. This is in marked contrast to the MWC model, in which a given conformation can bind any number of ligands up to the maximum value of t.

In both the MWC and the KNF models, the nature of the cooperativity depends on the choice of the L_h. All the interactions between sites are indirect, and are mediated by ligand-linked conformational changes. This mass action between allosteric forms is the essence of the allosteric concept. The MWC model represents an extreme choice, where all mixed polymeric conformations are excluded. This model shows only positive cooperativity. This is apparent when we expand the normalized MWC polynomial as

$$P(\text{MWC}) = 1 + t\bar{K}x + \cdots + \frac{t!\overline{K^j}x^j}{j!(t-j)!} + \cdots + \overline{K^t}x^t, \qquad (4.67)$$

where the bars denote the averages $(\overline{K^j} = \alpha_0 \kappa_R{}^j + \alpha_t \kappa_T{}^j)$. Since

$$\overline{K^j} > \overline{K^{j-1}} \cdot \bar{K},$$

the ratio of successive coefficients with statistical factors removed will always be greater than one; so the binding polynomial cannot be factored completely to linear terms (see Appendix 3.4 in Chapter 3).

In contrast to the MWC model, the induced-fit model can show both positive and negative cooperativity depending on the choice of allosteric constants. In terms of the Hill plot, this model may show Hill coefficients less than or greater than 1. Finally, the shape of the MWC binding curve is determined by two parameters, κ_T/κ_R and L_t, whereas the shape of the KNF binding curve is determined by t allosteric parameters, $L_1, L_2 \ldots L_t$ and is unaffected by the κ_R.

(c) *The hybrid model.* This model extends the MWC case to include an intermediate column of species from the square array. It has been used to explain reaction-rate data of the tetrameric enzyme pyruvate kinase by considering the principal species to be R_4, $R_2 T_2$, and T_4 (Buc *et al.*, 1973). The oxygen-binding properties of hexameric hemocyanins have also been explained by considering hybrid allosteric species of the form R_6, $R_3 T_3$, and T_6 (Arisaka and Van Holde, 1979). The binding partition function for such cases is given by

$$Q(\text{hybrid}) = (1 + \kappa_R x)^t + L_{t/2}[(1 + \kappa_R x)(1 + \kappa_T x)]^{t/2} + L_t(1 + \kappa_T x)^t.$$
$$(4.68)$$

As this expression shows, one additional parameter, $L_{t/2}$, is needed to characterize this model. This flexibility has enabled effects of various allosteric effectors to be accommodated through their influence on $L_{t/2}$ and L_t. An example of the application of this model to ghost shrimp hemocyanin under different pH conditions is shown in Figure 4-10.

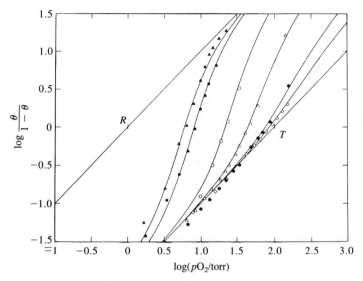

Figure 4-10.
Hill plot of oxygen binding to *C. Californiansis* hemocyanin under indicated pH conditions. The theoretical curves were generated using a MWC hybrid model with $t = 6$ for the binding polynomial given by equation (4.82) (Arisaka and Van Holde, 1979).

4.3.3   The Pauling and KNF Models

The Pauling (1935) model of cooperativity for oxygen binding was formulated by considering site-site interactions which depended on occupancy of a site by oxygen. The simple geometries of a square and a tetrahedron were used in setting up the rules of site interactions. Allen and Wyman (1950) extended the ideas to a rectangular geometry. The theoretical approach is completely different from the allosteric equilibrium concepts considered in the previous sections. In a general sense, we represent the binding process to the four-site hemoglobin molecule by means of two effects. The first effect of binding is the imagined intrinsic binding of an oxygen molecule to each site as though each site were identical and independent. The second effect is to include the influence of site-site interactions. These interactions can be envisioned as "bonds" between sites in the initial, completely unligated state of the macromolecule. The "bonds" will be disposed according to various imagined geometric schemes, and the effect of ligation will be to "break" the bonds according to simple selection rules. Each broken bond contributes to the free energy of a given macromolecular ligated form in an additive manner. Both positive and negative contributions can be considered. The standard-state free energy of various states of the ligated macromolecule can be then written in terms of the intrinsic binding, the "bond" free energies, and the free energy contribution from equivalent or degenerate ways of realizing a given ligated state. The equilibrium constant for the reaction from the unligated form to the state in question is determined by this standard-state free energy, and the binding polynomial can be written directly.

Koshland *et al.* (1966) considered the effects of site-site interactions from a view which combined aspects of the Pauling "bond" approach with certain features of the allosteric approach. The binding system is considered to consist of protomers that can exist in either an R or a T state. The initial unligated state of the macromolecule is described as having all protomers in the T state (T_4 for hemoglobin). The binding of ligand X, however, occurs only with the R form of the protomer, and thus the singly ligated allosteric form is T_3RX, and so forth. This is the basis of the name the *induced-fit* model. Each of these forms will have a particular set of new interaction free energies between subunit protomers.* The free energy of each form can then be considered in terms of broken "bond" contributions in the sense developed by Pauling. Thus the KNF models contain the same type of geometric selection rules, and for similar situations give the same results as formulated by Pauling. A wide variety of geometric situations with different arrangements of bond strengths and selection rules for the formation of ligated forms has been considered, and the general name for models based on this approach is the KNF model. Hess and Szabo (1979) discuss this model in terms of stabilizing cross-link "bonds" between unligated subunits. Salt bridges, as proposed by Perutz in his description of the stereochemical mechanism of subunit interaction in hemoglobin (Perutz, 1970), are considered as stabilizing bonds. Changes in interfacial contacts, ionization effects, and redistribution of solutes and water molecules may all be involved in the cumulative description of an interaction "bond."

The main case considered by Pauling postulated that the binding sites are located at the corners of a square. We depict the unligated form of this model as shown in Figure 4-11 by bonds drawn between the four subunits, represented as squares. Two things happen with the addition of ligand. First, a new ligand bond is formed, as depicted by the X-filled circle. The product of the intrinsic binding constant (κ) and the activity of the free ligand (x) raised to the power of the number of ligands bound gives the relative concentration

---

* We have seen in the discussion of the allosteric "parent" model how KNF models arise under particular conditions where each state of ligation has a particular allosteric form. Note that this view leads to the binding polynomial of equation (4.66). Allosteric free-energy changes are equivalent to broken "bond" free-energy values.

Structures:

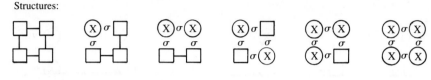

Concentrations:

$$1 \qquad 4\,\frac{(\kappa x)}{\sigma^2} \qquad 4\,\frac{(\kappa x)^2}{\sigma^3} \qquad 2\,\frac{(\kappa x)^2}{\sigma^4} \qquad 4\,\frac{(\kappa x)^3}{\sigma^4} \qquad \frac{(\kappa x)^4}{\sigma^4}$$

Figure 4-11.
Pauling "square"-bond interaction model for hemoglobin. Species are depicted by amounts of ligand bound and bonds broken (σ). Statistical factors indicate the number of ways a given species can be bound.

of the ligated form compared to the unligated form in the absence of site-site interaction. Second, the effect of site interactions is determined by the number of such interactions that are broken, each broken bond contributing a term to the free energy of a given ligated state (the broken "bond" free-energy contribution is $-RT \ln \sigma$). In the square model, each site-site bond gives a factor $1/\sigma$ (the reciprocal reflects the fact that the bond is broken on ligation) to the equilibrium constant for the reaction between unligated and specifically ligated species. The number of ways an equivalent species can be represented is described by its statistical factor. The partition function is the sum of all species concentrations relative to the unliganded form and in terms of the bond-interaction properties of the square model is given as

$$P(\text{KNF square}) = 1 + 4\,\frac{(\kappa x)}{\sigma^2} + 4\,\frac{(\kappa x)^2}{\sigma^3} + 2\,\frac{(\kappa x)^2}{\sigma^4} + 4\,\frac{(\kappa x)^3}{\sigma^4} + \frac{(\kappa x)^4}{\sigma^4}. \quad (4.69)$$

We see that this model reduces to the case of four identical sites when there is no site-site interaction, i.e., $\sigma = 1$. Furthermore, positive cooperativity occurs when $\sigma < 1$, and negative cooperativity occurs when $\sigma > 1$. Clearly only two parameters are needed to describe this model, κ and σ.

The median x_m is given by the last set of constants: $(\kappa/\sigma)^4 = \beta_4 = (1/x_m)^4$, or $x_m = \sigma/\kappa$. We may then normalize the activity to the median by letting $x = x_m x'$, and then obtain

$$P_N(\text{KNF square}) = 1 + \frac{4}{\sigma}x' + \left(\frac{4}{\sigma} + \frac{2}{\sigma^2}\right)x'^2 + \frac{4}{\sigma}x'^3 + x'^4. \quad (4.70)$$

Since the second and fourth terms have the same coefficient, this binding polynomial by necessity gives symmetric binding curves. Oxygen-binding curves to hemoglobin have a slight asymmetry; so this model cannot describe the hemoglobin system exactly.

A rectangular model with two long bonds of strength σ_1 and two short

Structures:

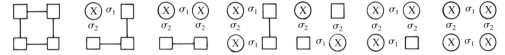

Concentrations:

$$1 \qquad 4\frac{(\kappa x)}{\sigma_1\sigma_2} \qquad 2\frac{(\kappa x)^2}{\sigma_1\sigma_2{}^2} \qquad 2\frac{(\kappa x)^2}{\sigma_1{}^2\sigma_2} \qquad 2\frac{(\kappa x)^2}{\sigma_1{}^2\sigma_2{}^2} \qquad 4\frac{(\kappa x)^3}{\sigma_1{}^2\sigma_2{}^2} \qquad \frac{(\kappa x)^4}{\sigma_1{}^2\sigma_2{}^2}$$

Figure 4-12.
Rectangular bond model for the hemoglobin partition-function interaction bonds of strength σ_1 and σ_2.

bonds of strength σ_2 leads by the same process, as seen in Figure 4-12, to the following binding polynomial.

$$P(\text{KNF rectangle}) = 1 + \frac{4\kappa x}{\sigma_1\sigma_2} + \frac{2(\kappa x)^2}{\sigma_1\sigma_2}\left(\frac{1}{\sigma_1} + \frac{1}{\sigma_2} + \frac{1}{\sigma_1\sigma_2}\right)$$

$$+ \frac{4(\kappa x)^3}{\sigma_1{}^2\sigma_2{}^2} + \frac{(\kappa x)^4}{\sigma_1{}^2\sigma_2{}^2}. \tag{4.71}$$

This is a three-parameter model, and by noting that the median is $x_m = (\sigma_1\sigma_2)^{1/2}/\kappa$, we find that the normalized polynomial has equal coefficients for the second and fourth terms, again indicating that only a symmetric binding curve can be obtained for such a model.

The effect of different intrinsic binding constants for various sites is easily introduced. Suppose there are two α and two β subunits with different intrinsic affinities, as might be the case for hemoglobin. For the "rectangle" model let the diagonal corners be α and β, with intrinsic binding constants of κ_α and κ_β. Then the binding polynomial will be found to be

$$P(\text{KNF rectangle, } \alpha\beta) = 1 + \frac{2(\kappa_\alpha + \kappa_\beta)}{\sigma_1\sigma_2}x$$

$$+ \frac{\kappa_\alpha\kappa_\beta}{\sigma_1\sigma_2}\left[\frac{2}{\sigma_1} + \frac{2}{\sigma_2} + \left(\frac{\kappa_\alpha}{\kappa_\beta} + \frac{\kappa_\beta}{\kappa_\alpha}\right)\frac{1}{\sigma_1\sigma_2}\right]x^2$$

$$+ \frac{2(\kappa_\alpha{}^2\kappa_\beta + \kappa_\alpha\kappa_\beta{}^2)}{\sigma_1{}^2\sigma_2{}^2}x^3 + \frac{\kappa_\alpha{}^2\kappa_\beta{}^2}{\sigma_1{}^2\sigma_2{}^2}x^4. \tag{4.72}$$

This four-parameter model, when written in median normalized form, is also symmetric.

Results for the median normalized form of the binding polynomial for several models ($t = 4$) are collected in Table 4.2. If we introduce some feature of asymmetry, such as the distorted square with one different interaction bond, or the square with one diagonal interaction bond, the coefficients of second and fourth terms of the binding polynomials are different. This is an example of a general principle pointed out previously by Wyman (in Allen *et al.*, 1950), that symmetry of function (namely, the shape of the binding curve) implies geometric symmetry of structure, and conversely.*

The asymmetric binding properties of the hemoglobin binding curve have led Weber (1982) and Peller (1982) to use an extended version of the $\alpha_2 \beta_2$ rectangle (diagonal $\alpha - \alpha$ interaction) model given in Table 4.2. They obtain conditions for $\kappa_\alpha / \kappa_\beta$ and τ in which the asymmetry observed for hemoglobin can be rationalized by such a model. As we have also seen, the simple MWC model can also give asymmetric binding curves that closely match those observed for hemoglobin. Thus the lack of observed symmetry is not sufficient to support a nonsymmetric KNF model over the simple MWC model.

4.4   NESTED ALLOSTERIC MODELS

As we have seen, allosteric phenomena can occur between molecular sub-units, between whole molecules, or between complex oligomeric forms. The combination of allosteric changes within simple subunit conformers with allosteric changes of larger structures made up of several subunits suggests the idea of *nesting*, a phenomenon which arises when there is a hierarchy of conformational changes in the most general type of allosteric systems.

The nesting concept was invoked (Wyman, 1964, 1968, 1972) to explain linkage phenomena and cooperativity observed in early studies of hemoglobin. The observation of the nearly invariant shape of the oxygen-binding curve at different pHs requires a similar pH dependence of the oxygen-binding constants for the subunits in the R and T forms. This dependence can be explained by letting the subunit itself exist in subconformational allosteric states whose equilibrium population shifts with pH. The nesting idea was also invoked to account for some early data (now realized to be erroneous) which implied that the dissociated $\alpha\beta$ dimer of hemoglobin was cooperative, and could be regarded as an allosteric unit within the larger allosteric tetramer form of hemoglobin itself (Wyman, 1967). The overall cooperativity of the hemoglobin molecule was then interpreted to arise from the intrinsic contribution of the allosteric dimers amplified through allosteric tetramer changes.

The concept of nested allosteric reactions is particularly compelling in dealing with cooperative oxygen-binding reactions with large multisubunit proteins, such as the hemocyanins and erythrocruorins. In arthropod hemocyanins, structures are composed typically of 6, 12, 24, and 48 protein

---

* Note however that the linear models also lead in general to asymmetric binding polynomials. The lack of interaction-bond symmetry here is pointed out by Whitehead (1980) to be the structural cause of a nonsymmetric binding polynomial.

Table 4.2
Median normalized KNF binding-polynomial coefficients (β_i') for various models of hemoglobin ($t = 4$)

Model	β_1'	β_2'	β_3'	Median x_m
Square	$4/\sigma$	$\dfrac{4}{\sigma} + \dfrac{2}{\sigma^2}$	$4/\sigma$	$\dfrac{\sigma}{\kappa}$
Tetrahedral	$\dfrac{4}{\sigma^{3/2}}$	$\dfrac{6}{\sigma^2}$	$\dfrac{4}{\sigma^{3/2}}$	$\dfrac{\sigma^{3/2}}{\kappa}$
Rectangular (identical sites)	$\dfrac{4}{\sqrt{\sigma_1\sigma_2}}$	$2\left(\dfrac{1}{\sigma_1} + \dfrac{1}{\sigma_2} + \dfrac{1}{\sigma_1\sigma_2}\right)$	$\dfrac{4}{\sqrt{\sigma_1\sigma_2}}$	$\dfrac{\sqrt{\sigma_1\sigma_2}}{\kappa}$
Rectangular (α, β sites)	$\dfrac{2\left(\sqrt{\dfrac{\kappa_\alpha}{\kappa_\beta}} + \sqrt{\dfrac{\kappa_\beta}{\kappa_\alpha}}\right)}{\sqrt{\sigma_1\sigma_2}}$	$2\left[\left(\dfrac{1}{\sigma_1} + \dfrac{1}{\sigma_2}\right) + \left(\dfrac{\kappa_\alpha}{\kappa_\beta} + \dfrac{\kappa_\beta}{\kappa_\alpha}\right)\dfrac{1}{\sigma_1\sigma_2}\right]$	$\dfrac{2\left(\sqrt{\dfrac{\kappa_\alpha}{\kappa_\beta}} + \sqrt{\dfrac{\kappa_\beta}{\kappa_\alpha}}\right)}{\sqrt{\sigma_1\sigma_2}}$	$\dfrac{\sqrt{\sigma_1\sigma_2}}{\sqrt{\kappa_\alpha\kappa_\beta}}$
Rectangular (α, β sites)	$\dfrac{2\left(\sqrt{\dfrac{\kappa_\alpha}{\kappa_\beta}} + \sqrt{\dfrac{\kappa_\beta}{\kappa_\alpha}}\right)}{\sqrt{\sigma_1\sigma_2}}$	$2\left(\dfrac{1}{\sigma_1} + \dfrac{1}{\sigma_1\sigma_2}\right) + \left(\dfrac{\kappa_\alpha}{\kappa_\beta} + \dfrac{\kappa_\beta}{\kappa_\alpha}\right)\sigma_1\sigma_2$	$\dfrac{2\left(\sqrt{\dfrac{\kappa_\alpha}{\kappa_\beta}} + \sqrt{\dfrac{\kappa_\beta}{\kappa_\alpha}}\right)}{\sqrt{\sigma_1\sigma_2}}$	$\dfrac{\sqrt{\sigma_1\sigma_2}}{\sqrt{\kappa_\alpha\kappa_\beta}}$
Distorted square	$(\tau\sigma^3)^{1/4}\left(\dfrac{2}{\sigma^2} + \dfrac{2}{\sigma\tau}\right)$	$(\tau\sigma^3)^{1/2}\left(\dfrac{3}{\tau\sigma^2} + \dfrac{1}{\sigma^3} + \dfrac{2}{\tau\sigma^3}\right)$	$4(\tau\sigma^3)^{-1/4}$	$\dfrac{\sqrt{\tau\sigma^3}}{\kappa}$

Table 4.2, continued
Median normalized KNF binding-polynomial coefficients (β_i') for various models of hemoglobin ($t = 4$)

Model	β_1'	β_2'	β_3'	Median x_m
Rectangle diagonal α-α (τ)	$\dfrac{2\tau^{1/4}}{\sqrt{\sigma_1\sigma_2}}\left(\dfrac{\sqrt{\kappa_\alpha}}{\tau\sqrt{\kappa_\beta}} + \sqrt{\dfrac{\kappa_\beta}{\kappa_\alpha}}\right)$	$\tau^{1/2}\left[\dfrac{1}{\sigma_2\tau} + \dfrac{1}{\sigma_1\tau} + \dfrac{1}{\sigma_1\sigma_2}\left(\dfrac{\kappa_\alpha}{\kappa_\beta\tau} + \dfrac{\kappa_\beta}{\kappa_\alpha}\right)\right]$	$\dfrac{2}{\tau^{1/4}\sqrt{\sigma_1\sigma_2}}\left(\dfrac{\sqrt{\kappa_\sigma}}{\sqrt{\kappa_\alpha}} + \sqrt{\dfrac{\kappa_\beta}{\kappa_\alpha}}\right)$	$\left(\dfrac{\sqrt{\sigma_1\sigma_2}\,\tau^{1/4}}{\sqrt{\kappa_\alpha\kappa_\beta}}\right)$
Square (diagonal) (τ)	$\dfrac{2\tau^{1/4}}{\sigma}\left(\dfrac{1}{\tau} + 1\right)$	$\dfrac{4\tau^{1/2}}{\sigma\tau} + \dfrac{\tau^{1/2}}{\sigma^2}\left(\dfrac{1}{\tau} + 1\right)$	$4/(\tau^{1/4}\sigma)$	$\dfrac{\sigma\tau^{1/4}}{\kappa}$
Linear	$2\left(1 + \dfrac{1}{\sigma}\right)\sigma^{-1/4}$	$3\left(1 + \dfrac{1}{\sigma}\right)\sigma^{-1/2}$	$4\sigma^{-3/4}$	$\dfrac{\sigma^{3/4}}{\kappa}$
Linear	$2\left(\dfrac{1}{\sigma_1} + \dfrac{1}{\sigma_1\sigma_2}\right)(\sigma_1^2\sigma_2)^{1/4}$	$\dfrac{1}{\sigma_1}\left(\dfrac{1}{\sigma_1} + \dfrac{2}{\sigma_2} + \dfrac{3}{\sigma_1\sigma_2}\right)\sigma_1\sigma_2^{1/2}$	$4(\sigma_1^2\sigma_2)^{-1/4}$	$\left(\dfrac{\sigma_1^2\sigma_2}{\kappa}\right)^{1/4}$

subunits (van Bruggen, 1983). The key building block in these aggregates is the hexameric unit, which itself shows positive cooperativity for oxygen binding ($n \cong 4$). As we form the higher oligomers, the cooperativity increases, and some Hill coefficients reach values > 7. The shape of the oxygen-binding curve for such large oligomers of *Eurypelma* (Decker *et al.*, 1983) hemocyanin shows that the simple two-state allosteric model is inadequate to describe the results, but a nested model can account for the observation. This is shown in Figure 4-13.

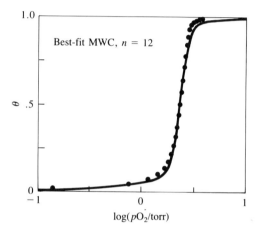

Figure 4-13.
Oxygen binding to *Eurypelma californicum* hemocyanin dodecamers (Decker *et al.*, 1983). Theoretical solid line shows that MWC model with $t = 12$ fails to describe the data accurately. See Figure 4-14 for the results fitted to a nested model.

A wide variety of nested models can be imagined. We wish to show how the partition function of the nested model can be formulated in terms of subunit and oligomer properties for a simple situation. Suppose we have a macromolecule made up of s oligomer substructures, and that these substructures are each made of r subunits. Thus there are $t = s \times r$ total subunits (binding sites). We could *a priori* consider a dodecameric molecule to be a trimer of tetramers or a dimer of hexamers. Thus in explaining a macromolecule's function with a nested model, we first must establish an appropriate hierarchy of structure. In this respect we will be guided primarily by structural information about the macromolecule obtained from crystallography, EM, or other techniques. In addition, several approaches have been taken in modeling the functional interactions that operate in nested models. Several constitute a hybrid approach that uses aspects of the Pauling or KNF models nested inside an MWC-type of interaction (Brunori *et al.*, 1986; Gill *et al.*, 1986). Others have made use of nested MWC representations (Decker *et al.*, 1986; Robert *et al.*, 1987). The basic concepts can be illustrated using a specific case, motivated by the complex functional and structural properties of the hemocyanin from the tarantula.

The tarantula hemocyanin is a 24-subunit macromolecule; each subunit binds a single oxygen molecule, and all are arranged as a pair of identical dodecamers. The structure and the oxygen-binding properties of the whole macromolecule and some of its dissociated parts were shown in Chapter 1. In the nested model we consider each subunit to bind oxygen noncooperatively, with a single-site binding polynomial of the form $1 + \kappa x$. Next we shall assume that the dodecameric assembly of subunits can exist in two allosteric conformations, R and T, and that the binding polynomial of the dodecamer can be written in the MWC form

$$1/(1 + L)(1 + \kappa_R x)^{12} + L/(1 + L)(1 + \kappa_T x)^{12}.$$

At this point we hypothesize that the entire macromolecule, composed of two of these dodecamers, can further exist in another, "super" allosteric conformation, and we designate this conformation A, as distinct from the original conformation, which we shall designate B. The presence of two alternative super conformations confers a total of four different environments in which a subunit of a dodecamer can exist: AR, AT, BR, and BT. A subunit in each of these conformations will have a characteristic binding affinity, indicated by κ_{AR}, etc. The R to T allosteric equilibrium constants are also subject to the super conformation; so they will be written L_A and L_B. The allosteric equilibria between the super conformations are described by Λ. (All allosteric equilibrium constants are defined in the absence of ligand.) Thus the binding polynomial for this dimer of dodecamers, interacting in two levels of allosteric equilibria described by the MWC principles, is

$$P = \frac{1}{1 + \Lambda}\left[\frac{1}{1 + L_A}(1 + \kappa_{AR}x)^{12} + \frac{L_A}{1 + L_A}(1 + \kappa_{AT}x)^{12}\right]^2$$

$$+ \frac{\Lambda}{1 + \Lambda}\left[\frac{1}{1 + L_B}(1 + \kappa_{BR}x)^{12} + \frac{L_B}{1 + L_B}(1 + \kappa_{BT}x)^{12}\right]^2. \quad (4.73)$$

This expression of the partition function reflects the nesting of the MWC partition functions for each dodecamer into the partition function of the whole molecule, and is found to describe the binding properties of oxygen to the tarantula hemocyanin. The oxygen-binding properties for *Eurypelma* spider hemocyanin in different subunit and native forms can be described as seen in Figure 4-14 by the nested MWC parameters (Decker *et al.*, 1986).

This model has been further tested by extension to include the identical linkage of carbon monoxide and oxygen binding. In this case the individual site-binding polynomials used in the preceding nesting equation have the form $1 + \kappa_{O_2}x + \kappa_{CO}y$, where x and y denote the oxygen and carbon monoxide activities, respectively. Results of such a study (Decker *et al.*, 1988) are

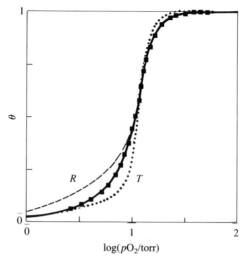

$\log(pO_2/\text{torr})$

Figure 4-14.
Oxygen-binding curves of tarantula (*E. californicum*) hemocyanin under highly cooperative solution conditions (Robert *et al.*, 1987). Small boxes about the data points are drawn two times the standard error of a point. The solid line is the best fit to a nested model with two allosteric dodecamer units that exist in gross structures of 24 binding sites and designated by *R* and *T*. Each dodecamer within these larger structures is assumed to undergo allosteric changes designated by *r* and *t*. The dashed lines show the underlying subbinding curves corresponding to the allosteric equilibria between *r* and *t* within a given gross *R* or *T* form.

illustrated by surfaces representing the saturation of either O_2 or CO as a function of the activities of the two gases. In Figure 4-15, we see that the CO binding curve is essentially noncooperative in the absence of oxygen, but becomes increasingly cooperative as the oxygen partial pressure is raised. This reflects the enhanced stability that oxygen provides to a macromolecular conformation in which CO has a markedly higher affinity. On the other hand, the oxygen binding curve (not shown here) remains essentially unchanged with respect to cooperativity as CO activity is increased, although the average affinity of the macromolecule for oxygen decreases.

For a nonbiological molecular situation, King (1981) has shown how an allosteric model with nested KNF forms may be used to explain the positive cooperative binding of cyanide ion in complexes of nickel and zinc ions. We might have expected that the addition of successive negative ions to the positive metal core would result in negative cooperativity because of large electrostatic repulsion effects, and this is observed for most such systems (for example, complexes of beryllium (II) and fluoride ion). However, quite the contrary is observed for these cyanide complexes. Knowing that each of the aquo metal ions (nickel and zinc) is octahedral, and the tetracyano zinc complex is tetrahedral, but the tetracyano nickel complex is square-planar, King

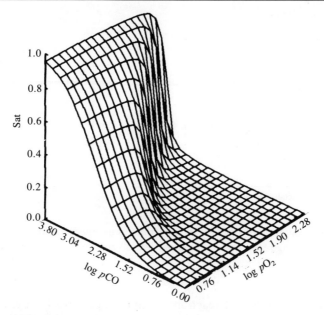

Figure 4-15.
Carbon monoxide binding (degree of saturation) as a function
of logarithmic values of oxygen and carbon monoxide partial
pressure for tarantula hemocyanin from data given by Decker
et al., 1988.

suggested an allosteric model. It might also be noted that hexaaquonickel
(II) ion is high-spin (paramagnetic) and tetracyanometal (II) ion is low-spin
(diamagnetic). Furthermore, within each allosteric form (octahedral, square-
planar, and tetrahedral), King proposed that the binding of CN^- was not
governed by the simple MWC idea of a single intrinsic binding constant, i.e.,
independent identical binding, but rather that the binding within each form
followed a Pauling or KNF model. Since, as we have seen in Section 4.3.2, the
KNF model is a specially selected model of the allosteric "square," King has
effectively used a model that falls within the idea of nesting.

We depict the essential ideas of his model schematically by Figure 4-16,
where the diagonals of the allosteric "squares" with six and four forms are
formulated by KNF rules, and the two general forms are in equilibrium with
each other.

As cyanide is added to the zinc system, a conversion to the tetrahedral form
occurs, since the cyanide has more affinity to the tetrahedral form than to the
octahedral form. However, at sufficiently high ligand concentration, it must
return to the form with the greatest number of ligands bound, i.e., the
octahedral form. Thus, we predict an interesting pathway in which octahedral
form is converted to tetrahedral form, and back to the octahedral form, as
ligand concentration increases.

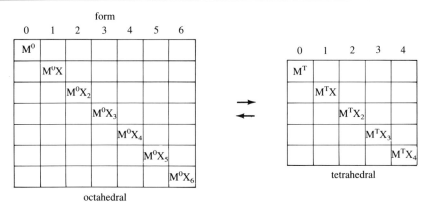

Figure 4-16.
Nested representation of the KNF octahedral and tetrahedral allosteric "square" formed by binding reactions of cyanide with aquo zinc complexes (King, 1981).

The concept of nested reactions within cooperative biological binding macromolecules has been used by Di Cera (Brunori *et al.*, 1986) to postulate the presence of a dimeric *cooperon* unit that can contain positive or negative interactions between its two subunits. The cooperon binding polynomial is then formulated by a simple KNF description, and nested within a MWC two-state model to obtain the binding polynomial for the whole system. This model handles a variety of complex data obtained on both arthropod and molluscan hemocyanins under various pH conditions.

A particularly challenging situation to which nesting ideas have been applied is to provide a model to represent dissociation free energies of ten different species of oxidized hybrids of $\alpha_2\beta_2$ hemoglobins studied by Smith and Ackers (1985). The electron binding polynomial, based on an overall two-state MWC process with a nested two-parameter KNF "square with diagonal," has been found to describe the quantitative properties of all ten different electron-ligated forms (Gill *et al.*, 1986).

4.5   AN ALLOSTERIC SYSTEM IN THE STEADY STATE

Almost of necessity we think about the physical world in terms of models. Indeed, to draw a sharp line between model and world is impossible. Among the most sophisticated and articulate models are those couched in the language of mathematics. These, particularly as they apply to physicochemical systems, are basically of two kinds, thermodynamic and kinetic (or dynamic). Thermodynamic models are built on the concept of equilibrium, from which time is excluded, although it ever lurks in the background, because of our recognition of irreversibility, or what Eddington called the "direction of time's arrow." Dynamic models, in contrast, involve time explicitly, and are formulated in terms of coupled differential equations, in which time enters as the independent variable. In spite of this basic difference, however, under certain conditions the two kinds of model lead to the same result, as when the differential equations have a unique, asymptotically stable critical point.

The relationship between the two types of model is brought out when we formulate the mass-action law, on which so much of the previous discussion is based, from these two points of view. Recall that the original mass-action law by Guldberg and Waage was formulated in terms of kinetics. (The kinetic approach is sometimes almost the only practical way to derive an equilibrium constant, for example, for the dissociation of hemoglobin into dimers; Smith and Ackers, 1985).

The simplest allosteric system is a single-site enzyme that can exist in two conformations, M_1 and M_2. Thus four species describe the system, and we shall assume that the kinetic transitions are single-step reactions. This model forms the basis of the "turning wheel" (Wyman, 1975b). The name comes from the net circulation that arises when an irreversible reaction with respect to a ligand X is incorporated. Such a scheme is shown in Figure 4-17.

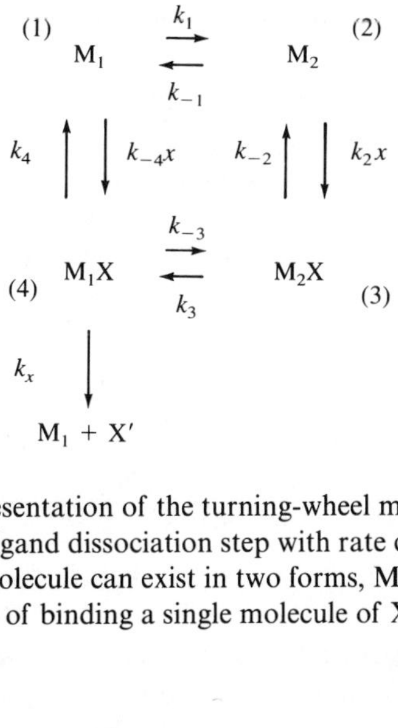

Figure 4-17.
Kinetic representation of the turning-wheel model with an irreversible ligand dissociation step with rate constant k_x. The macromolecule can exist in two forms, M_1 and M_2, each capable of binding a single molecule of X (Wyman, 1975b).

The system, no longer in equilibrium, is nevertheless in a steady state, maintained by interaction with its surroundings. The forward and backward rates of each elementary step are no longer equal, and the very existence of the steady state demands a constant "circulation" of the macromolecule around the square. It also follows from the existence of the steady state that there is a constant flow of ligand X, which is being converted to product X′ through the macromolecule. The *net* velocity of each transition, both in magnitude and sense, must be the same, for otherwise the amounts of enzyme in the various forms would be constantly changing. When the irreversible dissociation involves M_1X, the circulation is counterclockwise; when it involves the form M_2X, it will be clockwise. The key point is that the enzyme exists in two different forms that differ in their catalytic power. Such a model shows that in the steady state, where there is a constant conversion of substrate into product, there must be a continuous "circulation" of the enzyme through its various forms—a turnover.

The four rate equations governing this process may be written in matrix form as

$$
\begin{bmatrix} \dfrac{dM_1}{dt} \\[2mm] \dfrac{dM_2}{dt} \\[2mm] \dfrac{dM_1X}{dt} \\[2mm] \dfrac{dM_2X}{dt} \end{bmatrix} = \begin{bmatrix} -(k_1 + k_{-4}x) & k_{-1} & (k_4 + k_x) & 0 \\[2mm] k_1 & -(k_{-1} + k_2x) & 0 & k_{-2} \\[2mm] k_{-4}x & 0 & -(k_x + k_{-3} + k_4) & k_3 \\[2mm] 0 & k_2x & k_{-3} & -(k_{-2} + k_3) \end{bmatrix} \begin{bmatrix} M_1 \\[2mm] M_2 \\[2mm] M_1X \\[2mm] M_2X \end{bmatrix}.
$$

$$(4.74)$$

In the steady state the determinant of the matrix must be zero. If we write $k'_4 = k_x + k_4$, then the condition of equilibrium, namely, $k_{-4}k_{-3}k_{-2}k_{-1} = k'_4k_3k_2k_1$, cannot hold, since this condition is $k_{-4}k_{-3}k_{-2}k_{-1} = k_4k_3k_2k_1$. The difference, $k_xk_3k_2k_1$, determines the relative rate of the clockwise circulation. The relative amounts of M_1, M_2, M_1X, and M_2X in the steady state are given as

$$M_1 \sim (k_{-1}k_{-2}k_{-3} + k_{-1}k_{-2}k'_4 + k_{-1}k_3k'_4) + k_2k_3k'_4x,$$

$$M_2 \sim (k_{-2}k_{-3}k_1 + k_1k_{-2}k'_4 + k_1k_3k'_4) + k_{-2}k_{-3}k_{-4}x,$$

$$M_1X \sim (k_{-1}k_{-2}k_{-4} + k_{-1}k_3k_{-4} + k_1k_2k_3)x + k_2k_3k_{-4}x^2,$$

$$M_2X \sim (k_{-1}k_{-3}k_{-4} + k_1k_2k_{-3} + k_1k_2k'_4)x + k_2k_{-3}k_{-4}x^2.$$

$$(4.75)$$

At equilibrium, designated by *, where $k_x = 0$ and the conditions of detailed balance are satisfied, equations (4.75) reduce simply to

$$M^*_1 \ : \ M^*_2 \ : \ M_1X^* \ : M_2X^* =$$

$$k_{-1}k_{-2}k_4 : k_1k_{-2}k_4 : k_{-1}k_{-2}k_{-4}x : k_1k_2k_4x.$$

$$(4.76)$$

We can get some idea of the effect of the irreversible step by letting all the k's together with x be unity. Then $k'_4 = 2$, and we find that the steady-state concentrations are $M_1:M_2:M_1X:M_2X = 7:6:4:5$, as contrasted with the equilibrium values of $1:1:1:1$. The drop in free energy as we pass from M_1 to M_2 to M_2X to M_1X is given by

$$\Delta G_{(M_1 \to M_2 \to M_2X \to M_1X)} = RT \ln\frac{6}{7} + RT \ln\frac{5}{6} + RT \ln\frac{4}{5}. \qquad (4.77)$$

This is exactly balanced by the increase in passing from M_1X to M_1:

$$\Delta G_{(M_1X \to M_1)} = RT \ln\frac{7}{4}, \qquad (4.78)$$

which is paid for by the irreversible reaction $(X \to X')$. Since, as far as the macromolecule is concerned, the situation remains unchanged, we can ask what happens to the free energy liberated by the irreversible reaction. The answer is, of course, that it appears as heat. The situation may be likened to that of a man walking up a treadmill; the work he does in maintaining himself at a constant level likewise appears as heat.

To an observer unaware of the irreversible process going on and concerned only with the amount of substrate combined with enzyme in relation to substrate concentration (activity), the steady state would seem to be a true equilibrium: as the substrate activity changes, so does the amount of enzyme-substrate complex, in a unique manner. The steady state represents, in fact, a pseudoequilibrium, which deserves consideration. The ratio of the enzyme-substrate complex, in both forms, to the free enzyme, in both forms, is obtained at once from equations (4.75) as

$$\frac{M_1X + M_2X}{M_1 + M_2} = \frac{A_1x + B_1x^2}{A_2 + B_2x}, \qquad (4.79)$$

where A_1, B_1, A_2, and B_2 are constants expressible in terms of the velocity constants in (4.75). It is striking that this equation is of the same general form as that for the *true* equilibrium of a macromolecule containing not *one*, but *two*, binding sites for its ligand. The apparent cooperativity, or anticooperativity, of the pseudoequilibrium is determined by the relative values of the four constants A_1, B_1, A_2, and B_2.

It is assumed here that our measurements do not distinguish between the two liganded forms of the macromolecule M_1X and M_2X, or between the two unliganded forms M_1 and M_2. This will be true when our measurements are spectroscopic, and when the absorption coefficient of M_1X is the same as that of M_2X, and that of M_1 the same as that of M_2. If in the absence of spectroscopic measurements we take the overall enzyme activity as a criterion of binding, as is frequently done by enzymologists, then we obtain a slightly different picture. For simplicity, we again assume that only the M_1X form is active, and take as our measure of "binding" the ratio of the actual rate of product formation divided by the maximum rate when $x \to \infty$. Then the binding fraction is given by

$$\theta = \left[\frac{M_1 X}{M_1 X + M_2 X + M_1 + M_2}\right]_x \bigg/ \left[\frac{M_1 X}{M_1 X + M_2 X + M_1 + M_2}\right]_{x \to \infty},$$

(4.80)

where the relative amounts of the four forms of the enzyme are given by equations (4.75). By a suitable choice of the eight constants, we again obtain a variety of binding curves just as in the previous example. Thus, even though an allosteric enzyme has only a single site for the substrate, it *can* show high positive or negative cooperativity. Therefore it is quite unnecessary to explain deviations from simple Michaelis-Menten behavior by invoking a multisite-enzyme model. It might be pointed out that King (1956), using a different type of square model involving two different ligands, also obtained second-order dependence of enzyme activity on the substrate concentrations. A searching analysis of the Michaelis-Menten model has been given by J. D. Murray (1977).

We next suppose that the enzyme system can bind two substrates X and Y, which are converted into products X' and Y' by reversible reactions, as shown in equation (4.81):

$$
\begin{array}{c}
\text{(1)} \;\; M \underset{k_{-1}}{\overset{k_1 y}{\rightleftarrows}} \;\; \text{(2)} \;\; MY \underset{k_{-y}y'}{\overset{k_y}{\rightleftarrows}} M + Y' \\[4pt]
k_4 \Big\updownarrow k_{-4}x \qquad\qquad k_{-2} \Big\updownarrow k_2 x \\[4pt]
M + X' \underset{k_{-x}x'}{\overset{k_x}{\rightleftarrows}} MX \underset{k_3}{\overset{k_{-3}y}{\rightleftarrows}} MXY \\
\qquad\qquad (4) \qquad\qquad\qquad (3)
\end{array}
$$

(4.81)

The two reactions $MX \to M + X'$ and $MY \to M + Y'$ oppose each other, one calling for counterclockwise circulation, the other for clockwise circulation. Here the macromolecule provides a mechanism whereby one irreversible reaction may be made to drive another. The free energy liberated by the flow of X through the system and its conversion to X', instead of being wholly lost as heat, may be used, or partly used, to reverse the flow of Y through the system, and to pay for converting Y' into Y. It is possible, of course, that the X reaction may be photochemical, making the macromolecule function as a photo-chemical transducer, using the light energy absorbed in one process to drive another totally different one. The question of the efficiency of the overall irreversible process, which must depend on the speed of circulation, is a difficult one that we shall not go into here.

The kinetic coupling between the two ligands is given by the ratio of the rates of production of X' and Y' as follows:

$$\frac{dY'}{dt} = k_y[MY] - k_{-y}[M]y',$$

(4.82)

$$\frac{dX'}{dt} = k_x[MX] - k_{-x}[M]x',$$
(4.83)

whence

$$\frac{dY'}{dX'} = \frac{k_y[MY] - k_{-y}[M]y'}{k_x[MX] - k_{-x}[M]x'}.$$
(4.84)

Each of the equations (4.82) and (4.83), when normalized to the total amount of the macromolecule, gives the turnover number for the enzymatically catalyzed reaction.

That light can dissociate carbon monoxide from hemoglobin (HbCO) was discovered by Haldane and Smith (1897). John Edsall (personal communication) points out that A. V. Hill, 30 years later, told Otto Warburg about it, and Warburg and coworkers (1929) therefore investigated the high quantum yield of photodissociation and worked on the action spectrum of the respiratory ferment (cytochrome oridase), for which he received the Nobel Prize. The development of methods to study fast kinetics of CO binding to hemoglobin and myoglobin, utilizing photolysis, was pioneered largely by Gibson (1956).

The effect of light on the binding curves of carbon monoxide to hemoglobin has been studied quantitatively by Brunori et al. (1972). As seen in Figure 4-18,

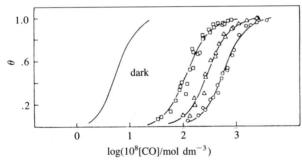

Figure 4-18.
Curves of carbon monoxide binding to hemoglobin in the presence of light of different intensities (Brunori et al., 1972).

binding curves are shifted to the right with increasing light intensity, indicating photolysis. The shape of the curves ($\bar{X}$ versus $\ln x$) remains unchanged for hemoglobin, although it is greatly modified in the more complex erythrocruorins. These observations are, in the broad sense, consistent with the concept of the turning wheel, in which the light of intensity I generates two different states of the macromolecule, one in its unligated form $M^\dagger$ (2) and one in its ligated form $M^\dagger X$ (3). The rate of excited-state generation is dependent on the absorption coefficients of the process. A simple model representing this situation is shown in equation (4.85):

$$(1) \ M \underset{k_{-1}}{\overset{k_1 I}{\rightleftarrows}} M^\dagger \ (2)$$

$$k_4 \Big\Updownarrow k_{-4} \qquad k_{-2} \Big\Updownarrow k_2 \qquad\qquad (4.85)$$

$$(4) \ MX \underset{k_3}{\overset{k_{-3}I}{\rightleftarrows}} M^\dagger X \ (3).$$

The influence of the light is analogous to that of the second ligand, Y, seen in equation (4.75). The presence of light clearly complicates the nature of the binding curve, and the existence of an excited state will in general affect the location and shape of the ligand binding curve. Studies of CO binding to myoglobin in the presence of light (Bonaventura $et\ al.$, 1973) indicate that the steady-state concentration ratio ($[MX]/[M]x$) is described by $l'/(l + \omega I)$, where l' and l are the association and dissociation rate constants in the absence of light, and ω is a proportionality constant determined by the quantum yield and the overall absorption coefficient. In terms of the photo-excited square model, if the rate constants $k_3 = k_2 = k_1 = 0$, then we obtain the result that $[MX]/[M]x = k_{-4}/(k_{-3}I + k_4)$, which conforms to the experimental situation found for myoglobin. Note that here $[M^\dagger X]/[MX] = k_{-3}I/k_{-2}$; so, taking $k_{-2} \gg k_{-3}I$, as it must be in these experiments, we have a negligibly small population of excited species. This model would be the same if the light impartially displaced the ligand from any liganded form. The detailed kinetic events involved in photolysis of CO from hemoglobin and myoglobin show additional complications not taken account of in this simple description. In particular, extremely rapid processes of CO escape from the heme pocket and the kinetics of allosteric changes have been detailed (Eisenstein and Frauenfelder, 1982, and Hofrichter $et\ al.$, 1983).

In a somewhat different context, we may apply the concept of the turning-wheel model to the reciprocal transport of oxygen and carbon dioxide by the circulating blood (Brunori, 1975), or alternatively to active transport across a membrane arising from facilitated diffusion of a carrier macromolecule (Wittenburg, 1959; Scholander, 1960; Murray and Wyman, 1971; Murray, 1977). In both cases the phenomenon involves spatial transport. The membrane represents a separation in space corresponding to the separation of lungs and tissues for the circulating blood. The question immediately presents itself as to what replaces the mechanical action of the heart in the membrane situation. The obvious answer would be the random motion of a carrier molecule in the membrane. For active transport there must, however, be a linkage between two reactions. One way of looking at the problem is to think of the macromolecule as an imperfect "Carnot engine."

A formulation of allosteric kinetic systems subject to linkage through contact with their surroundings has recently been examined in detail (Di Cera *et al.*, 1989b). The existence of a globally stable critical point has been studied in one case by Fichera *et al.* (1977). A general exposition of coupled kinetic processes is given by Hill (1985).

4.6   OVERVIEW

We have dealt with the allosteric model, in which cooperativity, whether homotropic or heterotropic, can be explained by the effect of ligands upon equilibria between various conformations, characterized by different ligand affinities. Within this very general overall picture we have discussed two specific cases: (1) the concerted model or MWC model; and (2) the Pauling or KNF model. The MWC model postulates only two conformations, each with t binding sites, and each conformation with its specific affinity. The KNF model recognizes $t + 1$ different allosteric states, each characterized by a specific number of ligands bound, thus giving rise to the name *induced-fit model*. The KNF or Pauling model assumes ligand-mediated "bond" interactions between subunits based on simple geometric and selection rules. Heterotropic linkage is introduced by inclusion of a second ligand species, and is explicitly expressed by inclusion of appropriate binding polynomial terms in the second ligand activity. The total free energy of ligation, even when the system is anticooperative, as the KNF model can be, is always reduced in the presence of allosteric equilibria. The concerted and induced-fit models can be further elaborated into the so-called *nested* models, involving a hierarchy of conformational changes within a large multisubunit structure. Such models have been invoked to explain detailed and complex results found in high-precision studies of both hemoglobin and large, multiple-binding-site proteins, such as hemocyanin.

The number of models that can be invoked to explain a given set of facts is unlimited. This is apparent if we suppose we have a model involving t parameters, $x_1, x_2, \ldots x_t$. Introduce a new set of parameters $y_1, y_2, \ldots y_t$, each a function of the xs. The resulting equations will necessarily explain the facts equally well. We have only to give them physical meaning to have a new, equally satisfactory model. We might indeed introduce a set of $t + s$ variables, together with s restrictions, to obtain a more complicated model. Between different models we can choose only on the basis of parsimony, plausibility, or aesthetic appeal, in the absence of additional facts.

Physical Binding Phenomena 5

5.1 INTRODUCTION

The analysis of both ligand-binding and thermal-transition phenomena has an extensive literature. In general each area has been treated separately, and the features common to both types of analysis have not been recognized. The intent of this chapter is to develop a theoretical framework that can deal with both kinds of phenomena. In an earlier paper (Wyman *et al.*, 1979) we considered the effect of temperature on the melting behavior of a nondissociating allosteric macromolecule. It was noted that a strong parallel exists between the description of transitions induced by heat and those induced by ligand binding. This parallelism can be exploited to draw many of the ideas of ligand-binding phenomena as they are affected by ligand activity into the broader picture that includes the influence of temperature and pressure.

The usual concept of binding is of specific interactions or structural changes that occur when a ligand reacts with a macromolecule. Our attention is focused on the amount of ligand bound to the macromolecule under given conditions of ligand activity. The idea of binding is then most obviously associated with the process of chemical ligand reactions. However, concomitant with any chemical ligand-binding process in general is a change in enthalpy (heat) and volume. We shall consider these terms to be physical binding parameters. Thus the generalized term *binding* may be used to include changes in amounts of ligand, enthalpy, or volume that are associated with particular reaction processes involving the macromolecule. We need to delineate the amounts of these quantities which are specifically attributed to the presence of the macromolecule. To evaluate specific binding parameters, we need a way to exclude nonspecific effects. Dialysis and spectroscopic procedures are useful in measuring specific chemical ligand binding. Calorimetry and densitometry allow us to measure changes in enthalpy and volume that result from macromolecular reactions. Just as we have found that ligand binding of macromolecular processes is conveniently represented by binding curves of amounts of ligand bound versus ligand activity, so also we will find that "heat-binding curves" may be described by heat absorbed by the macromolecule at different temperatures or different ligand activities. Underlying macromolecular changes are revealed by the nature of these binding curves. An example of heat binding as a function of temperature is shown in Figure 5-1 for lysozyme denaturation.

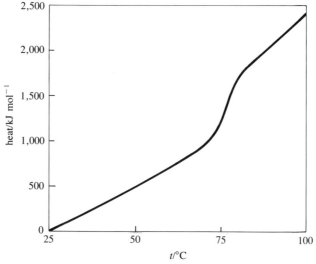

Figure 5-1.
Heat binding to lysozyme as a function of temperature from a zero point reference temperature of 25°C under solution conditions of pH 4.5. The curve was constructed from data of Privalov and Khechinashvili (1974). The midpoint transition temperature is 78.8°C, where the enthalpy of transition is 57 kJ mol^{-1} and the heat capacity change is $\Delta C_p = 5.4$ kJ K^{-1} mol^{-1}. The heat capacity of the native protein was taken as 18.0 kJ K^{-1} mol^{-1} at 25°C. Details of the pH dependence of this transition are given by Robert et al. (1989).

This curve reveals that a significant absorption of heat occurs over a temperature range centered at 78°C. From other physical studies we can attribute this change to a large allosteric transition from the native structure of lysozyme pictured in Figure 5-2 to a denatured random-coil polypeptide form. From the shape of the curve we seek to discover the principal macromolecular reactions that are involved. This kind of thermal binding study reveals information concerning the nature of the allosteric transitions. The analysis of such experiments has been described for conditions of fixed ligand activity (Privalov, 1979; Privalov and Filimonov, 1978; Freire and Biltonen, 1978a).

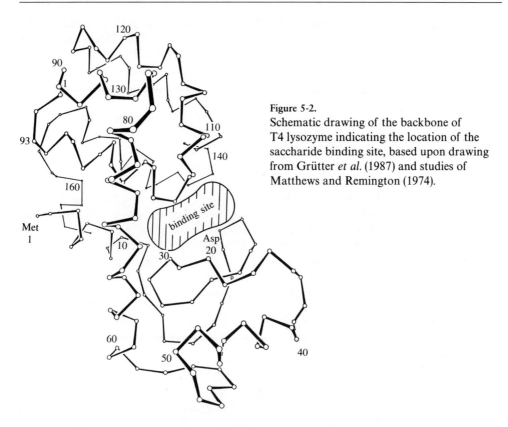

Figure 5-2.
Schematic drawing of the backbone of
T4 lysozyme indicating the location of the
saccharide binding site, based upon drawing
from Grütter *et al.* (1987) and studies of
Matthews and Remington (1974).

The incorporation of accompanying ligand-binding reactions has not been
developed in specific detail in the analysis of thermal denaturation. However,
the general concepts of linkage between ligand activity and thermal transition
temperatures (Privalov and Ptitsyn, 1969), and enthalpy change accompanying isothermal titration of a macromolecule from one ligand activity to
another, have been used to establish the state function properties of proteins as a function of temperature and ligand activity (Pfeil and Privalov,
1976a, b, c). Changes in enthalpy as a function of ligand activity will provide information regarding the linkage relation between enthalpic changes
and chemical ligand-binding processes for the macromolecular system. The
exploration of volume changes as a function of pressure (experiments not
practically realized at present) or as a function of ligand activity would provide
further characterization of the significant thermodynamic states and reactions
of biological macromolecules.

By recognizing that allosteric macromolecular and ligand-binding reactions have common thermodynamic effects, we can describe them by means
of a single theory. We wish to show how this is done for a macromolecule that
can undergo allosteric transitions to different states, each of which can bind a
specific ligand. The formulation of these ideas is made possible by generalizing
the binding partition function to include enthalpy and volume changes for

allosteric transition and ligand-binding reactions (Gill *et al.*, 1985, 1988). Schellman (1975), Freire and Biltonen (1978a, b, c), Hill (1960), and others have also treated various aspects of this problem. In this chapter we shall restrict ourselves to consideration of nondissociating macromolecules.

5.2   EFFECTS OF PRESSURE AND TEMPERATURE ON THE BINDING PARTITION FUNCTION

In this section we examine the effects of temperature, pressure, and chemical-ligand activity on the state of a macromolecular system. As in Chapter 4, we will consider macromolecules that can exist in several different conformations in equilibrium with one another. We assume that each of these allosteric forms has one or more binding sites for one or more chemical ligands.*

We shall consider a macromolecule that has $q + 1$ conformations, $0, 1, \ldots q$, each of which has t binding sites for a ligand X. Figure 5-3 represents the macromolecule in the different states specified by conformational form and number of X ligands bound. We follow the same line developed in Chapter 4

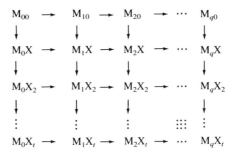

Figure 5-3.
Array of conformational and chemically ligated species. Columns represent different conformational forms, and rows denote different amounts of ligand X bound.

by reproducing equation (4.1), showing that chemical ligation and conformational change from the zero reference state can be represented by

$$M_{00} + iX \rightarrow M_h X_i. \tag{5.1}$$

Here M_{00} is the unligated macromolecule in the zeroth conformational form, i is the number of ligands involved in the specific binding reaction, and $M_h X_i$ is the macromolecule in the hth conformational form with i ligands of X bound. The reaction is characterized by changes in the amount of X ligand bound

---

* Recall that the familiar two-state MWC allosteric model has only two conformations, each of which can bind ligands independently (Monod *et al.*, 1965). In Chapter 4 we saw how the general form of this model could be used in describing cooperative effects found in the binding of chemical ligands.

$(\Delta \bar{X}_{hi})$, in the enthalpy $(\Delta \bar{H}_{hi})$, and in the volume $(\Delta \bar{V}_{hi})$; for the unligated reference state, $\Delta \bar{X}_{hi} = i$.

Our first interest in the use of equation (5.1) is to connect the concentration of the $M_h X_i$ species with the concentration of M_{00} and to formulate the partition function. By the law of mass action, the concentration of $M_h X_i$ is proportional to M_{00} at given temperature, pressure, and chemical activity of X. We wish to emphasize this generality in order to show the parallel features of heat, volume, and ligand binding. Thus instead of equation (4.2) we write

$$[M_h X_i] = [M_{00}]\Lambda_{hi}. \tag{5.2}$$

Here we have defined Λ_{hi} to be a general equilibrium constant for the reaction, which now depends on ligand activity, x, as well as on temperature and pressure. (In previous notation, at a given temperature and pressure, $\Lambda_{hi} = \beta_{hi}x^i$.) The binding partition function Q is then given by the sum of all species concentrations taken relative to the reference species, here chosen as M_{00}. Thus we obtain

$$Q = \sum_{h=0}^{q} \sum_{i=0}^{t} \frac{[M_h X_i]}{[M_{00}]} = \sum_{h=0}^{q} \sum_{i=0}^{t} \Lambda_{hi}. \tag{5.3}$$

The partition function* given by (5.3) represents the rectangular array of species shown in Figure 5-3. As such it depicts all the species concentrations of the array relative to the reference species. These concentrations might be

---

* Equation (5.3) may also be obtained from the traditional partition function given by the sum of all states for a system,

$$Q = \sum g_n e^{-\varepsilon_n/kT},$$

where g_n is the degeneracy of energy state ε_n. The number of molecules in state n, N_n, is then given as

$$N_n = N g_n e^{-\varepsilon_n/kT}/Q,$$

where N is the total number of molecules. In terms of the ground state $(n = 0)$,

$$N_n = N_0(g_n/g_0)e^{-(\varepsilon_n - \varepsilon_0)/kT},$$

which then allows Q to be expressed as

$$Q = g_0 e^{-\varepsilon_0/kT} \sum(N_n/N_0).$$

Defining the free energy as $G_n = \varepsilon_n - kT \ln g_n$ and setting $G_0 = 0$ yields

$$Q = \sum(N_n/N_0).$$

This expression is equivalent to equation (5.3), if we specify the state of a molecule in terms of the degree of ligation and allosteric form.

described by arrows of appropriate length Λ_{hi} erected from M_{00} to each point on the species array lattice. Changes in ligand activity affect these concentrations by the ith power of the activity, and changes in temperature and pressure affect these concentrations through factors that include enthalpy and volume changes. We can also describe the partition function as a collection of allosteric species with different amounts of ligation, or as a collection of specifically ligated species with different allosteric forms. Thus the array can be reduced in two ways: (1) collecting all the various states of ligation according to their specific allosteric forms; or (2) collecting the allosteric forms according to their ligand stoichiometry. In procedure (1) we initially sum the elements of the array over the degree of ligation for each allosteric form h; i.e., we take the sum of a column in the array. This sum defines the equilibrium constant L_h that represents the concentration of all chemically ligated forms of the allosteric state h relative to the reference species M_{00}:

$$L_h = \sum_{i=0}^{t} \Lambda_{hi}. \tag{5.4}$$

In terms of the concentrations of given allosteric forms, Q is obtained by adding all the columns together:

$$Q = \sum_{h=0}^{q} L_h. \tag{5.5}$$

In procedure (2) we initially sum the concentrations of a given row (defined by iX ligand bound) for the various allosteric forms. This yields the ligated state equilibrium constants, defined as Λ_i, which represent the total concentrations of all species with i ligands bound, relative to the concentration of the M_{00} reference species. These summations are expressed explicitly as follows:

$$\Lambda_i = \sum_{h=0}^{q} \Lambda_{hi}. \tag{5.6}$$

By adding the rows together, we again obtain the full partition function

$$Q = \sum_{i=0}^{t} \Lambda_i. \tag{5.7}$$

In studies of chemical ligand binding, it is usual to choose the reference state to include all the unligated allosteric forms. This is accomplished by normalizing the partition function of equation (5.7) by dividing by Λ_0. This gives Q in the form in which the various coefficients define the Adair parameters. Normalization by the unligated species terms yields the partition function in the form we have specifically denoted as the binding polynomial, P. The first term is unity, and the Λ_i terms contain the ligand activity (x) to the ith power.

The influence of ligand activity, x, of temperature, T, and of pressure, p, on an equilibrium constant for a chemical reaction is incorporated by explicitly bringing in the thermodynamic factors that influence the free-energy change of a given reaction process. These are expressed by partial differentiation of $\ln \Lambda_{hi}$ with respect to the appropriate independent variables of the system as follows:

$$\frac{\partial \ln \Lambda_{hi}}{\partial \ln x} = \Delta \bar{X}_{hi}, \tag{5.8}$$

$$\frac{\partial \ln \Lambda_{hi}}{\partial \tau} = \frac{-\Delta \bar{H}_{hi}}{R}, \qquad \tau = 1/T, \tag{5.9}$$

$$\frac{\partial \ln \Lambda_{hi}}{\partial p} = \frac{-\Delta \bar{V}_{hi}}{RT}, \tag{5.10}$$

where $\Delta \bar{X}_{hi}$, $\Delta \bar{H}_{hi}$, and $\Delta \bar{V}_{hi}$ represent the changes in X moles, enthalpy, and volume for the reaction given by equation (5.1). The second equation, for heat, is known as the *van't Hoff equation*.

In order to obtain the total amount of ligand, enthalpy, or volume change which occurs when the macromolecular system changes from its reference state to any other state, we differentiate $\ln Q$ with respect to the appropriate independent variable. For chemical ligation, this gives

$$\frac{\partial \ln Q}{\partial \ln x} = \frac{1}{Q} \sum_h \sum_i \frac{\partial \ln \Lambda_{hi}}{\partial \ln x} \Lambda_{hi} = \frac{1}{Q} \sum_h \sum_i (\Delta \bar{X}_{hi}) \Lambda_{hi} = \bar{X} - \bar{X}_{00}. \tag{5.11}$$

The term $\bar{X}_{00}$ represents the amount of X ligand bound in the reference state, here taken to equal 0. It is, of course, arbitrary which state we choose to be the reference state. The fraction of macromolecules of the type represented by $M_h X_i$ is given by Λ_{hi}/Q. This expression allows us to see that the last term of equation (5.11) is obtained by taking the weighted sum of the $\Delta \bar{X}_{hi}$ values over all species.

Similarly, the amounts of enthalpy and volume change, when the macromolecule goes from the reference state to some other state, $\bar{H} - \bar{H}_{00}$ and $\bar{V} - \bar{V}_{00}$, are obtained by differentiating $\ln Q$ with respect to τ and p. Here $\bar{H}_{00}$ and $\bar{V}_{00}$ must be included because the enthalpy and volume for the M_{00} reference state are not zero. In summary, we write

$$\bar{X} - \bar{X}_{00} = \frac{\partial \ln Q}{\partial \ln x}, \tag{5.12}$$

$$\bar{H} - \bar{H}_{00} = -R \frac{\partial \ln Q}{\partial \tau}, \tag{5.13}$$

$$\bar{V} - \bar{V}_{00} = -RT \frac{\partial \ln Q}{\partial p}. \tag{5.14}$$

The parallel form of these expressions emphasizes how chemical and physical binding phenomena (namely, heat and volume associated with macro-molecular reactions) can be considered in the same way. As we have seen in earlier chapters on ligand binding, the most fundamental way of depicting chemical binding curves is by $\bar{X}$ versus $\ln x$. From the preceding equations, we see that plots of $\bar{H} - \bar{H}_{00}$ might be made against $1/T$, and plots of $\bar{V} - \bar{V}_{00}$ might be made against p in order to provide the most direct connection to the partition function of the system.

The phenomenological results expressed as $\bar{X}$, $\bar{H}$, and $\bar{V}$ are determined, as we have seen, by the properties of each macromolecular species and its relative concentration. In terms of the fraction of the macromolecules in the h form with i ligands bound, α_{hi},

$$\alpha_{hi} = \frac{1}{Q} \Lambda_{hi}. \tag{5.15}$$

The average amount of chemical ligand bound per mole of macromolecule is then equal to the sum of the fraction of molecules in each state times the amount of ligand bound to that state. The average enthalpy and volume are expressed in a similar manner. The resulting equations are

$$\bar{X} - \bar{X}_{00} = \sum_h \sum_i \Delta \bar{X}_{hi} \alpha_{hi}, \tag{5.16}$$

$$\bar{H} - \bar{H}_{00} = \sum_h \sum_i \Delta \bar{H}_{hi} \alpha_{hi}, \tag{5.17}$$

$$\bar{V} - \bar{V}_{00} = \sum_h \sum_i \Delta \bar{V}_{hi} \alpha_{hi}. \tag{5.18}$$

As we can see, in order to evaluate $\bar{X}$, $\bar{H}$, or $\bar{V}$ in any specific problem, we need the array of species parameters, $\Delta \bar{H}_{hi}$, $\Delta \bar{V}_{hi}$, and $\Delta \bar{X}_{hi}$, along with the values of the species fractions α_{hi}. In chemical ligand binding, $\Delta \bar{X}_{hi}$ ranges in integer values from 0 to t. In thermal binding the values of $\Delta \bar{H}_{hi}$ are not necessarily integer or positive, as is also true for the values of $\Delta \bar{V}_{hi}$. Hence the description of chemical ligand binding is inherently much simpler than that for heat and volume effects.

In order to describe the explicit dependence of Q on the independent variables $\ln x$, τ, and p, we need to express Λ_{hi} in terms of these variables. This can be done by integrating equations (5.8–5.10) as follows:

$$\int_{\ln(\Lambda_{hi})_0}^{\ln \Lambda_{hi}} d \ln \Lambda_{hi} = -\int_{\tau_0}^{\tau} \frac{\Delta \bar{H}_{hi}}{R} d\tau - \int_{p_0}^{p} \frac{\Delta \bar{V}_{hi}}{RT} dp + \int_{\ln x_0}^{\ln x} \Delta \bar{X}_{hi} d \ln x. \tag{5.19}$$

For simplicity let us assume that $\Delta \bar{H}_{hi}$ is independent of temperature (i.e., the heat-capacity change $\Delta \bar{C}_{hi}$ is zero), that $\Delta \bar{V}_{hi}$ is independent of pressure (i.e., the compressibility is the same for all species), and that $\Delta \bar{X}_{hi} = i$ (i.e., the reference state M_{00} has no ligand bound). Integration from the reference condition of τ_0, p_0, and $\ln x_0$ then gives the expression for the equilibrium constant between any form and the reference form M_{00} as

$$\Lambda_{hi} = (\Lambda_{hi})_0 \exp[-(\Delta \bar{H}_{hi}/R)(\tau - \tau_0)] \exp[-(\Delta \bar{V}_{hi}/RT)(p - p_0)]$$

$$\times \exp[i(\ln x - \ln x_0)]. \tag{5.20}$$

Here $(\Lambda_{hi})_0$ is the equilibrium constant under the reference-state conditions defined by τ_0, p_0, and x_0.*

The partition function Q as found by substitution into equation (5.3) is

$$Q = \sum_{h=0}^{q} \sum_{i=0}^{r} (\Lambda_{ij})_0 \exp[-(\Delta \bar{H}_{hi}/R)(\tau - \tau_0)] \exp[-(\Delta \bar{V}_{hi}/RT)(p - p_0)]$$

$$\times \exp[i(\ln x - \ln x_0)]. \tag{5.21}$$

The first two exponentials in this expression account for the effect of the physical variables T and p; the third exponential accounts for the effect of the chemical ligand X. The presence of additional ligands will contribute exponential terms analogous to that of X with appropriate summations.

5.2.1   Allosteric Forms with Equal Heat Capacities

The preceding development has been directed toward showing what features of multi-state equilibria are common to the description of thermal- and ligand-binding phenomena. For practical situations, this general formulation has far too many parameters to evaluate; so we must then resort to simplifying assumptions. In this section we wish to develop a description for the total enthalpy and heat capacity of a system in which the difference between the heat capacities of allosteric forms is effectively zero. This description will be useful for systems whose allosteric forms do not show appreciable intrinsic heat-capacity differences, and whose heats of ligand binding are small compared to the heats of allosteric transitions. Studies on thermal denaturation have shown that tRNAs generally satisfy these criteria, whereas proteins almost certainly do not (Privalov, 1979).

By assuming that the heat of ligation is small compared to the heat of transition, we focus attention on the average enthalpy change during transitions from one allosteric form to another. The average enthalpy change $(\Delta \bar{H}_h)$ during the transition from the M_{00} reference state to the h

---

* If the heat-capacity change $\Delta \bar{C}_{hi}$ is not zero, an additional factor,

$$(\tau/\tau_0)^{-\Delta \bar{C}_{hi}/R} \exp[(\Delta \bar{C}_{hi}/R\tau_0)(\tau - \tau_0)],$$

needs to be included in equation (5.20).

allosteric state is obtained by summation over the liganded species of the h form:

$$\Delta\bar{H}_h = \frac{\sum_i \alpha_{hi}\Delta\bar{H}_{hi}}{\sum_i \alpha_{hi}}. \tag{5.22}$$

For the special case under consideration the heat-capacity change is effectively zero. Then the effect of temperature on the equilibrium constant, L_h [defined by equation (5.4) as the ratio of concentrations of all the hth form species to the M_{00} species], for this transition may be written as

$$L_h = L_h{}^o \exp[(-\Delta\bar{H}_h/R)(\tau - \tau_0)], \tag{5.23}$$

where $L_h{}^o$ is the equilibrium constant at τ_0 and ligand activity x. The partition function for this system of allosteric forms is just $\sum L_h$.

In a usual thermal denaturation experiment the total enthalpy of the macromolecular system is measured relative to the enthalpy of its native form at low temperature. In general, this form consists of a number of species with different amounts of ligand bound. We thus need a new reference state that includes all such species of the zeroth or native allosteric form. This is accomplished by normalizing the partition function given by equation (5.5), by dividing by the sum of all zeroth-form species, i.e., $\sum \Lambda_{0i}$, which gives L_0. An asterisk ($*$) is used to denote quantities based on this total zeroth-form allosteric reference state. With this reference state we define the partition function Q^* as

$$Q^* = \frac{Q}{L_0} = \frac{\sum L_h}{L_0} = \sum L_h{}^*, \tag{5.24}$$

where $L_h{}^* = L_h/L_0$. In terms of this reference state, equation (5.23) becomes

$$L_h{}^* = L_h{}^{*o} \exp[(-\Delta\bar{H}_h{}^*/R)(\tau - \tau_0)], \tag{5.25}$$

where $L_h{}^{*o}$ is the standard state ($\tau = \tau_0$) equilibrium constant and $\Delta\bar{H}_h{}^*$ is the change in enthalpy for the reaction between the hth and zeroth forms. A particularly convenient representation of equation (5.25) is to define a reciprocal midtemperature τ_{mh} where $L_h{}^* = 1$, e.g., when there are equal populations of the zeroth and hth allosteric forms. This then gives

$$L_h{}^{*o} = \exp[(\Delta\bar{H}_h{}^*/R)(\tau_{mh} - \tau_0)] \tag{5.26}$$

or

$$L_h{}^* = \exp[(-\Delta\bar{H}_h{}^*/R)(\tau - \tau_{mh})]. \tag{5.27}$$

The fraction α_h of macromolecules in the hth form is given as

$$\alpha_h = \frac{L_h^{*o} \exp[-\Delta \bar{H}_h^*(\tau - \tau_0)/R]}{\sum L_h^{*o} \exp[-\Delta \bar{H}_h^*(\tau - \tau_0)/R]}. \tag{5.28}$$

The total enthalpy $\bar{H}$ minus the enthalpy of the zeroth form is found by differentiation of the logarithm of the partition function Q^* [equation (5.24)] with respect to $1/T$ as indicated by equation (5.13). The result is

$$\bar{H} - \bar{H}_0 = \frac{\sum \Delta \bar{H}_h^* L_h^{*o} \exp[-\Delta \bar{H}_h^*(\tau - \tau_0)/R]}{\sum L_h^{*o} \exp[-\Delta \bar{H}_h^*(\tau - \tau_0)/R]}. \tag{5.29}$$

The apparent excess heat capacity of the system as found by differentiating the enthalpy with respect to T is

$$\bar{C} - \bar{C}_0 = \frac{\tau^2}{R} \left\{ \frac{\sum (\Delta \bar{H}_h^*)^2 L_h^{*o} \exp[-\Delta \bar{H}_h^*(\tau_h - \tau_0)/R]}{\sum L_h^{*o} \exp[-\Delta \bar{H}_h^*(\tau - \tau_0)/R]} \right.$$
$$\left. - \frac{(\sum \Delta \bar{H}_h^* L_h^{*o} \exp[-\Delta \bar{H}_h^*(\tau - \tau_0)/R])^2}{(\sum L_h^{*o} \exp[-\Delta \bar{H}_h^*(\tau - \tau_0)/R])^2} \right\}. \tag{5.30}$$

Equation (5.30) reflects the heat-capacity effects which are associated with alterations in the distribution of allosteric forms brought about by a change in temperature. Even in this simplified case, where the enthalpy changes between forms are assumed to be independent of temperature, two parameters are needed to describe the binding of enthalpy to each form in the system: the relative enthalpy of the ith form ($\Delta \bar{H}_h^*$) and the value of L_h^{*o} at τ_0. We again wish to emphasize that for chemical ligand binding the quantity analogous to the enthalpy change for the ith reaction is given simply by the integer i itself. It is also worth noting that the equilibrium constant L_h^{*o} and the enthalpy change $\Delta \bar{H}_h^*$ will in general depend on the chemical-ligand activity. The reference state equilibrium constant will be affected by ligand activity through the ratio of the X-binding polynomials in the hth and zeroth forms. The enthalpy change at the reference temperature will likewise depend on the degree of ligation of the various ligated states of the zeroth and hth allosteric forms. If the heats of ligation are large, then, as the temperature is changed, so will the population of the ligated states of a given allosteric form change. And the enthalpy change between the zeroth and hth form will not be constant. In phenomenological terms, this dependency of the heat of the allosteric transition on temperature would be observed as an overall heat-capacity change in the allosteric forms. Such effects appear to be quite large in proteins, but not so in nucleic-acid transitions. We shall examine such effects in more detail in Section 5.3. At this point the first-order approximation of constant values for the enthalpy of transitions between allosteric forms as given by equation (5.29) serves to define the initial choice of analysis of thermally induced transitions of nondissociating macromolecules. An example of a three-state allosteric system subject to thermal scanning is shown in Figure 5-4. Note how the asymptotes of the enthalpy plot are horizontal, indicative of the condition of equal heat capacities of initial and final species, and consequently how the heat-capacity difference returns to zero at high temperatures.

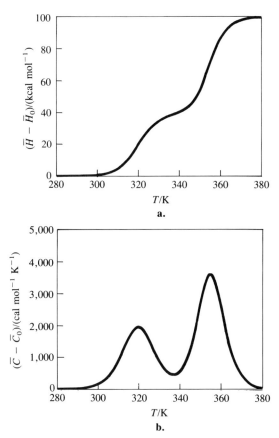

Figure 5-4.
Hypothetical plot of enthalpy $(\bar{H} - \bar{H}_0)$ versus temperature T(a), and of heat capacity $(\bar{C} - \bar{C}_0)$ versus temperature T(b) for a three-state system defined with $\Delta H_1 = 40$ kcal, $\tau_{m1} = 1/320$ K^{-1}, $\Delta H_2 = 100$ kcal, $\tau_{m2} = 1/340$ K^{-1}.

5.2.2   The Independent-Transition Model

Independent ligand-binding reactions and independent thermal transitions present the simplest case to consider in modeling the thermodynamics of a macromolecular system. Thermal melting curves of tRNA have been analyzed using this approach (Privalov and Filimonov, 1978). The independent transition model assumes that the macromolecule consists of a set of n independent segments or domains, each of which exists in only two conformations (such as native or denatured). The total number of allosteric states of such a macromolecule then consists of all combinations of the independent substates. Assuming that each substate is uniquely characterized by a set of thermodynamic parameters, then the total number of allosteric states will be 2^n. The partition function for this situation is obtained by multiplication of the partition functions for each individual domain. The partition function for the ith domain (2 states) is simply

$$q_i = 1 + \lambda_i, \tag{5.31}$$

where λ_i represents the equilibrium constant for the melting of this domain. The value of λ_i will depend, as we have seen, on the X ligand activity, the temperature, and the pressure. The essential feature we wish to illustrate is the temperature dependence of λ_i, assuming the heat capacity of the domain transition is zero. This is shown explicitly as

$$q_i = 1 + \lambda_i^o \exp[-\Delta H_i(\tau - \tau_i^o)/R], \tag{5.32}$$

where λ_i^o is the equilibrium constant for the ith transition at τ_i^o (and will depend in general on ligand activity). The enthalpy change for the transition of the ith segment is ΔH_i, and we have assumed that it is independent of temperature. If the reference reciprocal temperature, τ_i^o, is chosen at the midpoint temperature of the ith transition, then $\lambda_i^o = 1$. Here the reference reciprocal temperature is denoted by τ_{mi}. This choice is also indicated by equation (5.26).

The partition function, Q^{indep}, for the entire macromolecule with n independent segments is given by the product of the partition functions for each segment:

$$Q^{indep} = \prod_{i=1}^{n} q_i. \tag{5.33}$$

For the situation defined by equation (5.32) in terms of the midpoint reciprocal temperature, we obtain

$$Q^{indep} = \prod_{i=1}^{n} (1 + \exp[-\Delta H_i(\tau - \tau_{mi})/R]). \tag{5.34}$$

We can see by expansion of this expression that each term in the resulting sum represents an allosteric state whose properties are determined by the particular combination of the independent substate (domain) properties. Each allosteric state is then described by specifying those segments that have melted. The total enthalpy per mole of macromolecule $\bar{H}$ is given from equation (5.13) as

$$\bar{H} = \bar{H}_0 + \sum_{i=1}^{n} \frac{\Delta H_i \exp[-\Delta H_i(\tau - \tau_{mi})/R]}{1 + \exp[-\Delta H_i(\tau - \tau_{mi})/R]}, \qquad (5.35)$$

where $\bar{H}_0$ is the enthalpy of the unmelted native state. As might be expected, this result shows that the enthalpy of the system is the sum of the segment enthalpy changes weighted by the fraction of the particular segment melted.

The heat capacity is found by differentiation of equation (5.36) with respect to T:

$$\bar{C} = \bar{C}_0 + \frac{\tau^2}{R} \sum_{i=1}^{n} \frac{(\Delta H_i)^2 \exp[-\Delta H_i(\tau - \tau_{mi})/R]}{\{1 + \exp[-\Delta H_i(\tau - \tau_{mi})/R]\}^2}, \qquad (5.36)$$

where $\bar{C}_0$ is the heat capacity of the reference state. The simplicity of this equation results from the fact that each segment transition contributes separately to the total heat capacity. In the general allosteric situation, the heat capacity [equation (5.30)] cannot be separated into contributions from each specific allosteric state. In the general case, the thermal properties of the various states are interwoven.

If a second transition is assumed to occur for each domain, an additional term (e.g., ω_i) may be added to the partition function for the domain, giving

$$q_i = 1 + \lambda_i + \omega_i. \qquad (5.37)$$

The preceding formulation of the resulting thermal properties can be easily carried out for such a case. This situation is analogous to the competitive binding of two ligands at a given site and represents a situation of *identical linkage*.

The independent-site model has been used extensively in the analysis of thermal transition data obtained by scanning calorimetry (Privalov, 1979), as we will see next.

5.3   APPLICATIONS

5.3.1   Scanning Calorimetry

We wish to show how the preceding general theoretical development applies to the analysis of specific experimental data. The extensive experimental work done on the melting of transfer RNA (Privalov and Filimonov, 1978; Filimonov *et al.*, 1976) is particularly well-suited for analysis in terms of the two alternative models developed here (Gill *et al.*, 1985). Privalov and Filimonov (1978) have presented results on the thermal denaturation of various tRNAs. They give their results in terms of transition enthalpies and midpoint temperatures as obtained by fitting the experimental data to the independent-transition model. Since they show that this analysis reproduces the data within experimental error, it is possible to reconstruct the experimental curves from their published parameters. We shall consider these reconstructed melting curves to be equivalent to the original experimental data. The original data are estimated to be reproducible within an error of a few percent (Privalov and Filimonov, 1978).

It is informative to analyze these data in terms of the general thermal-state treatment given by equation (5.30). From this viewpoint we seek to find the minimum number of allosteric forms that are required to describe the heat-capacity data in accordance with the macromolecular partition function given by equations (5.24) and (5.25). All the states are ordered according to their enthalpy content, with the reference state being set equal to zero. Each state is characterized by a particular enthalpy difference, $\Delta \bar{H}_h^*$, and by a reciprocal midtemperature τ_{mh}, where L_h^* is unity.

The choice of the minimum number of enthalpy states is essentially governed by the fit between the theoretical and experimental heat-capacity curves. Trial cases with different numbers of allosteric forms are used to generate best-fit heat-capacity curves. This procedure is terminated when the error of the fit is approximately equal to the actual experimental error.

To illustrate this analysis, we have taken the five independent transition enthalpies and temperatures obtained by Privalov and Filimonov (1978) for tRNA^{Phe} in 20mM and 150mM NaCl, and generated heat-capacity differences for integral temperature values from 0° to 100°C using equation (5.36). This gives the means for reconstructing the original observations. We then found by nonlinear least-square analysis the best values for the enthalpy changes $\Delta \bar{H}_h^*$ and associated τ_{mh} parameters for cases with various numbers of allosteric forms, using equations (5.26) and (5.30). The criterion of fit determined from the least-squares analysis is the standard error of a point. The value of this measure decreases as more allosteric forms are included in the fitting procedure. The results are shown in Table 5.1.

From the data of Privalov and Filimonov, the actual experimental error appears to be about 1 percent of the maximum excess heat-capacity value. Thus it is seen that the analysis with six allosteric forms fits the data well within these criteria. Figure 5-5 shows the curves obtained for five and six forms; the system with five forms gives an inadequate fit, whereas that with six gives a curve that is virtually indistinguishable from the constructed experimental curve.

How can the six-form allosteric model given here represent the same data originally obtained from the independent-transition model with 2^5 different allosteric forms? Figure 5-6 illustrates the comparison between the enthalpy states for the independent-transition model for tRNA^{Phe} and the six energy levels of the six-state allosteric model. There is no obvious relation between these two enthalpy level diagrams. However, since the two schemes both fit the

Table 5.1
Enthalpy and temperature parameters for thermal-state treatment of tRNA[Phe] melting in 0.020M NaCl[a]

State i	4-State model		5-State model		6-State model		7-State model	
	$\Delta \bar{H}_h{}^*$	$T_{mh}{}^b$	$\Delta \bar{H}_h{}^*$	T_{mh}	$\Delta \bar{H}_h{}^*$	T_{mh}	$\Delta \bar{H}_h{}^*$	T_{mh}
1	457773	312.95	223232	301.72	190961	299.19	187998	299.09
2	886084	317.16	617757	309.27	453993	306.64	381719	307.10
3	1252000	321.89	968116	313.9	722787	310.0	498676	307.82
4			1252000	318.34	1010530	313.82	729380	310.80
5					1252000	317.75	1011390	313.80
6							1252000	317.71
Error[c]	.17		.046		.00012		.00010	

[a] Parameters determined by least-square analysis of heat-capacity data from Privalov and Filimonov (1978) on tRNA[Phe].
[b] The units for $\Delta \bar{H}_h{}^*$ are joule/mole and for T_{mh} are °K. For convenience T_{mh} is defined as $T_{mh} = 1/\tau_{mh}$, which means that the reference-state temperature is chosen at which $L_h{}^* = 1$ in equation (5.25).
[c] This is the standard error of a point for the fit divided by the maximum value of the heat capacity of the data.

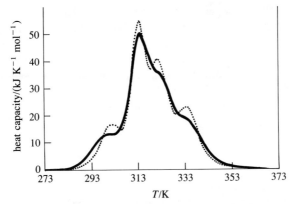

Figure 5-5.
A comparison of fit between the general allosteric state analysis [equation (5.30)] with five states (·····) and the calorimetrically determined melting curve (——) of tRNA^{Phe} in 20 mM NaCl solution as measured by Privalov and Filimonov (1978). The parameters for the fits are listed in Table 5.2. The inclusion of a sixth state provides a theoretical curve which is indistinguishable from the experimental data. Taken from Gill *et al.*, 1985.

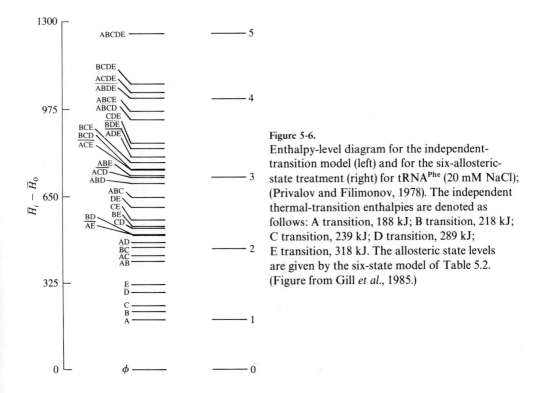

Figure 5-6.
Enthalpy-level diagram for the independent-transition model (left) and for the six-allosteric-state treatment (right) for tRNA^{Phe} (20 mM NaCl); (Privalov and Filimonov, 1978). The independent thermal-transition enthalpies are denoted as follows: A transition, 188 kJ; B transition, 218 kJ; C transition, 239 kJ; D transition, 289 kJ; E transition, 318 kJ. The allosteric state levels are given by the six-state model of Table 5.2. (Figure from Gill *et al.*, 1985.)

experimental data, we would expect to find an underlying connection. This is seen by considering the fractions of the various allosteric species as a function of temperature. The fraction of macromolecules in the h form, α_h, is given by equation (5.28). The fractional occupancy of any level in the independent model is found by expanding the partition function given by equation (5.34), and noting that each term is proportional to the concentration of a particular species. The fraction is computed by normalizing to the sum of all species. The fractional occupancy* for both schemes is shown in Figure 5-7. We see that only a few of the 32 states of the independent-transition model are significantly populated. The population of these states as a function of temperature closely corresponds to the population of the six states found in the general allosteric treatment.

As seen, the experimental data can be described by either model. The underlying correspondence between the independent-transition model and the general allosteric approach is due to the selection of the significant states in each. The general allosteric method as described selects the significant allosteric states directly, whereas the independent-transition model finds the same significant states while implying the existence of many other unnecessary forms. The general approach also allows us to avoid making any assumption about the interactions or lack of interactions between various regions of the macromolecule.

In a broad sense, the formulation of the thermal transition problem in terms of different allosteric forms is analogous to the formulation of chemical ligand binding by the Adair form of the partition function. However, for ligand binding, the binding polynomial is characterized by terms that contain integer powers of the ligand activity, whereas in thermal binding each term contains a power depending on the enthalpy of that form. Thus, in general, there are twice as many parameters needed to represent thermal binding: an equilibrium constant and enthalpy change for each reaction. Representation of chemical ligand binding requires just an equilibrium constant.

---

* The maximum amount of any species occurs at the temperature corresponding to the point at which the enthalpy added to the system is equal to the enthalpy of that state. This result is analogous to the general rule in ligand binding that the maximum amount of ith species occurs at the extent of reaction corresponding to i moles of ligand bound. The fraction of form h, α_h, is given using (5.23) as L_h/Q, and differentiation with respect to τ gives

$$\frac{\partial \ln \alpha_h}{\partial \tau} = -\frac{\Delta \bar{H}_h}{R} + \frac{\sum_h \alpha_h \Delta \bar{H}_h}{R}.$$

When set equal to zero, this shows that the maximum in α_h occurs when

$$\sum \alpha_h \Delta \bar{H}_h = \bar{H} - \bar{H}_0 = \Delta \bar{H}_h.$$

Thus at the temperature where $\bar{H} - \bar{H}_0 = \Delta \bar{H}_h$ there is a maximum concentration of α_h. An example is shown in Figure 5-7.

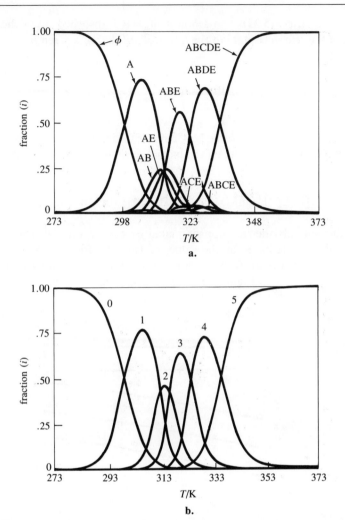

Figure 5-7.
The species fractions as a function of temperature computed for the independent-transition model (a) and the six-allosteric-state formulation (b). The (a) figure labels correspond to the combinations of independent transitions given in Figure 5-6, and the (b) figure labels correspond to the states given in Table 5.1. (Figure from Gill *et al.*, 1985.)

The influence of the ligand NaCl upon thermal denaturation processes of the tRNA system can be examined either in specific terms by proposing ligand binding reactions to the various allosteric forms or in general terms by applying linkage rules [Wyman (1964)]. The linkage effect of ligand concentration upon an allosteric equilibrium constant determines the change in the moles of ligand for the allosteric reaction. At a given temperature, the equilibrium constant between the reference form and the ith-form species, $L_h{}^*$, is given by equation (5.25). The amount of NaCl absorbed upon the transition from the reference state to the h state, $\Delta n_h(\text{NaCl})$, is given by the linkage rule as

$$\left(\frac{\partial \ln L_h^*}{\partial \ln a_{\text{NaCl}}}\right)_T = \Delta n_h(\text{NaCl}), \tag{5.38}$$

where a_{NaCl} is the activity of the NaCl in solution at temperature T. To apply this expression we approximate the partial-derivative term in equation (5.38) by

$$[\ln L_h^*(150\text{mM}) - \ln L_h^*(20\text{mM})]/(\ln 150 - \ln 20),$$

where the salt activities are approximated by concentrations. The results of this calculation are based on the values in Table 5.1 for 0.020 M NaCl along with reported values for 0.150 M NaCl (Gill et al., 1985) and are plotted as $\Delta n_h(\text{NaCl})$ versus T in Figure 5-8. The most significant feature is the negative

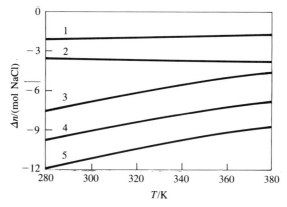

Figure 5-8.
The calculated change in the moles of NaCl bound for the allosteric transition of tRNA^{Phe} between the reference and ith state, $\Delta n_{\text{NaCl}}(i)$, as a function of temperature. The lines labeled 1, 2, 3, 4, and 5 correspond to the transition from the zeroth-form reference state to the labeled state. The average NaCl concentration is approximately 0.1 M. (Figure from Gill et al., 1985.)

value found for $\Delta n_h(\text{NaCl})$ in all transitions. This indicates that NaCl is released upon melting.

The Manning (1978) theory of counterion condensation on highly charged polyelectrolytes predicts that double-stranded nucleic acid, with its higher charge density, will bind more counterions (Na$^+$) than the single-strand form, with its lower charge density. Thus the melting of double-stranded regions in tRNA should cause a release of Na^+ ions from the tRNA molecule. Qualitatively, this agrees with the negative values of $\Delta n_h(NaCl)$ observed by application of the linkage equation.

5.3.2 Isothermal Titration Calorimetry: Single-Site Reaction

The generalized binding partition function may also be used to describe the heat effects that occur upon binding ligands to allosteric macromolecules under conditions of constant temperature. Such heats are conveniently measured by calorimetric titrations.

Single-site binding reactions to several allosteric forms have been discussed by Eftink *et al.* (1983), who show that significant heat-capacity changes can be attributed to ligand-binding effects. Thermal titrations of the L-arabinose binding protein (Fukada *et al.*, 1983), which has a single sugar-binding site, show large heat-capacity changes for the L-arabinose binding reaction. The authors of this study chose to treat the heat-capacity change as a phenomenological observation. However, there is a strong implication that an allosteric transition occurs during the binding reaction. X-ray structural data show different structural forms for the protein when sugar is either bound or not bound (Newcomer *et al.*, 1981). The observed heat effects may also be formulated in terms of the allosteric model. The simple MWC formulation given may be used, and must be normalized by the sum of terms representing the unligated species. For two allosteric forms, the reaction as shown in Figure 5-1 is

$$
\begin{array}{ccc}
M_{00} & \to & M_{10} \\
\downarrow & & \downarrow \\
M_0X & \to & M_1X
\end{array},
$$

where each allosteric form binds only one ligand. We find that the stoichiometric binding constant, β_1, is then given as

$$
\beta_1 = \frac{\kappa_0 + \Lambda_{10}\kappa_1}{1 + \Lambda_{10}}. \tag{5.39}
$$

Here the allosteric equilibrium constant of the unligated species is Λ_{10}, and the intrinsic sugar binding constants to the zeroth and first allosteric forms are κ_0 and κ_1. Each of these parameters depends on temperature as mediated by the enthalpy changes of the underlying reaction processes that define each term [see equation (5.9)].

Since we can observe that the stoichiometric reaction has a significant heat-capacity change, $\Delta \bar{C}_p$, we must include this term in the phenomenological description of the temperature behavior of β_1. Alternatively, the overall result for β_1 from (5.39) is obtained by writing the van't Hoff expression for κ_0,

κ_1, and Λ_{10}. The experimental data for the equilibrium binding constant β_1 at 25°C are given by Clark *et al.* (1982), and values for $\Delta\bar{H}°$ and $\Delta\bar{C}_p$ have been established by Fukada *et al.* (1983). These data may be used much as the scanning calorimetric data were used in the previous section; that is, we generate a set of values for β_1 for each temperature between 8° and 30°C, and find (Gill *et al.*, 1985) values of the six reaction parameters by equation (5.39) as given in Figure 5-9. We could also simplify the problem by assuming that

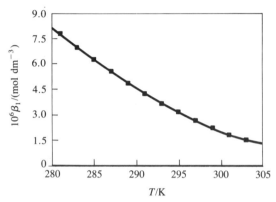

Figure 5-9.
Temperature dependence of the binding constant for l-arabinose to l-arabinose binding protein. The squares (■) represent the phenomenological values of the constant calculated from the literature values of β_1 at 25°C of 2.40×10^6 dm³ mol⁻¹ (Clark *et al.*, 1982), $\Delta\bar{H}°$ at 25°C of -15.26 kcal/mole, and $\Delta\bar{C}_p$ of -436 cal/mole-deg (Fukada *et al.*, 1983). The solid line shows the results obtained using the two-state allosteric model given by equation (5.39). The values obtained for the allosteric parameters at 25°C, along with their estimated standard errors, are as follows (Gill *et al.*, 1985):

$(\kappa_0)_0 = 4.8 \times 10^6 \pm 8 \times 10^4$ dm³ mol⁻¹ $\Delta\bar{H}_0 = -5.8 \pm 0.1$ kcal/mole

$(\kappa_1)_0 = 5 \times 10^5 \pm 1 \times 10^5$ dm³ mol⁻¹ $\Delta\bar{H}_1 = -5.2 \pm 3.6$ kcal/mole

$(\Lambda_{10})_0 = 1.29 \pm 0.05$ $\Delta\bar{H}_{10} = 21.66 \pm 0.62$ kcal/mole

ligand binding occurs to only one form of the macromolecule, and still obtain a reasonable representation of the temperature dependence of β_1.

This analysis has used purely phenomenological data, in the form of an equilibrium constant and enthalpy change under standard-state conditions, along with the heat-capacity change for the reaction. As shown, these data can be fit to a simple two-state allosteric model. The important result of this analysis is that the allosteric model is able to account fully for the thermal- and ligand-binding properties for this system. Binding-curve analysis at a single temperature can provide a value for only one average binding constant; so the full characterization of all the reaction constants for this simplest MWC case can be carried out only by studies at various temperatures. We should find a similar result for a two-site binding macromolecule, where we can find values for only two Adair equilibrium constants at each given temperature. Examination of the binding process as a function of temperature, either by finding accurate values of the Adair constant or, better, by a combination of calorimetric and binding measurements, provides the additional facts we need to explicate the underlying reaction processes.

5.3.3   Isothermal Titration Calorimetry: Multiple-Site Reactions

Thermal titrations of more complex ligand bindings usually present a more difficult problem. We wish to describe some of the general features of such processes in terms of the preceding development. We must first of all formulate the partition function for the system under consideration. For ligand titration processes, the usual reference state is given by the sum of unligated species (however, for proton titrations the reference state may be chosen quite differently; e.g., it may be the species at pH 7). The temperature dependence of each species term is expressed in the partition function, and the enthalpy (per mole of macromolecule) relative to the reference state is evaluated by partial differentiation, as in equation (5.13). The resulting expression will reflect the dependence of $\bar{H} - \bar{H}_0$ on both the temperature and the ligand activity. Our interest in isothermal calorimetry is that it measures the enthalpy change upon a change of added ligand at a given temperature. Thus the experimental results will correspond to the theoretical equations, if we know the ligand activity at each point along the titration process. The ligand activity, however, is usually not what is known directly, unless the experiment includes special ligand electrodes. What is generally known is the total amount of ligand added to the system; so we seek to calculate the amount of ligand bound, and the difference will give the amount free, and hence the ligand activity. As might be expected, using mass balance to calculate the activity yields equations that are (except in the simplest binding situations) sensitive to binding-parameter guesses used in least-square analysis of titration data. The most favorable situation is when we know the ligand activity at each point in the titration from separate experimental measurements. We can then express the results of the enthalpy of the macromolecule versus the logarithm of the ligand activity in a form analogous to the usual ligand-binding curve. Such curves might be called heat-binding titration curves. An example of such a curve is shown in Figure 5-10 from a calorimetric study of the hemocyanin from lobster *H. americanus* (Parody-Morreale *et al.*, 1986). The calorimetric data were obtained by titrating a solution of the macromolecule with oxygen-saturated buffer. The heat evolved during a titration step as we go from ligand activity x_{i-1} to x_i with c moles of hemocyanin in the system is

$$q = c[(\bar{H} - \bar{H}_0)_i - (\bar{H} - \bar{H}_0)_{i-1}]. \qquad (5.40)$$

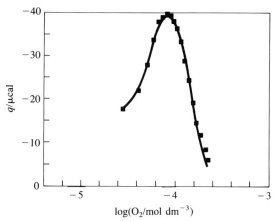

Figure 5-10.
Calorimetric titration by additions of 7 nmoles of dissolved oxygen to 80 nmoles of *H. americanus* hemocyanin binding sites 0.1 M Tris pH 7.4, 20 mM $CaCl_2$. Theoretical line was obtained using a six-site MWC model (Parody-Morreale *et al.*, 1986).

At each titration step we calculate the value of the ligand activity, using separate measurements of the binding constants for the system and the amount of ligand added to the system.

We have used a six-site MWC description for the oxygen-binding properties of this molecule in formulating the amount of ligand bound and the average enthalpy of the system. The results are shown for stepwise additions in Figure 5-10, and the accumulated effects, normalized to the moles of hexamer, are shown in Figure 5-11.

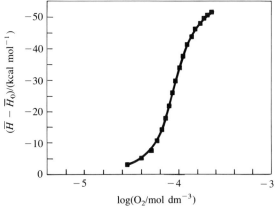

Figure 5-11.
Calorimetric data from Figure 5-10 for oxygen titration of *H. americanus* hemocyanin plotted in the form of a "heat-binding" curve. Theoretical line was obtained using a six-site MWC model. The mol unit is the hexamer (Parody-Morreale *et al.*, 1986).

As a final example, we show the results of calculations using parameters obtained in calorimetric and ligand-binding studies on the reaction of CO and Trout I hemoglobin (Barisas and Gill, 1979). Values of the enthalpy change as enough ligand is added to reach a given activity are shown in Figure 5-12 for several temperatures. As we have mentioned, this mode of presentation is

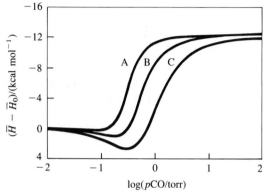

Figure 5-12.
Enthalpy change per mole of Trout I hemoglobin versus logarithm of CO ligand activity at various temperatures: (A) 278°K, (B) 298°K, (C) 318°K. These curves were calculated from enthalpy and equilibrium constant values given by Barisas and Gill (1979) using equation (5.13) with the Adair form of the binding polynomial. From Gill et al., 1985.

analogous to the way ligand-binding curves are often represented. One similarity between these two binding phenomena is the saturation effects exhibited at high ligand activity. The main difference between ligand and enthalpy binding is shown in this example by the presence of both positive and negative enthalpy changes. This contrasts with ligand binding, where only positive changes in ligation occur with increasing ligand activity. Another difference is that ligand binding is characterized by integer stoichiometry, whereas thermal binding is governed by noninteger enthalpy changes. Because of these differences, the analysis of thermal-binding curves requires both the equilibrium constants and their associated reaction enthalpy changes, whereas ligand-binding curves require only the equilibrium constants. Thus, as noted before, the description of thermal-binding curves at a given temperature requires twice as many parameters as ligand-binding curves require.

We see by these specific applications how the general partition function may be used to analyze and simulate a variety of heat and chemical ligand-binding phenomena. When heat effects are ascribed to specific macromolecular and chemical ligand-binding reactions, then we note a strong parallel to the description of chemical ligand binding. In this way it becomes useful to regard such heat and chemical ligand effects in terms of a generalized concept of "binding," where the physical parameters (enthalpy and volume) play a role that is formally analogous to that of chemical ligation.

5.4   GENERAL PROPERTIES OF HEAT-BINDING CURVES

We have seen in the preceding sections how we may define the enthalpy $\bar{H} - \bar{H}_0$ of a complex set of macromolecular species in equilibrium in terms of the partial derivative of the partition function of the macromolecule with respect to τ, the reciprocal absolute temperature. The exact relation is $\bar{H} - \bar{H}_0 = -R(\partial \ln Q / \partial \tau)$. We speak of $\bar{H} - \bar{H}_0$ as the excess enthalpy of the macromolecule above the ground state. This is an experimentally measurable quantity, and plots of $\bar{H} - \bar{H}_0$ versus τ or $\ln x$ yield what may be called *enthalpy* or *heat-binding curves*. In this section we wish to explore some of the more general properties of the heat absorbed considered as a function of reciprocal temperature. As we shall discover, the properties of these curves are analogous to those for chemical ligand binding, with characteristic median values and other properties for each situation.

Suppose we start with a simple, two-state transition, described by $A_0 \rightarrow A_1$, with an enthalpy of reaction of ΔH. Then the partition function can be derived from equation (5.32) simply as

$$Q = 1 + \exp\left[-\frac{\Delta H}{R}(\tau - \tau_m) \right], \tag{5.41}$$

where τ_m is the reciprocal temperature where the concentrations of A_0 and A_1 are equal. The excess enthalpy is found by taking the derivative of Q as

$$\bar{H} - \bar{H}_0 = -R \frac{\partial \ln Q}{\partial \tau} = \frac{\Delta H \exp[-(\Delta H / R)(\tau - \tau_m)]}{1 + \exp[-(\Delta H / R)(\tau - \tau_m)]}. \tag{5.42}$$

A plot of this function for $\Delta H = 1,000$ cal and $\tau_m = 0.00200$ K^{-1} (or $T_m = 500°$K) is shown in Figure 5-13. We note that at low values of τ, i.e., high temperatures, the excess enthalpy approaches a value around 750 cal/mole, indicating that the reaction cannot be driven to completion at high temperature. The "complete" binding curve can be obtained, however, by extending the range of τ to hypothetical negative values, i.e., to negative temperatures. This is shown in Figure 5-13. The full binding curve then shows the expected symmetry of a two-state reaction. This mode of plotting heat-binding data can obviously be extended to complex multistate processes.

The area under the heat-binding curve from τ to $\tau = \infty$ provides a direct way to evaluate Q:

$$\frac{1}{R} \int_{\tau}^{\tau = \infty} (\bar{H} - \bar{H}_0) \, d\tau = -\int_{Q}^{Q(\tau = \infty) = 1} d \ln Q = \ln Q, \tag{5.43}$$

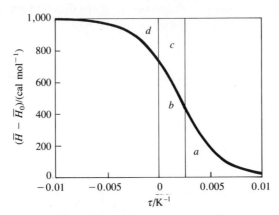

Figure 5-13.
Excess enthalpy $(\bar{H} - \bar{H}_0)$ versus τ for two-state transition ($\Delta H = 1,000$ cal, $\tau_m = 0.00200$ K^{-1}). Note that the rectangular area $(b + c)$ equals the area beneath the binding curve $(a + b - d)$.

where $Q = 1$ at low temperature. This equation has an exact counterpart for relating the area under ligand-binding curves to partition functions of ligand binding.

A median reciprocal temperature (τ_{med}) may be defined as the point where the roughly triangular areas (vertical sides at τ_{med}) above and below the heat-binding curve are equal, i.e., $(c + d) = (a)$ in Figure 5-13. Equivalently, the rectangular area $(b + c)$ equals the difference between the two triangular areas (vertical sides at $\tau = 0$) below and above the heat-binding curve, $(a + b - d)$. The area $(a + b)$ from equation (5.43) equals $R \ln Q(\tau = 0)$; the area (d) may be shown to equal $[R \ln Q(\tau = 0) - (\Delta H_t)\tau_{\text{mt}}]$, where τ_{mt} is mid-reciprocal temperature of the terminal allosteric transition with an enthalpy of reaction given by ΔH_t. Thus the difference is $(\Delta H_t)\tau_{\text{mt}}$, which also is given by the equivalent rectangular area $(b + c)$, i.e., $(\bar{H}_t - \bar{H}_0)\tau_{\text{med}}$. Since the enthalpy change ΔH_t of the terminal transition is the same as $(\bar{H}_t - \bar{H}_0)$, we see that median reciprocal temperature is exactly the same as the mid-reciprocal temperature of the last allosteric transition. Indeed, this result might have been anticipated from the analogous result in ligand binding, where the median activity is determined simply by the overall binding constant to the terminal species.

Heat-binding curves can also be obtained for systems with multiple-state transitions. For example, a system in which the molecule undergoes two independent transitions with equal ΔH values (1,000 cal), but different reciprocal midtemperature values ($\tau_m = 1/100$ and $1/1,000$ K^{-1}), follows the partition function given by

$$Q = \left\{1 + \exp\left[-\frac{1,000}{R}(\tau - .01)\right]\right\}\left\{1 + \exp\left[-\frac{1,000}{R}(\tau - .001)\right]\right\}. \quad (5.44)$$

The median temperature is found to be 182°K for this example, and the heat-binding curve takes the form shown in Figure 5-14.

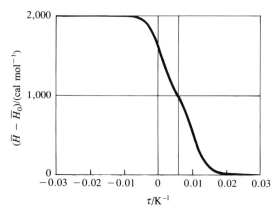

Figure 5-14.
Heat-binding curve for a macromolecule with two independent transitions ($\Delta H_1 = 1{,}000$ cal, $\tau_{m_1} = .01$ K^{-1}, and $\Delta H_2 = 1{,}000$ cal, $\tau_{m_2} = .001$ K^{-1}).

5.5 THE INCLUSION OF HEAT CAPACITY CHANGES IN THERMAL BINDING CURVES

We have concentrated on the key ideas of thermal binding, assuming that all heat capacities of the various allosteric forms are the same. This leads to heat-binding curves with horizontal asymptotes, similar to what we have found for chemical-ligand binding. However, for many biopolymer transitions, for example, protein denaturation, there are significant heat-capacity differences between native and denatured forms; so we must consider the consequences of such changes (Wyman *et al.*, 1979). We shall assume that the pertinent allosteric reactions are given by the following set of reactions:

$$A_0 \rightarrow A_1 \cdots A_h \rightarrow A_q. \tag{5.45}$$

The enthalpy change for $A_0 \rightarrow A_h$, is ΔH_h, and its temperature dependence is affected to the first approximation by the heat-capacity change for the reaction, ΔC_h. Thus we obtain

$$\Delta H_h = \Delta H_h^o + \Delta C_h(T - T_0), \tag{5.46}$$

where ΔH_h^o is the enthalpy of reaction at the reference temperature T_0. The temperature dependence of the equilibrium constant L_h is expressed in terms of the van't Hoff relation as

$$\frac{\partial \ln L_h}{\partial \tau} = -\frac{\Delta H_h}{R} = -\frac{\Delta H_h^o}{R} + \frac{\Delta C_h/\tau_0}{R} - \frac{\Delta C_h/\tau}{R}. \qquad (5.47)$$

When this is integrated between τ_0 and τ, we obtain

$$L_h = L_h^o \exp\left[-\frac{\Delta H_h^o}{R}(\tau - \tau_0)\right] \exp\left[\frac{\Delta C_h}{R\tau_0}(\tau - \tau_0)\right] \exp\left[-\frac{\Delta C_h}{R} \ln \frac{\tau}{\tau_0}\right]. \qquad (5.48)$$

This equation can be arranged to give

$$L_h = L_h^o \left(\frac{\tau}{\tau_0}\right)^{-(\Delta C_h)/R} \exp\left[-\frac{\Delta H_h^o}{R}(\tau - \tau_0)\right] \exp\left[\frac{\Delta C_h}{R\tau_0}(\tau - \tau_0)\right], \qquad (5.49)$$

which was partly included in the footnote on p. 173 without derivation. The partition function Q is given by the sum of all species concentrations in the system, normalized to the ground-state species, and is given by $\sum L_h$. The enthalpy bound above the ground state is then found from $-R(\partial \ln Q/\partial \tau)$, or in general terms

$$\bar{H} - \bar{H}_0 = \frac{\sum L_h \Delta H_h}{\sum L_h} = \sum \alpha_h \Delta H_h, \qquad (5.50)$$

where α_h is the fraction of h-form species in the system. This equation can be used to generate heat-binding situations where ΔH_h is itself temperature-dependent. The average heat capacity of the macromolecule above its reference state $\bar{C} - \bar{C}_0$ is then

$$\bar{C} - \bar{C}_0 = \frac{\partial(\bar{H} - \bar{H}_0)}{\partial T}, \qquad (5.51)$$

from which we find, using (5.50), (5.47), and (5.46),

$$\bar{C} - \bar{C}_0 = \frac{\tau^2}{R}\left[\sum(\Delta H_h)^2 \alpha_h - \left(\sum \Delta H_h \alpha_h\right)^2 + \sum \Delta C_h \alpha_h R/\tau^2\right]. \qquad (5.52)$$

We see that this expression has the same form as (5.30) except for the inclusion of ΔC_h. A system of two allosteric species is characterized by L^o, ΔH^o, and ΔC, and a system of q forms, all allosteric, is characterized by $3(q-1)$ parameters. Some unusual heat-binding curves can arise because of the influence of ΔC_h. The protein lysozyme shows a curve of heat capacity versus temperature like

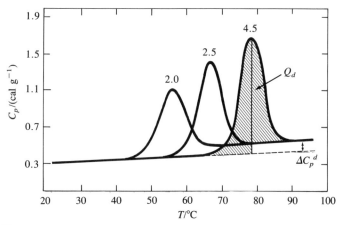

Figure 5-15.
Specific heat capacity of lysozyme as a function of T at different pH values
(Privalov, 1979). The shaded region denotes the heat of transition Q_d at a temperature of 78°C. The heat capacity change ΔC_p^d for denaturation is indicated by the
doubled arrow.

that shown in Figure 5-15. This experimental result indicates that there can be
large values of ΔC between the native form and the denatured form. In Figure 5-16 we show a hypothetical situation for enthalpy binding for a two-state
case. The excess heat capacity for the same situation is shown in Figure 5-17.
The fractions of the two forms as a function of temperature are shown in Figure 5-18. As these figures illustrate, the ground state is stable at intermediate
temperatures, and as temperature is either raised or lowered, the molecule is
converted to the denatured form. This behavior is caused by the large heat-
capacity difference between forms, so that the enthalpy change of the
transition reverses sign at some temperature, as is shown by equation (5.46).

This difference in behavior caused by large heat-capacity differences
between allosteric forms obviously complicates the analysis of scanning
calorimetric data in all but the simplest cases, but it leads to the very
interesting phenomenon of cold denaturation, which is observed in myoglobin
(Privalov *et al.*, 1986).

5.6   EFFECT OF PRESSURE ON MACROMOLECULAR
REACTIONS

The effects of pressure on the partition function can be analyzed in the same
way as those of temperature. The general effects of temperature, pressure,
and ligand activity on the macromolecular partition function have been discussed in Section 5.2. We saw that the equilibrium constant (Λ_{hi}), which describes the reaction between the zeroth and hth allosteric forms accompanied
by binding of iX ligands, is influenced by changes in temperature, pressure,
and ligand activity, as mediated by the conjugate parameters of enthalpy,

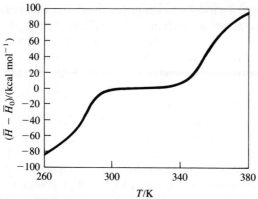

Figure 5-16.
Excess-enthalpy binding curve for a two-state case: $\Delta C_1 = 1,500$ cal/mole-deg, $\Delta H_1^o = 50,000$ cal/mole, $L_1^o = 1$, and $T_0 = 350°$K.

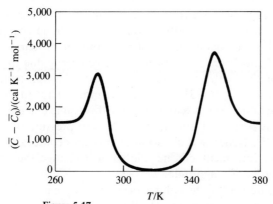

Figure 5-17.
Excess heat capacity for a two-state transition
with parameters as given in Figure 5-16.

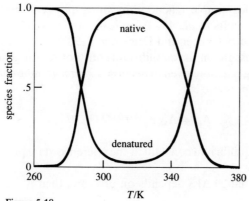

Figure 5-18.
Fractions of two-state transition forms as a function
of T for parameters given in Figure 5-16.

volume, and moles of ligand that change for the designated reaction. Equation (5.19) summarizes the calculation of these effects. The application of this equation to macromolecular problems dealing with temperature scanning and titration calorimetry has been outlined in detail in the preceding sections. Extensive thermal investigations have been made with high-sensitivity temperature devices because of the relatively large enthalpy changes encountered in macromolecular transitions.

Pressure and volume change logically represent variables of as much thermodynamic importance as temperature and enthalpy change. The full thermodynamic characterization of a macromolecular system requires knowledge of all these effects. Compared to thermal investigations, relatively little is known about the volume changes in, and effects of pressure on, reactions involving macromolecules, primarily because experimental measurements of such volume changes with pressure are quite difficult. Recent review articles describe the situation (Morild, 1981; Heremans, 1982; Weber and Drickamer, 1983).

The practical range of pressure for studies in liquid water is less than 12 kbar (1 kb = 986.92 atm = 1.0197 kg/cm^2). The volume change for typical reactions with small ligands is 10 ml/mol, and for protein unfolding is 50 ml/mol at 25°C. At room temperature the free energy due to a pressure of 1 kbar for a reaction with a volume change of 25 ml is approximately RT (a convenient unit for R is 0.08314 kbar cm^3/K mole). Thus the equilibrium constant for a reaction at room temperature with volume change ΔV (ml) at pressure p (kbar) is perturbed from its value at zero pressure by a factor of $e^{-p\Delta V/25} = 10^{-p\Delta V/57}$. Hence in a situation of protein denaturation (if $\Delta V = 57$ ml), a pressure increment of one kilobar will change the equilibrium constant by one order of magnitude.

The direct measurement of the volume occupied by the molecule as a function of pressure would represent the ideal thermodynamic way to study the influence of pressure. This would be the analog of scanning calorimetry. Unfortunately, a precise way to measure volume change as a function of pressure is not available. We therefore must characterize the macromolecular equilibrium constant for simple reactions by other physical methods, such as optical density (Brandts et al., 1970), optical rotation (Gill and Glogoasky, 1965), and fluorimetry (Weber and Drickamer, 1983).

The effect of pressure on the equilibrium constant Λ_{hi} for general allosteric and ligand-binding reaction given in Section 5.2 for a volume change $\Delta\bar{V}_{hi}$ that is independent of pressure is

$$\Lambda_{hi} = \Lambda_{hi}{}^{o}e^{-(\Delta\bar{V}_{hi})/(RT)(p - p_0)}, \tag{5.53}$$

where $\Lambda_{hi}{}^{o}$ is the equilibrium constant at the reference-state pressure, typically 1 atm.

If the volume change $\Delta\bar{V}_{hi}$ depends on pressure, then we characterize the first-order dependence by the change in compressibility $\Delta\beta_{hi}$ for the relevant states. The compressibility of a given form is defined by

$$\beta = -(1/V)(\partial V/\partial p)_T.$$

The appropriate first-order expression for the influence of pressure on $\Delta\bar{V}_{hi}$ is

$$\Delta\bar{V}_{hi} = \Delta\bar{V}_{hi}{}^o + \frac{\partial\,\Delta\bar{V}_{hi}}{\partial p}(p - p_0) \tag{5.54}$$

or

$$\Delta\bar{V}_{hi} = \Delta\bar{V}_{hi}{}^o - \bar{V}\Delta\beta_{hi}(p - p_0), \tag{5.55}$$

where $\bar{V}$ is the molar volume of the macromolecule. In writing equation (5.55) we assume that the molar volumes of native and denatured forms are nearly the same. Integration of equation (5.19) then gives

$$\Lambda_{hi} = \Lambda_{hi}{}^o \exp\left[-\frac{\Delta\bar{V}_{hi}}{RT}(p - p_0)\right]\exp\left[+\frac{\bar{V}\Delta\beta_{hi}}{2RT}(p - p_0)^2\right]. \tag{5.56}$$

This equation applies as it stands to fixed temperature and ligand activity conditions. We have seen (in our earlier study of temperature effects on macromolecular allosteric and ligation reactions) that the sum of such equilibrium-constant terms represents the partition function of the entire system. In practice, we cannot evaluate the relevant parameters except for the simplest macromolecular reactions. Even then we must resort to selection of the reactions that contain the largest volume change, and absorb the volume-change effects of other reactions in the compressibility term.

A detailed study by Brandts *et al.* (1970) on the pressure denaturation of ribonuclease A illustrates the principles we have discussed. A simple two-state reaction (native → denatured), as detected by optical-density changes, was analyzed in terms of an equilibrium constant L that depends on pressure by

$$L = L^o \exp\left[-\frac{\Delta\bar{V}^o}{RT}(p - p_0)\right]\exp\left[+\frac{\bar{V}\Delta\beta}{2RT}(p - p_0)^2\right]. \tag{5.57}$$

where L^o is the reference equilibrium constant at p_0 and depends also on pH and T. The terms $\Delta\bar{V}^o$, $\bar{V}$, and $\Delta\beta$ represent molar volume change, molar volume, and change in compressibility of ribonuclease A at a given temperature and pH. Table 5.2 summarizes the results. The fraction of denaturation α is given by $L/(1 + L)$, and its pressure dependence is illustrated in Figure 5-19 for three conditions selected from Table 5.2. The full transition was not observed under the conditions used. Further, the steepness of the transition depends on the value of $\Delta\bar{V}^o$, which is strongly influenced by the difference in compressibility $\Delta\beta$. These effects are brought out in a logarithmic plot of

Table 5.2
Parameters for the denaturation of ribonuclease A

pH	Temp/(°C)	$\Delta\bar{V}°$/(ml/mole)	$\Delta\beta$/(kbar^{-1} × 10^{-3})	$\Delta G°$/kcal
2.0	23.7	−46.5	1.5	.823
2.0	27.5	−43.0	2.0	.176
2.6	35.5	−27.0	0.9	.823
2.6	38.2	−27.0	1.0	.382
2.6	41.6	−20.0	1.6	.294
4.0	47.4	−7.5	1.1	2.000
4.0	51.7	−6.5	1.3	1.060
4.0	55.1	−4.5	1.5	.088

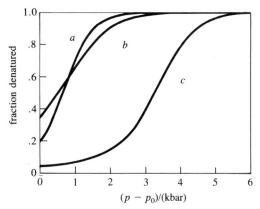

Figure 5-19.
Fractional denaturation of ribonuclease A as a function of pressure ($p_0 = 1$ atm) for three conditions given in detail in Table 5.3: (a) pH 2.0, 23.7°C; (b) pH 2.6, 38.2°C; (c) pH 4.0, 47.4°C. Note that the molar volume of ribonuclease was taken as 10,000 ml/mole.

(5.57) versus the pressure expressed as

$$RT[1/(p - p_0)] \ln(L/L°) = -\Delta\bar{V}° + \frac{\bar{V}\Delta\beta}{2}(p - p_0) = -\Delta\bar{V}. \quad (5.58)$$

The three examples in Figure 5-19 are plotted in this form in Figure 5-20, which shows the importance of the change in the compressibility upon ΔV at a given pressure.

A detailed study of the effects of pressure and temperature on the reversible denaturation of chymotrypsinogen at pH 2.07 was made by Hawley (1971),

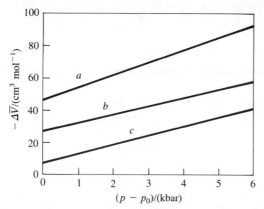

Figure 5-20.
Negative molar volume change for denaturation of ribonuclease A as a function of pressure [see equation (5.62)] for conditions (a) pH 2.0, 23.7°C; (b) pH 2.6, 38.2°C; (c) pH 4.0, 47.4°C of Figure 5-19.

who followed optical absorbance to measure the extent of reaction. The data were fit to terms including compressibility change and heat-capacity change. The fitted data gave $\Delta \bar{V}^{\circ} = -14.3$ ml/mole, and a change in compressibility of comparable magnitude was found as for the ribonuclease system. That the extent of denaturation depends on temperature and pressure is illustrated in Figure 5-21, which shows the contours of given fractions of denaturation. In it a combination of starting pressures and temperatures can be found, such as 3,000 kg/cm² and 0°C, where the protein is essentially in its denatured form.

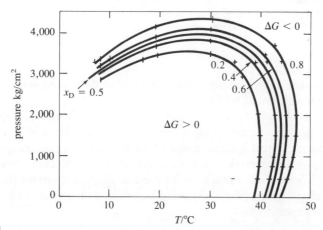

Figure 5-21.
Denaturation of chymotrypsinogen as a function of pressure and temperature at pH 2.07. Contours are drawn at constant fraction of denaturation through experimental points (+). (Taken from Hawley, 1971.)

Upon increase in temperature at this pressure, the protein is converted first to its native configuration (25°C), and then denatured as the temperature is raised above 40°C.

The effects of temperature, pressure, and pH have also been explored in a study of the denaturation of metmyoglobin by Zipp and Kauzmann (1973). This system is especially suitable for pressure studies, because a large optical change occurs upon denaturation, and the volume change for denaturation is nearly − 100 ml. They analyzed their data assuming a two-state transition and a pressure-independent volume change. The conditions where $\Delta G^o = 0$, i.e., the midpoint of the transitions, are plotted in Figure 5-22. From this figure we

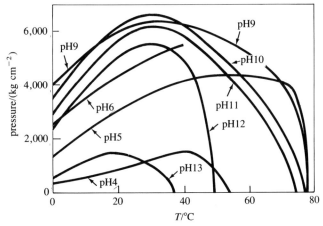

Figure 5-22.
Contours of constant pH in the pressure-temperature plane at which $\Delta G^o = 0$ for the denaturation of metmyoglobin. The native form is stable within the contour, and the denatured state is stable outside the contour (Zipp and Kauzmann, 1973).

can predict that metMb at pH5 and 3 kbar will be denatured at 0°C, native at 40°C, and denatured at 80°C.

The results of these studies have been obtained by indirect measurements of the pressure dependence on equilibrium constants evaluated from optical measurements. Direct measurements of volume change and compressibility change upon denaturation are complicated by significant experimental problems. There is still a real need for precise, direct measurements of molar volumes of proteins under denaturing conditions of pressure, temperature, and ligand concentration.

5.7 SUMMARY

In this chapter we have seen how the physical properties of enthalpy and volume change that accompany ligand binding and allosteric reactions in macromolecules can be treated in the same way as chemical ligand-binding processes. The procedure involves expressing the binding partition function in terms of equilibrium constants for the relevant species of the system. Each of the terms depends on temperature, pressure, and ligand activity by the change in enthalpy, volume, and ligand stoichiometry of the specific reaction process. The average enthalpy, volume, or bound ligand relative to an arbitrary reference state (per mole of macromolecule) is then determined by an appropriate partial derivative of the binding partition function with respect to temperature, pressure, or ligand activity. The general and similar nature of this procedure for describing the physical and chemical changes of macro- molecular systems leads us to regard "binding" in a general sense, which then includes heat and volume as well as chemical binding. Such a view allows a systematic and uniform treatment of complex reaction processes as they are influenced by changes in temperature, pressure, and ligand activity.

Ligand Control of Aggregation 6

The regulation of the association and dissociation of macromolecules is of obvious importance in many biological events. The construction of complex macromolecular aggregates begins by the synthesis of each of the component subunits, and then · proceeds by specific selection and regulation to the formation of larger units (often called oligomers) consisting of the simpler subunit forms. The oligomers themselves often serve as the building blocks of still larger assemblies. In hemoglobin we start with the α and β chain subunits, and the favored assembly of these is the familiar $\alpha_2\beta_2$ tetramer. But higher-aggregated structures are well-known, particularly for sickle-cell hemoglobin, which forms extensive fibers under conditions of low oxygen activity and sufficient hemoglobin concentration. The complex aggregates of hemocyanins from both arthropod and molluscan species offer striking examples of the way nature has created unique assemblies of oxygen-carrying macromolecules to fulfill the requirements imposed by diverse environmental conditions. Many enzymatic systems consist of several subunits of different proteins, organized to perform particular chemical processes.

Our insight into the relationships between structure and function for macromolecular assemblies is just in its infancy, but we can well imagine that the powerful structural tools developed in the last decade or two, especially X-ray crystallography, electron microscopy, and nuclear magnetic resonance, will provide many details that will help us understand the function of complex aggregates. The high-resolution structural information on aspartate transcarbamylase (Krause *et al.*, 1985) gives us a unique glimpse of the specific organization of regulatory and catalytic subunits in this enzyme (see Figure 6-1).

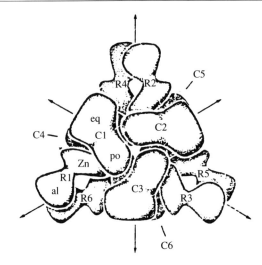

Figure 6-1.
Aggregate structure of aspartate transcarbamylase showing arrangement of regulatory (R) and catalytic (C) protein subunits. Domains of catalytic (C) chains are equatorial (eq) and polar (po); those of the regulatory (R) chains are allosteric (al) or zinc-containing (Zn) (Krause *et al.*, 1985).

The assembly of various subunits into even larger structures, such as viruses or microtubules, leads to the diversity of molecules that underlies biological phenomena. A flu virus (Daniels *et al.*, 1985; Wilson *et al.*, 1981) that attaches itself to the cell wall in preparation for invasion once pH has dropped has a triple-subunit structure that shields its hydrophobic legs until invasion occurs. The structure is pictured in Figure 6-2.

The structures of large viruses, tobacco and phage, are simply large, precise assemblies of various subunits; they provide packages for transmission of nucleic acid that leads to the propagation of the virus itself. The architecture of such particles shows the artistic diversity of nature. An example is given in Figure 6-3.

In this chapter we will outline the physical-chemical principles of aggregate formation or its converse, aggregate dissociation. As we shall see, one of the key parameters of such processes is the subunit concentration. The degree of aggregation depends on concentration, or, put another way, on the solvent activity. Thus the role of water becomes of major importance in aggregation processes. In nondissociating macromolecules, the effect of water is generally not detectable. For aggregating systems we should expect to find ligand-binding curves sensitive to concentration, and reciprocally we should anticipate that the degree of aggregation will be sensitive to ligand binding. These systems have the simple elements that demonstrate how aggregation processes can be controlled by reacting ligands. Follow-

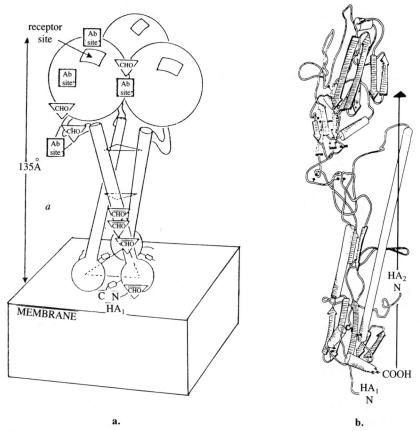

Figure 6-2.
Schematic structural features of hemagglutinin membrane glycoprotein of influenza virus (Wilson *et al.*, 1981). (a) Diagram of trimeric molecule showing carbohydrate attachment locations (CHO), antigenic sites (Absite), host cell receptor binding site, and end attachment to membrane. (b) Monomer chain consisting of two disulfide linked polypeptide chains with N-terminal residues labeled HA_1 and HA_2. Three-fold symmetry axis designated by arrow. The trimer is stabilized principally through interaction between long α-helices (cylinders) of the monomers. Details of the structure and its relevance to functional properties are reviewed by Wiley and Skehel (1987).

ing the procedures of preceding chapters, we formulate details of binding reactions for reversible or equilibrium conditions in terms of simple mass-action laws. We deal with two general problems: (1) ligand-linked aggregation within a homogeneous solution phase; (2) ligand-controlled phase formation. The second problem can be considered an outgrowth of the first, where aggregation is so extensive that it forms a second phase as in a crystal in equilibrium with a solution phase. This will be dealt with in Chapter 7.

Figure 6-3.
Model of the tobacco mosaic virus, showing outer
protein subunits wrapped around the helical RNA
core (Klug and Caspar, 1960).

6.1   HOMOGENEOUS SOLUTIONS: LIGAND-LINKED AGGREGATION; EFFECT OF LIGAND ACTIVITY ON MACROMOLECULAR REACTION EQUILIBRIUM CONSTANTS

We have shown in detail in the preceding chapters how ligand activity, say, x
for ligand X, affects any equilibrium constant through the ratio of X-binding
polynomials for the reaction species. It is a simple matter to extend this idea to
more general cases where the moles of macromolecules change in the reaction
process. Let a moles of M_A plus b moles of M_B react to form c moles of M_C:

$$aM_A + bM_B \rightarrow cM_C \tag{6.1}$$

The equilibrium constant of this reaction in the absence of X is K_0, and is
determined by the concentrations of the unliganded macromolecules, given as
$[M_A{}^o]$, $[M_B{}^o]$, and $[M_C{}^o]$, as

$$K_0 = \frac{[M_C{}^o]^c}{[M_A{}^o]^a[M_B{}^o]^b}. \tag{6.2}$$

In the presence of ligand X, at activity x, we then have various ligated species
of each form of macromolecule as determined by the X-binding polynomial
for each form, i.e., P_{AX}, P_{BX}, P_{CX}; and the general equilibrium constant K is

given as

$$K = \frac{[M_C]^c}{[M_A]^a[M_B]^b} = \frac{[M_C^\circ]P_{CX}^c}{[M_A^\circ]^a P_{AX}^a [M_B^\circ]^b P_{BX}^b}. \tag{6.3}$$

This gives the expected linkage result in terms of polynomial ratios

$$K = K_0 \frac{P_{CX}^c}{P_{AX}^a P_{BX}^b}. \tag{6.4}$$

Since the equilibrium constant expresses a stoichiometrically weighted set of macromolecular concentrations, a change in ligand activity x will in general cause a shift in the macromolecular concentrations, except for the special situation where the weighted polynomials cancel each other. The explicit dependence of K on the ligand activity is derived from (6.4) from what we know about the ligand-activity derivatives of the X-binding polynomials, namely, the moles of X bound per mole of given macromolecule, i.e., $\bar{X}_A = \partial \ln P_{AX}/\partial \ln x$, etc. Thus, we take the logarithm of K and differentiate partially with respect to $\ln x$ to obtain

$$\frac{\partial \ln K}{\partial \ln x} = c\bar{X}_C - b\bar{X}_B - a\bar{X}_A = \Delta\bar{X}, \tag{6.5}$$

where $\Delta\bar{X}$ denotes the difference in the moles of X that are bound in going from reactants to product macromolecules as specified by reaction (6.1). The value of $\Delta\bar{X}$ depends explicitly on the binding polynomials as follows:

$$\Delta\bar{X} = c\frac{\partial \ln P_{CX}}{\partial \ln x} - b\frac{\partial \ln P_{BX}}{\partial \ln x} - a\frac{\partial \ln P_{AX}}{\partial \ln x}. \tag{6.6}$$

An experimental study of K as a function of ligand activity x enables us to calculate the ratio of binding polynomials of the various macromolecules in the reaction, and gives information about the X-binding reactions to the different forms.

As an example, consider the combination of $\alpha\beta$ dimers to form tetrameric hemoglobin, $\alpha_2\beta_2$. The reaction is

$$2\alpha\beta \rightarrow \alpha_2\beta_2. \tag{6.7}$$

What happens to this equilibrium in the presence of different activities of an organic phosphate ligand like IHP? Assume oxygen is absent, and assume IHP binds only to the tetramer, $\alpha_2\beta_2$, with a binding constant K_I. Then the IHP-binding polynomials are $P_{\alpha\beta,\text{IHP}} = 1$ and $P_{\alpha_2\beta_2,\text{IHP}} = 1 + K_I[IHP]$, and we obtain for (6.4)

$$K = K_0\{1 + K_I[IHP]\}. \tag{6.8}$$

The change in IHP bound, $\Delta\overline{IHP}$, per unit of tetramer-forming reaction is then computed from (6.6) as

$$\Delta\overline{IHP} = \frac{K_I[IHP]}{1 + K_I[IHP]}.\tag{6.9}$$

The value of K will continue to increase linearly with IHP concentrations, even though $\Delta\overline{IHP}$ reaches a saturation value of 1 at high IHP concentrations.

6.2 BINDING CURVES

It is frequently much easier to find out how much ligand is bound to an aggregating macromolecular system than to calculate the equilibrium constant for the aggregation reaction. As we have already noted in Chapter 3, there are often spectroscopic methods to follow the extent of binding, and binding curves may be generated from experiments conducted at different ligand activities. Such curves reveal the underlying reaction processes.

We develop the principles of how aggregation affects binding curves by starting with a simple example. Consider the formation of a dimer from subunits denoted by M, each of which can bind one X ligand. Actually, this situation has been found in the dimeric heme molecule of *Chromatium vinosum* cytochrome c' upon binding carbon monoxide to the reduced form (Doyle *et al.*, 1986). The molecule from the species *Rhodospirillum molischianum* shows no effect of cooperativity or dependence of protein concentration on CO binding (Doyle *et al.*, 1985). One striking molecular feature found in the structure of *R. molischianum* (Weber and Salemme, 1982) is the presence of a salt bridge through a lysine on one chain to a propionate group on the heme of the opposite chain. This pair of salt links, shown in Figure 6-4, is absent in the *C. vinosum* species. There are other residue changes in the contact interface as well. The reaction process can be described as shown in Figure 6-5. All species in the array in Figure 6-5 can be related to the unligated monomer concentrations $[M]$ and X activity by means of mass-action law equations as follows:

$$[M_2] = L_{20}[M]^2;$$

$$[MX] = \beta_{11}[M]x;$$

$$[M_2X] = L_{20}\beta_{21}[M]^2x;\tag{6.10}$$

$$[M_2X_2] = L_{20}\beta_{22}[M]^2x^2.$$

Although the molar amounts of aggregated forms will in general vary in a given ligation experiment, the moles of subunits, or in this example the total X-binding sites, will remain constant. Thus the relevant measure of binding is

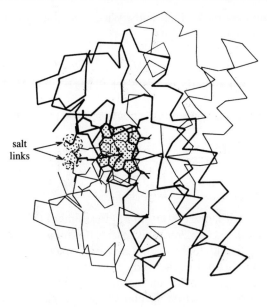

salt
links

Figure 6-4.
Structure of dimeric cytochrome c' from *R. molischianum* with explicit inclusion of
the lysine-propionate salt bridge between one chain and the opposite heme. This salt
bridge is absent in cytochrome c' from *C. vinosum*, which dissociates on binding
carbon monoxide. (Structure coordinates from Weber and Salemme, 1982.)

$$2\,M \longrightarrow M_2$$
$$L_{20}$$

$$\downarrow \beta_{11} \qquad\qquad \downarrow \beta_{21}$$

$$MX + M \longrightarrow M_2X$$
$$L_{21}$$

$$\downarrow \beta_{11} \qquad\qquad \downarrow K_{22}$$

$$2\,MX \longrightarrow M_2X_2$$
$$L_{22}$$

Figure 6-5.
Reaction species array for monomer-dimer reaction
with single-site binding of ligand X to each monomer
subunit. Equilibrium constants beside the arrows
apply to those reactions. The reaction between M_2
and $2X$ to form M_2X_2 is described by the equilibrium
constant $\beta_{22} = \beta_{21}K_{22}$.

moles of X bound per mole of subunits. We denote this by $\bar{n}_X$ and proceed to write down this quantity as follows:

$$\bar{n}_X = \frac{[MX] + [M_2X] + 2[M_2X_2]}{[M] + 2[M_2] + [MX] + 2[M_2X] + 2[M_2X_2]}. \tag{6.11}$$

With the mass-action law relations [equation (6.10)] we obtain

$$\bar{n}_X = \frac{\beta_{11}[M]x + L_{20}\beta_{21}[M]^2x + 2L_{20}\beta_{22}[M]^2x^2}{[M] + 2L_{20}[M]^2 + \beta_{11}[M]x + 2L_{20}\beta_{21}[M]^2x + 2L_{20}\beta_{22}[M]^2x^2}. \tag{6.12}$$

Although we can cancel one power of $[M]$ throughout this equation, second-order terms retain this parameter. This reflects the linkage of concentration (or solvent acting as a ligand) to the X-binding curve for aggregating systems. This is a nontrivial complication in the study of such processes, because in general we have no direct methods for measuring the unligated concentration (or activity) of the subunit macromolecular species. In place of direct measurement we must consider the mass-balance relation of the total subunit concentration, m_0, i.e., the sum of all macromolecular concentrations in the system weighted by the number of subunits in each species. This is the denominator of equations (6.11) and (6.12):

$$m_0 = [M] + [MX] + 2[M_2] + 2[M_2X] + 2[M_2X_2]; \tag{6.13}$$

$$m_0 = [M] + \beta_{11}[M]x + 2L_{20}[M]^2 + 2L_{20}\beta_{21}[M]^2x$$
$$+ 2L_{20}\beta_{22}[M]^2x^2; \tag{6.14}$$

$$m_0 = [M](1 + \beta_{11}x) + 2L_{20}[M]^2(1 + \beta_{21}x + \beta_{22}x^2). \tag{6.15}$$

The value of m_0 will presumably be known and fixed for a given experiment in which the ligand activity x and consequently $[M]$ are varied. The value of $[M]$ can be found from equation (6.15) for given values of m_0, x, and binding constants. Substitution into (6.12) provides the relation between $\bar{n}_X$ and x at given m_0 values. The result is complicated, as we anticipated, even for this relatively simple case. However, since equation (6.15) is a quadratic, we can explicitly solve for $[M]$, and write the solution in detail as

$$2L_{20}(1 + \beta_{21}x + \beta_{22}x^2)[M]^2 + (1 + \beta_{11}x)[M] - m_0 = 0. \tag{6.16}$$

This yields the desired relation between $[M]$ and x and m_0:

$$[M] = \frac{-(1 + \beta_{11}x) + [(1 + \beta_{11}x)^2 + 8L_{20}(1 + \beta_{21}x + \beta_{22}x^2)m_0]^{1/2}}{4L_{20}(1 + \beta_{21}x + \beta_{22}x^2)}. \tag{6.17}$$

The influence of the total concentration of sites (m_0) is shown by the binding curves generated for selected values of $\beta_{11}, L_{20}, \beta_{21}, \beta_{22}$, and m_0 in Figure 6-6.

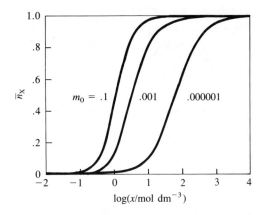

Figure 6-6.
Binding, curves for dimer aggregation
($\beta_{11} = 0.01$ M^{-1}; $L_{20} = 100$ M^{-1}; $\beta_{21} = 0.1$ M^{-1}, and $\beta_{22} = 1$ M^{-2}) for indicated
subunit concentrations m_0. At high con-
centration the binding curve is dominated
by the properties of the dimer, and at low
concentration by the properties of the
monomer.

These curves have been generated using equations (6.17) and (6.12).

The actual situation found for the binding of carbon monoxide to *C. vinosum* cytochrome c′ was that, for practically usable concentrations, no dissociation of the unligated dimer could be detected. Thus the relevant species for which binding curves could be made involved the species at the right and along the bottom of Figure 6-5. In that situation we formulate the analysis in terms of those equilibria. Hill plots of experimental results and the theoretical derived curves from this analysis are shown in Figure 6-7, which

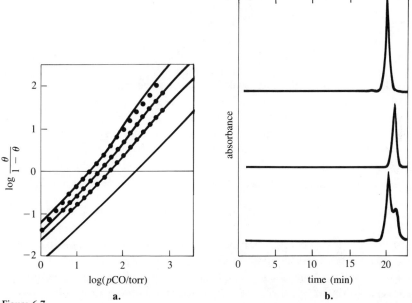

a.   b.

Figure 6-7.
(a) Hill plots of carbon monoxide binding to *C. vinosum* cytochrome c′ at 25°C and concentrations (left to right) 250 μM, 70 μM, and 20 μM heme along with theoretical lines based on equilibria between dimer and ligated monomer species. The theoretical lower line represents CO binding to pure dimer. (b) Liquid chromatography of same system with no CO present (middle), saturated with CO (top), and partially saturated (bottom), showing dissociation from dimer to monomeric form (Doyle *et al.*, 1986).

211

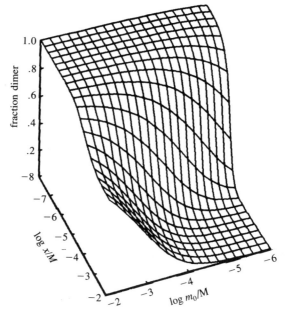

Figure 6-8.
Surface showing fraction of dimer (monomer units) as a function of total subunit concentration (m_0) and carbon monoxide concentration (x) for *C. vinosum* cytochrome c' (taken from Doyle *et al.*, 1986).

also shows chromatographic results indicating the presence of monomeric subunits in the presence of carbon monoxide. A three-dimensional plot (Figure 6-8) shows the fraction of dimeric species of this cytochrome c' as a function of total subunit concentration and carbon monoxide activity. As can be seen, essentially all subunits are aggregated into dimers in the absence of ligand.

6.3   PARTITION FUNCTION FOR AGGREGATING SYSTEMS

The key feature of a general partition function Q is that it represents the sum of all species concentrations. In dilute aggregating solutions, where ideal solution behavior applies, Q may be found directly by methods that find the number of macromolecular particles, i.e., measure the average molecular weight. Osmotic-pressure measurements could provide such a value. Since aggregation depends strongly on concentration, we retain this feature in the generalized definition of the partition function as a sum of unnormalized macromolecular concentrations. For simplicity we still retain the symbol Q.

Again, let us elaborate the partition function by continuing our discussion of simple dimerization. The partition function is then given directly from equations (6.13) to (6.15) as

$$Q = [M] + [MX] + [M_2] + [M_2X] + [M_2X_2], \tag{6.18}$$

$$Q = [M] + \beta_{11}[M]x + [M_2] + \beta_{21}[M_2]x + \beta_{22}[M_2]x^2, \tag{6.19}$$

or

$$Q = [M](1 + \beta_{11}x) + L_{20}[M]^2(1 + \beta_{21}x + \beta_{22}x^2), \tag{6.20}$$

where the unligated dimer $[M_2]$ concentration has here been related by the mass-action law to the unligated monomer. As usual, we note the ever-present binding polynomials reflecting for each aggregated form the relative amounts of their applicable species. The first set of terms in equation (6.20) gives the monomer species, and the second set gives the dimer species. Q is clearly a function of two variables, $[M]$ and x.

Partial derivatives of Q with respect to $\ln[M]$ and $\ln x$ give the total molar concentration of subunit sites, m_0, and the molar concentration of bound X ligand $[X_{bound}]$, respectively. This may be seen for our dimer example as

$$\frac{\partial Q}{\partial \ln x} = [M]\beta_{11}x + L_{20}[M]^2(\beta_{21}x + 2\beta_{22}x^2) = [X_{bound}] \tag{6.21}$$

and

$$\frac{\partial Q}{\partial \ln[M]} = [M](1 + \beta_{11}x) + 2L_{20}[M]^2(1 + \beta_{21}x + \beta_{22}x^2) = m_0. \tag{6.22}$$

In general we may find the moles of X bound per mole of binding sites from the result*

---

* Since

$$\frac{\left(\dfrac{\partial Q}{\partial \ln x}\right)_{[M]}}{\left(\dfrac{\partial Q}{\partial \ln[M]}\right)_x} = -\left(\frac{\partial \ln[M]}{\partial \ln x}\right)_Q,$$

we also obtain the formal result

$$\bar{n}_X = -\left(\frac{\partial \ln[M]}{\partial \ln x}\right)_Q.$$

$$\bar{n}_{\mathrm{X}} = \frac{[\mathrm{X}_{\mathrm{bound}}]}{m_0} = \frac{\dfrac{\partial Q}{\partial \ln x}}{\dfrac{\partial Q}{\partial \ln [M]}} = \frac{\dfrac{\partial Q}{\partial \ln x}}{m_0}. \tag{6.23}$$

We also see from the preceding example that Q may be expressed in general in terms of the X-binding polynomials P_i for the ith aggregate as

$$Q = \sum_{i=1} [M_i] P_i = \sum_{i=1} [M]^i L_{i0} P_i, \tag{6.24}$$

where $L_{10} = 1$. Then by partial differentiation of Q with respect to $\ln x$, we find, by substitution of equation (6.23),

$$\bar{n}_{\mathrm{X}} = \frac{1}{m_0} \sum_{i=1} [M]^i L_{i0} P'_i x, \tag{6.25}$$

where P'_i is the x derivative, i.e., $\partial P_i / \partial x$; and m_0 is given by the general expression

$$m_0 = \sum_{i=1}^{t} i [M]^i L_{i0} P_i. \tag{6.26}$$

The binding curve for complex aggregation systems may thus be generated by first solving for $[M]$ at given values of m_0 and x, and then substituting the result into equation (6.25).

6.4   MEDIAN AND FREE-ENERGY PROPERTIES OF BINDING CURVES OF AGGREGATING SYSTEMS

We next explore some of the general properties of the binding curves that occur for aggregating systems. As we have seen in nonaggregating systems, the areas under and above such curves reveal important information about the general thermodynamic behavior of the system, in particular, the free energy of saturating all sites. Johnson *et al.* (1976) have derived how the median activity depends on the concentration of macromolecule for the case of dimer association to tetramer, and we shall generalize this result by a different procedure. The area under the binding curve A_u is given by

$$A_u = \int_{x=0}^{x} \bar{n}_{\mathrm{X}} \, d \ln x. \tag{6.27}$$

To evaluate this, first note that the derivative of the partition function in the two variables, $\ln x$ and $\ln [M]$, is

$$dQ = \frac{\partial Q}{\partial \ln x} d\ln x + \frac{\partial Q}{\partial \ln [M]} d\ln [M]. \tag{6.28}$$

Substitution of (6.23) yields

$$dQ = \bar{n}_x m_0 \, d\ln x + m_0 \, d\ln [M] \tag{6.29}$$

or

$$\bar{n}_x \, d\ln x = \frac{dQ}{m_0} - d\ln [M]. \tag{6.30}$$

Then substitution into (6.27) and integration give the final, simple result

$$A_u = \frac{1}{m_0}(Q - Q_0) - \ln \frac{[M]}{[M_0]}, \tag{6.31}$$

where Q_0 and $[M_0]$ are the values of Q and $[M]$ when $x = 0$. From (6.24)

$$Q_0 = \sum [M_0]^i L_{i0}$$

and from (6.26)

$$m_0 = \sum i[M_0]^i L_{i0}.$$

The area above the binding curve A_a is given as

$$A_a = \int_{x=x}^{x=\infty} (1 - \bar{n}_x) d\ln x. \tag{6.32}$$

Upon substitution of equation (6.30) and integration, we obtain

$$A_a = \ln \frac{x_\infty}{x} - \frac{1}{m_0}(Q_\infty - Q) + \ln \frac{[M_\infty]}{[M]}, \tag{6.33}$$

where the subscript ∞ denotes the value of a given term as $x \to \infty$. We can evaluate Q_∞ by considering the highest-power term in x in each polynomial term, i.e., $[M]^i x^i$, from equation (6.24) as

$$Q_\infty = \sum_i L_{i0} \beta_{ii}[M_\infty]^i x_\infty^i, \tag{6.34}$$

and also realizing from equation (6.26) that

$$m_0 = \sum_i iL_{i0}\beta_{ii}[M_\infty]^i x_\infty^i. \tag{6.35}$$

Thus the product term $[M_\infty]x_\infty$ must be a finite value, say f, which is a function of m_0. The factor Q_∞/m_0 is determined by m_0 and the various constants $L_{i0}\beta_{ii}$. At $x = \infty$, the macromolecular system is driven into a mixed set of aggregate forms depending on these parameters. Substitution of equations (6.34) and (6.35) into (6.33) yields the general result for A_a for aggregating systems:

$$A_a = -\ln x - \frac{Q_\infty}{m_0} + \frac{Q}{m_0} + \ln f - \ln [M]. \tag{6.36}$$

Here $f = [M_\infty]x_\infty$, and Q_∞ is given by evaluation of equation (6.34) as

$$Q_\infty = \sum_i L_{i0}\beta_{ii}f^i. \tag{6.37}$$

From the areas under and above the binding curve at a given activity, we can now derive the expression for the median value of x, i.e., x_m, for an aggregating system. We equate A_a to A_u and thus find from equations (6.31) and (6.36) that

$$\ln x_m = \frac{Q_0 - Q_\infty}{m_0} + \ln \frac{f}{[M_0]}. \tag{6.38}$$

As we have seen, Q_∞ is given by equation (6.37),

$$Q_0 = \sum [M_0]^i L_{i0}, \tag{6.39}$$

and f is given by solving from equation (6.35), i.e., the mass-balance equation,

$$m_0 = \sum if^i L_{i0}\beta_{ii}. \tag{6.40}$$

These results have been derived for the general case of aggregating systems. What they show is that the median activity of X may be evaluated for complex aggregating systems. Recall that this value in turn determines the total free energy for saturating the system under the specified conditions of macromolecular concentration.

To illustrate these findings, let us consider the ligand-mediated monomer-dimer formation with binding constants defined by (6.10). The partition function in the absence of ligand is

$$Q_0 = [M_0] + L_{20}[M_0]^2, \tag{6.41}$$

and the mass-balance equation at $x = 0$ is

$$m_0 = [M_0] + 2L_{20}[M_0]^2. \qquad (6.42)$$

Similarly, the partition function and m_0 evaluated at x_∞ are

$$Q_\infty = \beta_{11}f + L_{20}\beta_{22}f^2, \qquad (6.43)$$

$$m_0 = \beta_{11}f + 2L_{20}\overline{\beta_{22}}f^2. \qquad (6.44)$$

Then $[M_0]$ and f may be found explicitly by solving equations (6.42) and (6.44) to give

$$[M_0] = \frac{-1 + (1 + 8m_0 L_{20})^{1/2}}{4L_{20}} \qquad (6.45)$$

and

$$f = \frac{-\beta_{11} + (\beta_{11}{}^2 + 8m_0 L_{20}\beta_{22})^{1/2}}{4L_{20}\beta_{22}} = \frac{-1 + (1 + 8m_0 L_{20}\beta_{22}/\beta_{11}{}^2)^{1/2}}{4L_{20}\beta_{22}/\beta_{11}}. \qquad (6.46)$$

We can then solve the various terms that determine the median x_m in equation (6.38) as follows:

$$\frac{Q_0}{m_0} = \frac{1 + L_{20}[M_0]}{1 + 2L_{20}[M_0]} = \frac{1 - 1/4 + 1/4(1 + 8m_0 L_{20})^{1/2}}{1 - 1/2 + 1/2(1 + 8m_0 L_{20})^{1/2}}, \qquad (6.47)$$

$$\frac{Q_\infty}{m_0} = \frac{1 + \dfrac{L_{20}\beta_{22}}{\beta_{11}}f}{1 + 2\dfrac{L_{20}\beta_{22}}{\beta_{11}}f} = \frac{1 - 1/4 + 1/4(1 + 8m_0 L_{20}\beta_{22}/\beta_{11}{}^2)^{1/2}}{1 - 1/2 + 1/2(1 + 8m_0 L_{20}\beta_{22}/\beta_{11}{}^2)^{1/2}}, \qquad (6.48)$$

and

$$\frac{f}{[M_0]} = \left(\frac{-1 + (1 + 8m_0 L_{20}\beta_{22}/\beta_{11}{}^2)^{1/2}}{-1 + (1 + 8m_0 L_{20})^{1/2}}\right)^{1/2} \frac{\beta_{11}}{\beta_{22}}. \qquad (6.49)$$

These equations, when substituted in the expression for $\ln x_m$ given by (6.38), give an explicit form of the dependence of x_m on m_0, L_{20}, β_{11}, and β_{22}. As $m_0 \to 0$, these expressions allow us to see that $x_m(m_0 \to 0) = 1/\beta_{11}$, as indeed we would expect, since at infinite dilution only monomer exists. See Figure 6-9.

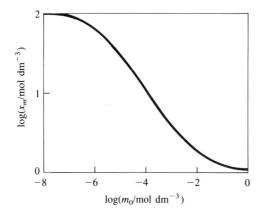

Figure 6-9.
Dependence of $\log x_m$ on $\log m_0$ for the monomer-dimer case given in Figure 6-6.

6.5 FREE ENERGY OF LIGAND BINDING TO AGGREGATING SYSTEMS

The work of saturating any system with X ligand is given by $RT \ln x_m$. However, the real question is what is the free-energy gain in saturating the freely adjusting aggregating system compared to that in a system frozen in its initial distribution of macromolecular forms. Such a comparison will indicate the extent of positive cooperativity in the freely adjusting system. We thus need to examine the binding properties of the "frozen" system and to find the median activity for the frozen case, designated by x_m^F.

We illustrate the idea by again drawing on the simple monomer-dimer case. The frozen partition function Q^F consists of monomer and dimer species with no relation between the two, and subject to the condition that the total amount of monomer and dimer stays the same as the initial values:

$$Q^F = [M](1 + \beta_{11}x) + [D](1 + \beta_{21}x + \beta_{22}x^2). \qquad (6.50)$$

Here the unligated monomer is $[M]$, and the unligated dimer is written simply as $[D]$ in what follows. Further, the concentration of all monomer species is equal to its initial value $[M_0]$ and likewise for the dimers, $[D_0]$:

$$[M_0] = [M](1 + \beta_{11}x), \qquad (6.51)$$

$$[D_0] = [D](1 + \beta_{21}x + \beta_{22}x^2). \qquad (6.52)$$

To obtain the binding curve of a frozen system, we carry out the following operations:

$$\bar{n}_X^F = \frac{1}{m_0}\frac{\partial Q^F}{\partial \ln x} = \frac{[M]\beta_{11}x}{m_0} + \frac{[D](\beta_{21}x + 2\beta_{22}x^2)}{m_0}. \qquad (6.53)$$

But $[M]$ and $[D]$ are given in terms of $[M_0]$ and $[D_0]$; so we obtain the result

$$\bar{n}_X^F = \frac{[M_0]}{m_0} \frac{\beta_{11}x}{1 + \beta_{11}x} + \frac{[D_0]}{m_0} \frac{\beta_{21}x + 2\beta_{22}x^2}{1 + \beta_{21}x + \beta_{22}x^2}. \tag{6.54}$$

As expected, the total binding curve is weighted by the proportions of the monomer and the dimer. This result can in general be written in terms of the separate binding polynomials P_1 and P_2, and their x derivatives P'_1 and P'_2, as

$$\bar{n}_X^F = \frac{[M_0]}{m_0} \frac{P'_1 x}{P_1} + \frac{[D_0]}{m_0} \frac{P'_2 x}{P_2}, \tag{6.55}$$

which may also be written as

$$\bar{n}_X^F = \frac{1}{m_0} \frac{\partial \ln (P_1^{[M_0]})}{\partial \ln x} + \frac{1}{m_0} \frac{\partial \ln (P_2^{[D_0]})}{\partial \ln x}. \tag{6.56}$$

Thus the partition function for the frozen case normalized to the total moles of   subunits gives the binding polynomial

$$P^F = P_1^{[M_0]/m_0} P_2^{[D_0]/m_0}. \tag{6.57}$$

When the argument of the logarithm is expanded, the lead term is 1; if we use the notation of Section 3.4 the highest-power term gives $\beta_1 x$. For the dimer example we have

$$\beta_1 x = (\beta_{11}x)^{[M_0]/m_0}(\beta_{22}x^2)^{[D_0]/m_0} \tag{6.58}$$

or

$$\beta_1 = \beta_{11}^{[M_0]/m_0} \beta_{22}^{2[D_0]/m_0} = \frac{1}{x_m^F}. \tag{6.59}$$

Thus we obtain the expression for the median of the frozen situation:

$$\ln x_m^F = -\frac{[M_0]}{m_0} \ln \beta_{11} - \frac{2[D_0]}{m_0} \ln \beta_{22}, \tag{6.60}$$

where $[D_0] = L_{20}[M_0]^2$ and $[M_0]$ is evaluated from (6.45). The binding curve for a frozen situation is contrasted with the free situation in Figure 6-10.

The free-energy difference between the free [see equation (6.38)] and the frozen (6.60) situation is given by $RT \ln (x_m^F/x_m)$. The free energy of saturating the frozen system is always greater than for the freely responding system (Wyman, 1967). An example of plots of $\log x_m$ for the free and frozen cases is shown in Figure 6-11.

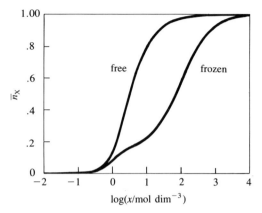

Figure 6-10.
Free and frozen binding curves for monomer-dimer case with equilibrium constants given in Figure 6-6 and $m_0 = 0.001$ M.

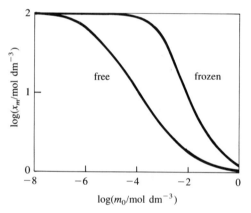

Figure 6-11.
Logarithm of medians x_m for free and frozen cases of monomer-dimer aggregation with constants of Figure 6-6. The difference in free energy of saturation at a given concentration is represented by the separation between the two curves.

We have illustrated the formulation of binding curves and their partition functions in terms of the simple monomer-dimer situation. However, it is apparent how this extends to many more complex sets of equilibria involving single monomer species. We can either (1) write the appropriate reactions to form a given complex species C from the monomer and X-ligand species, express C in terms of the equilibrium constant of the reaction, and collect all species written this way to give the partition function, or (2) write the unligated equilibria, multiply the unligated species by their specific ligand-binding polynomials, and collect the sum of all terms to arrive at the partition function. The second procedure is equivalent to what has been used in preceding chapters in assessing the effects of several ligands and allosteric forms.

6.6 AGGREGATION WITH DIFFERENT SUBUNITS: HEMOGLOBIN

So far we have dealt with aggregates composed of the same subunit monomer. Many biological complexes are composed of different monomeric subunits, for example, hemoglobin and ATCase. We wish to formulate the partition function and derive the binding curve for such complexes. In this section we shall illustrate these ideas specifically for hemoglobin, which is known to dissociate to identical dimers and dissimilar monomers (individual α and β chains). Important aspects of this general problem have been dealt with by Ackers and colleagues (e.g., Ackers and Halvorson, 1974; Mills *et al.*, 1976; Ip and Ackers, 1977).

We shall begin with the simplest system, a dimer formed from two different monomers, α and β. The possible equilibria along with specified equilibrium constants can be represented as

$$
\begin{array}{ccccc}
\alpha & + & \beta & \xrightarrow{\;L_{20}\;} & \alpha\beta \\[2mm]
\Big\downarrow{\scriptstyle \beta_\alpha} & & \Big\downarrow{\scriptstyle \beta_\beta} & & \Big\downarrow{\scriptstyle \beta_{21}} \\[2mm]
 & & & & \alpha\beta X \quad\Big] \beta_{22}. \\[2mm]
 & & & & \Big\downarrow \\[2mm]
\alpha X & + & \beta X & \longrightarrow & \alpha\beta X_2
\end{array}
\tag{6.61}
$$

If the concentrations of the unligated monomers α and β are denoted by $[M_\alpha]$ and $[M_\beta]$, we can express all species concentrations in terms of these. When added together, they give the aggregation partition function:

$$
Q = [M_\alpha] + [M_\beta] + \beta_\alpha[M_\alpha]x + \beta_\beta[M_\beta]x + L_{20}[M_\alpha][M_\beta]
$$
$$
+ L_{20}\beta_{21}[M_\alpha][M_\beta]x + L_{20}\beta_{22}[M_\alpha][M_\beta]x^2
\tag{6.62}
$$

or

$$
Q = [M_\alpha](1 + \beta_\alpha x) + [M_\beta](1 + \beta_\beta x) + L_{20}[M_\alpha][M_\beta](1 + \beta_{21}x + \beta_{22}x^2).
\tag{6.63}
$$

The ratio of sites filled to moles of binding sites is $\bar{n}_X$, and is written as

$$
\bar{n}_X = \frac{\beta_\alpha[M_\alpha]x + \beta_\beta[M_\beta]x + L_{20}\beta_{21}[M_\alpha][M_\beta]x + 2L_{20}\beta_{22}[M_\alpha][M_\beta]x^2}{[M_\alpha] + [M_\beta] + \beta_\alpha[M_\alpha]x + \beta_\beta[M_\beta]x + 2L_{20}[M_\alpha][M_\beta] + \\ 2L_{20}\beta_{21}[M_\alpha][M_\beta]x + 2L_{20}\beta_{22}[M_\alpha][M_\beta]x^2}.
\tag{6.64}
$$

This result is also obtained from the procedure used previously to obtain the total number of sites filled. By dividing $\partial Q/\partial \ln x$ by the total number of sites, $m_0 = m_{0\alpha} + m_{0\beta} = (\partial Q/\partial \ln [M_\alpha]) + (\partial Q/\partial \ln [M_\beta])$:

$$\bar{n}_X = \frac{\dfrac{\partial Q}{\partial \ln x}}{\dfrac{\partial Q}{\partial \ln [M_\alpha]} + \dfrac{\partial Q}{\partial \ln [M_\beta]}} = \frac{\dfrac{\partial Q}{\partial \ln x}}{m_{0\alpha} + m_{0\beta}}. \tag{6.65}$$

The areas beneath such binding curves may be evaluated by means of the procedure given by (6.27) to (6.31), extended now to include the variables $[M_\alpha]$ and $[M_\beta]$, to yield

$$A_u = \frac{1}{m_0}(Q - Q_0) - \frac{m_{0\alpha}}{m_0}\ln\frac{[M_\alpha]}{[M_{\alpha 0}]} - \frac{m_{0\beta}}{m_0}\ln\frac{[M_\beta]}{[M_{\beta 0}]}, \tag{6.66}$$

where Q, $[M_{\alpha 0}]$, and $[M_{\beta 0}]$ apply in the limit as $x \to 0$. The area above the binding curve as defined by (6.32) is given by

$$A_a = \ln\frac{x_\infty}{x} - \frac{1}{m_0}(Q_\infty - Q) + \frac{m_{0\alpha}}{m_0}\ln\frac{[M_{\alpha\infty}]}{[M_\alpha]} + \frac{m_{0\beta}}{m_0}\ln\frac{[M_{\beta\infty}]}{[M_\beta]}, \tag{6.67}$$

where Q_∞, $[M_{\alpha\infty}]$, and $[M_{\beta\infty}]$ apply in the limit as $x \to \infty$ denoted by x_∞. The median value of x, x_m, is found by equating A_u to A_a:

$$\ln x_m = \frac{1}{m_0}(Q_0 - Q_\infty) + \frac{m_{0\alpha}}{m_0}\ln\frac{[M_{\alpha\infty}]x_\infty}{[M_{\alpha 0}]} + \frac{m_{0\beta}}{m_0}\ln\frac{[M_{\beta\infty}]x_\infty}{[M_{\beta 0}]}. \tag{6.68}$$

The evaluation of $[Q]$, $[M_\alpha]$, and $[M_\beta]$ under the limiting conditions of $x = 0$ and $x \to \infty$ leads to various complicated expressions that depend on the total concentrations of α and β subunits. These can be worked out by using mass-balance conditions similar to those used for the identical-subunit dimers [equations (6.41) to (6.49)]. Briefly,

$$m_{0\alpha} = [M_\alpha]P_\alpha + L_{20}[M_\alpha][M_\beta]P_{\alpha\beta}, \tag{6.69}$$

$$m_{0\beta} = [M_\beta]P_\beta + L_{20}[M_\alpha][M_\beta]P_{\alpha\beta}, \tag{6.70}$$

where P_α, P_β, and $P_{\alpha\beta}$ are the X-binding polynomials to α, β, and $\alpha\beta$. Solving these expressions leads to

$$[M_\alpha] = \frac{(m_{0\beta} - m_{0\alpha}) \pm [(m_{0\beta} - m_{0\alpha})^2 + 4m_{0\alpha}L_{20}P_\alpha P_\beta/P_{\alpha\beta}]^{1/2}}{2P_\alpha} \tag{6.71}$$

and

$$[M_\beta] = \frac{(m_{0\beta} - m_{0\alpha}) \pm [(m_{0\beta} - m_{0\alpha})^2 + 4m_{0\beta}L_{20}P_\alpha P_\beta/P_{\alpha\beta}]^{1/2}}{2P_\beta}. \quad (6.72)$$

Insertion of these equations into (6.64) gives the expression of the binding curve, $\bar{n}_X$. Evaluation under limiting conditions of X ligand concentration provides the terms needed to evaluate the median by (6.68).

In hemoglobin the aggregation to the $\alpha\beta$ dimer continues and forms the $\alpha_2\beta_2$ tetramer, which is the cooperative functional unit. We thus have the general reaction scheme (without writing the X-bound species, as described by vertical columns with binding polynomials P_α, P_β, $P_{\alpha\beta}$, and $P_{\alpha_2\beta_2}$):

$$\begin{array}{c} \xrightarrow{\quad L_{41} \quad} \\ 2\alpha + 2\beta \xrightarrow{\ L_{21}{}^2\ } 2\alpha\beta \xrightarrow{\ L_{42}\ } \alpha_2\beta_2 \end{array} \quad (6.73)$$

Then the aggregation function is given by

$$Q = \lfloor M_\alpha \rfloor P_\alpha + [M_\beta]P_\beta + [M_\alpha][M_\beta]L_{21}P_{\alpha\beta} + [M_\alpha]^2[M_\beta]^2 L_{41}P_{\alpha_2\beta_2}, \quad (6.74)$$

where

$$P_\alpha = 1 + \beta_\alpha x, \quad (6.75)$$

$$P_\beta = 1 + \beta_\beta x, \quad (6.76)$$

$$P_{\alpha\beta} = 1 + \beta_{21}x + \beta_{22}x^2, \quad (6.77)$$

$$P_{\alpha_2\beta_2} = 1 + \beta_{41}x + \beta_{42}x^2 + \beta_{43}x^3 + \beta_{44}x^4. \quad (6.78)$$

The binding curve is described by the operational expression

$$\bar{n}_X = \frac{\dfrac{\partial Q}{\partial \ln x}}{m_{0\alpha} + m_{0\beta}}. \quad (6.79)$$

There are ten binding constants along with two mass-balance equations ($m_{0\alpha}$ and $m_{0\beta}$), which are needed to specify the binding curves. If β_α and β_β are equal, and the $\alpha\beta$ dimer is assumed to function noncooperatively with the same α or β intrinsic constant, then seven binding constants are needed to specify the system. If the monomer concentrations $[M_\alpha]$ and $[M_\beta]$ are negligible compared to that of the $\alpha\beta$ dimer, then the first two terms of equation (6.74) are absent, and the $\alpha\beta$ dimer concentration, $[M_{\alpha\beta}] = L_{21}[M_\alpha][M_\beta]$, allows us to write the dimer partition function Q_D in terms of two-site dimer concentration:

$$Q_D = [M_{\alpha\beta}]P_{\alpha\beta} + \frac{L_{41}}{L_{21}^2}[M_{\alpha\beta}]^2 P_{\alpha_2\beta_2}. \tag{6.80}$$

From (6.73) $L_{42} = L_{41}/L_{21}^2$, i.e., the dimer to tetramer equilibrium constant. Since the dimer is the reference form in this equation, the binding curve (moles X bound/mole reaction site) is

$$\bar{n}_X = \frac{\dfrac{\partial Q_D}{\partial \ln x}}{2\dfrac{\partial Q}{\partial \ln [M_{\alpha\beta}]}} = \frac{\dfrac{\partial Q_D}{\partial \ln x}}{m_0}, \tag{6.81}$$

where m_0 is the moles of subunits. The result of these calculations is summarized as

$$\bar{n}_X = \frac{[M_{\alpha\beta}]P'_{\alpha\beta}x + L_{42}[M_{\alpha\beta}]^2 P'_{\alpha_2\beta_2}x}{[M_{\alpha\beta}]P_{\alpha\beta} + 2L_{42}[M_{\alpha\beta}]^2 P_{\alpha_2\beta_2}} \tag{6.82}$$

and

$$m_0 = 2\{[M_{\alpha\beta}]P_{\alpha\beta} + 2L_{42}[M_{\alpha\beta}]^2 P_{\alpha_2\beta_2}\}, \tag{6.83}$$

where $P'_{\alpha\beta}$ and $P'_{\alpha_2\beta_2}$ denote derivatives with respect to x. Thus

$$[M_{\alpha\beta}] = \frac{-P_{\alpha\beta} + \sqrt{P_{\alpha\beta}^2 + 4L_{42}m_0 P_{\alpha_2\beta_2}}}{4L_{42}P_{\alpha_2\beta_2}}. \tag{6.84}$$

This situation requires specification of L_{42}, β_{21}, β_{22}, and β_{41}, β_{42}, β_{43}, and β_{44}, i.e., seven parameters. If the dimer consists of identical noncooperative binding sites, then β_{21} and β_{22} may be expressed by a single constant, and only six parameters are required. Ackers and Halvorson (1974) have formulated this same result from a somewhat different approach. High-precision studies of both oxygen-binding curves (Mills *et al.*, 1976) and dimer-tetramer association constants (Ip *et al.*, 1976; Ip and Ackers, 1977) have been carried out for HbA and Hb Kansas (Atha *et al.*, 1979). They found that the $\alpha\beta$ dimer binding to oxygen was described by identical and independent binding sites to HbA but not to Hb Kansas. Their results have been used to evaluate the specified parameters at 21.5°C in Table 6.1. The reaction scheme that defines the intrinsic free-energy changes for the oxygen binding and dimerization

Table 6.1

Hemoglobin-dimer-tetramer oxygen-binding constants (Johnson and Ackers, 1982)

Equilibrium constant	Hemoglobin A	Hemoglobin Kansas
$L_{42} = \exp\left(-\dfrac{^{o}\Delta G_2}{RT}\right)$	4.6×10^{10} M^{-1}	1.3×10^{10} M^{-1}
$\beta_{21} = 2\exp\left(-\dfrac{\Delta G_{21}}{RT}\right)$	3.3×10^{6} M^{-1}	3.4×10^{6} M^{-1}
$\beta_{22} = \exp\left[\dfrac{-(\Delta G_{21} + \Delta G_{22})}{RT}\right]$	2.7×10^{12} M^{-2}	4.7×10^{11} M^{-2}
$\beta_{41} = 4\exp\left(-\dfrac{\Delta G_{41}}{RT}\right)$	4.4×10^{4} M^{-1}	8.1×10^{4} M^{-1}
$\beta_{42} = 6\exp\left[\dfrac{-(\Delta G_{41} + \Delta G_{42})}{RT}\right]$	5.4×10^{8} M^{-2}	1.3×10^{9} M^{-2}
$\beta_{43} = 4\exp\left[\dfrac{-(\Delta G_{41} + \Delta G_{42} + \Delta G_{43})}{RT}\right]$	2.2×10^{14} M^{-3}	1.2×10^{13} M^{-3}
$\beta_{44} = \exp\left[\dfrac{-(\Delta G_{41} + \Delta G_{42} + \Delta G_{43} + \Delta G_{44})}{RT}\right]$	1.4×10^{20} M^{-4}	1.5×10^{13} M^{-4}

Intrinsic free-energy change[a]	Statistical term	HbA	Hb Kansas
ΔG_2	$RT \ln 1$	-14.38 kcal/mole	-13.63 kcal/mole
ΔG_{21}	$RT \ln 2$	-8.38	-8.40
ΔG_{22}	$RT \ln 1/2$	-8.38	-7.34
ΔG_{41}	$RT \ln 4$	-5.45	-5.81
ΔG_{42}	$RT \ln 3/2$	-5.28	-5.41
ΔG_{43}	$RT \ln 2/3$	-7.80	-5.59
ΔG_{44}	$RT \ln 1/4$	-8.65	-6.36

[a] The intrinsic free-energy change is obtained by subtraction of the statistical term from the measured macroscopic free-energy change.

processes is shown in Figure 6-12. We have used these constants to generate binding curves to hemoglobin A as a function of total monomer concentration m_0 as illustrated in Figure 6-13. As seen by these figures the cooperativity increases with concentration. The binding curves are asymmetric except at extreme concentrations, where either the dimer form dominates or the tetramer functions with close symmetry.

Ackers has designated the difference in oxygen-binding free energy between the tetramer and dimer forms as the total "regulatory energy" which is gained

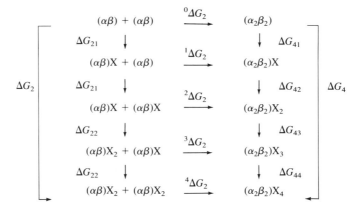

Figure 6-12.
Reaction scheme for dimer $(\alpha\beta)$ tetramer $(\alpha_2\beta_2)$ formation involving various forms of x-ligated species. Free energy changes associated with various reactions are denoted beside reaction process arrows.

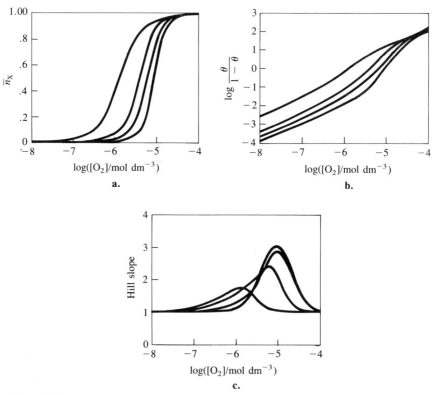

Figure 6-13.
Binding curves for HbA as a function of oxygen concentration (10^{-9}, 10^{-7}, 10^{-5}, and 10^{-3} M heme, left to right): (a) normal binding curve; (b) Hill plot; (c) Hill slope of pO_2. Reaction parameters taken from Johnson and Ackers (1982).

in the native tetramer. This difference, $\Delta G_4 - \Delta G_2$, in the preceding scheme is equivalent to the difference in association energy of the ligated and unligated dimer forms, $^4\Delta G_2 - {}^0\Delta G_2$. Experimentally these later terms can be evaluated by careful chromatographic measurements. The regulatory energy of HbA is 6.3 kcal, whereas mutants with substituted amino acids in the critical region of the $\alpha_1\beta_2$ contact show a significant loss in regulatory energy. Mutants with changes located external to the $\alpha_1\beta_2$ interface show similar regulatory free energy as HbA. This has led Ackers and his colleagues to the conclusion that the $\alpha_1\beta_2$ interface is the principal location of the energy changes that determine cooperativity in oxygen binding to hemoglobin (Pettigrew *et al.*, 1982). A detailed review is given by Ackers and Smith (1987).

6.7   LARGE AGGREGATION PROCESSES

The formation of microtubules or large polymerized filaments seen in sickle-cell hemoglobin aggregates must be very complicated. But the essence of such a process can be explored by considering the simple formation of an *n*-mer aggregate from monomers:

$$nM \xrightarrow{\; L_n \;} M_n. \tag{6.85}$$

Each species has an appropriate X-binding polynomial P_1 and P_n, and the aggregation partition function is given as

$$Q = [M]P_1 + L_n[M]^nP_n. \tag{6.86}$$

The binding curve expressed in terms of total subunit concentration is then obtained as

$$\bar{n}_X = \frac{\dfrac{\partial Q}{\partial \ln x}}{\dfrac{\partial Q}{\partial \ln [M]}} = \frac{[M]P_1'x + L_n[M]^nP_n'x}{m_0}, \tag{6.87}$$

where P_1' and P_n' are the x derivatives of P_1 and P_n, and m_0 is the total monomer concentration, given as

$$m_0 = [M]P_1 + nL_n[M]^nP_n. \tag{6.88}$$

To illustrate some of the features of this type of system, we consider the noncooperative binding polynomials

$$P_1 = (1 + \kappa_1 x), \tag{6.89}$$

$$P_n = (1 + \kappa_n x)^n, \tag{6.90}$$

where κ_1 and κ_n are the intrinsic binding constants of X to monomeric and aggregate forms. In order to generate comparable binding curves, we choose L_n such that at the unit concentration of total monomer, half are $[M]$ and half are $n[M_n]$. This means that $L_n = (1/n)(1/2)^{1-n}$. Binding curves are generated for different values of n, setting $\kappa_1 = 1$, $\kappa_n = 0.1$, and $m_0 = 10$ in Figure 6-14. Note how a sudden change in Hill slope can occur with large aggregate sizes. Such a phenomenon is similar to that encountered in sickle-cell hemoglobin at a critical value of oxygen-ligand concentration (see Figure 1-7).

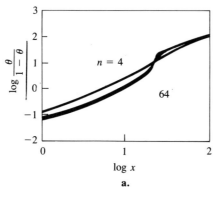

a.

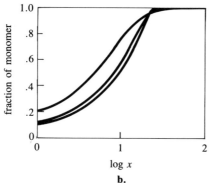

b.

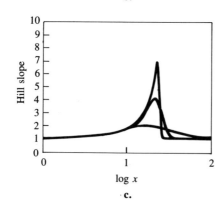

c.

Figure 6-14.
Binding curves of n-mer aggregation as a function of aggregation state ($n = 4, 16, 64$), monomer concentration 10, aggregate X binding constant 0.01 and monomer X binding constant 1: (a) Hill plot; (b) monomer fraction plot; (c) Hill slope plot.

6.8   WATER ACTIVITY AND HETEROTROPIC LINKAGE IN AGGREGATING SYSTEMS

In a broad sense, the linkage between a ligand X and the state of aggregation is equivalent to linkage between ligand X activity and solvent water activity. The water activity a_w for a macromolecular system may be calculated from osmotic pressure, sedimentation equilibrium, or light-scattering experiments. For osmotic pressure (π), the relation is

$$\pi = -\frac{RT}{\bar{V}_1^o} \ln a_w, \tag{6.91}$$

where $\bar{V}_1^o$ is the molar volume of water. In ideal solutions a_w is the mole fraction of the solvent, and in dilute solutions is given approximately by $1 - (n_2/n_w)$, where n_2 and n_w are the moles of all macromolecular species and water, respectively. Under these conditions, the concentration of macromolecular species is given by the partition function aggregation Q. We may put these ideas together by the expression $n_2/(n_w \bar{V}_1^o) = Q$. In a dilute solution there is a simple result relating water activity and the partition function by

$$a_w = 1 - Q\bar{V}_1^o. \tag{6.92}$$

From equation (6.91) we see that the determination of osmotic pressure permits a direct evaluation of Q in terms of the total macromolecular species, but does not give any details about their populations. This all assumes that the solution is sufficiently dilute that we can neglect activity-coefficient effects.

The prescription for formulating Q in terms of variables that describe the state of the system is given as follows:

(1) We have already shown how to develop Q in terms of mass-action laws between the unligated monomer concentration $[M]$ and the ligand activity x, i.e., $Q([M], x)$.

(2) By introduction of the mass balance, we may express $[M]$ in terms of m_0 and x, and the partition function is then described by $Q(m_0, x)$.

(3) $Q(a_w, x)$ employs (6.92) in relating Q to a_w, which is regulated by x.

As we have seen, the binding curve, $\bar{n}_X$, is derived directly from the partial derivative of $Q([M], x)$. We may then consider $\bar{n}_X$ a function of any two of x, or $[M]$, or a_w, or m_0. This leads to the homotropic derivatives of the binding curve, such as

$$\left(\frac{\partial \bar{n}_X}{\partial \ln x}\right)_{[M]}, \left(\frac{\partial \bar{n}_X}{\partial \ln x}\right)_{a_w}, \left(\frac{\partial \bar{n}_X}{\partial \ln x}\right)_{m_0}, \tag{6.93}$$

which express the homotropic cooperativity of the system under various choices of fixed conditions. Some of these are difficult to realize in practical situations. The left derivative of (6.93) requires holding $[M]$ constant, i.e., holding the unligated monomer constant, as X binding proceeds. Perhaps some type of phase equilibrium with a pure unliganded monomer phase would accomplish this, but in general it would be hard to achieve. The second derivative, at constant water activity, is equivalent to holding the osmotic pressure of the system constant as X binding is changed. This is certainly possible, but difficult, to do by an osmometer in which we could concentrate or dilute the solution of macromolecules to keep the osmotic pressure at a fixed value. The third derivative is by far the most practical, since the constraint is to hold the total concentration of macromolecule fixed as the amount of X binding is changed. This would represent the usual way in which binding data are measured.

The homotropic cooperative properties of ligand binding are reflected in the derivatives (6.93), but the heterotropic properties are revealed by derivatives such as

$$\left(\frac{\partial \bar{n}_X}{\partial \ln [M]}\right)_x, \left(\frac{\partial \bar{n}_X}{\partial \ln a_w}\right)_x, \left(\frac{\partial \bar{n}_X}{\partial m_0}\right)_x. \tag{6.94}$$

These represent the displacement of the binding curves with change in concentration of the macromolecule in the system. Of course, if there is no concentration effect on the binding curve, then such heterotropic linkage is absent.

6.9   THE MACROMOLECULAR CHEMICAL POTENTIAL

A particularly useful way of describing the underlying properties of complex aggregating systems with ligand binding is to use the chemical potential of the unligated macromolecular species, M_i, consisting of i subunits (Schellman, 1975; Gill, 1981; Benedict et al., 1981a). The macromolecular chemical potential is given for an ideal solution by

$$\mu_{M_i} = \mu_{M_i}^{\,o} + RT \ln [M_i], \tag{6.95}$$

where $[M_i]$ is the unliganded concentration of the i-mer macromolecule. Nonideal solution effects require the introduction of activity coefficients into (6.95). The concentration of the unligated macromolecule $[M_i]$ is related to the total macromolecular concentration of the ith species $[M_i]_T$ by the binding polynomial for that species P_i by

$$[M_i]_T = [M_i] P_i. \tag{6.96}$$

Thus the macromolecular chemical potential may be written as

$$\mu_{M_i} = \mu_{M_i}^{\,o} + RT \ln [M_i]_T - RT \ln P_i, \tag{6.97}$$

which is the form given by Schellman (1975).

We may then derive the general linkage rules for aggregating systems by recognizing that the stoichiometrically weighted sum of the chemical potentials of product minus reactants is equal to zero at equilibrium. For the general reaction

$$aA + bB \rightarrow cC, \tag{6.98}$$

or

$$c\mu_C - a\mu_A - b\mu_B = 0, \tag{6.99}$$

and with (6.97),

$$-(c\mu_C^\circ - a\mu_A^\circ - b\mu_B^\circ) = RT \ln \frac{[M_C]_T^c}{[M_A]_T^a[M_B]_T^b} - RT \ln \frac{P_C^c}{P_A^a P_B^b}. \tag{6.100}$$

The first term of standard-state chemical potentials gives $RT \ln K_0$, K_0 being the equilibrium constant of the unliganded species. The second term contains the ratio of total concentrations designated by K. Introducing these terms gives

$$RT \ln K_0 = RT \ln K - RT \ln \frac{P_C^c}{P_A^a P_B^b}, \tag{6.101}$$

or finally

$$K = K_0 \frac{P_C^c}{P_A^a P_B^b}. \tag{6.102}$$

For binding a single ligand X, we see that this is the same result as equation (6.14).

The macromolecular potential is of special use in providing a quantitative basis for equilibria between different phases. In the following chapter we consider such phenomena in detail.

Tanford (1969) has used a formulation of this type to consider the effects of water activity on the association of macromolecules.

6.10   ENTHALPY CHANGES AND EFFECTS OF TEMPERATURE

We have shown in Chapter 5 how the macromolecular enthalpy of a nondissociating macromolecule, $\bar{H} - \bar{H}_0$, may be evaluated by differentiation of the partition function with respect to temperature. The same ideas carry over to aggregating or dissociating systems with the recognition that the enthalpy is expressed per mole of subunit. Here we consider a few examples to illustrate the general idea.

Simple dimerization yields the partition function given by equation (6.20). The reference state is the unligated monomer, and the temperature dependence of the equilibrium constants will be determined by simple van't Hoff factors if the heat-capacity changes are neglected (or included if important). Thus, the temperature, ligand activity, and subunit concentration dependence of the partition function would appear as

$$
Q = [M]\left\{1 + \beta_{11}{}^{\circ}x \exp\left[-\frac{\Delta H_{11}{}^{\circ}}{R}\left(\frac{1}{T} - \frac{1}{T_0}\right)\right]\right\}
$$

$$
+ [M]^2 L_{20}{}^{\circ}\exp\left[-\frac{\Delta H_{20}{}^{\circ}}{R}\left(\frac{1}{T} - \frac{1}{T_0}\right)\right]
$$

$$
\times \left\{1 + \beta_{21}{}^{\circ}x \exp\left[-\frac{\Delta H_{21}{}^{\circ}}{R}\left(\frac{1}{T} - \frac{1}{T_0}\right)\right] + \beta_{22}{}^{\circ}x^2 \exp\left[-\frac{\Delta H_{22}{}^{\circ}}{R}\left(\frac{1}{T} - \frac{1}{T_0}\right)\right]\right\},
$$

$$(6.103)$$

where the standard enthalpy changes $\Delta H_{ij}{}^{\circ}$ correspond to the appropriate reaction processes, and the zero-superscripted equilibrium constants indicate values taken at reference-state temperature T_0. The relative enthalpy per mole of subunit is

$$
\bar{H} - \bar{H}_{00} = \frac{-R}{m_0}\frac{\partial Q}{\partial(1/T)}, \qquad (6.104)
$$

where

$$
m_0 = \frac{\partial Q}{\partial \ln[M]}
$$

as noted before. When (6.104) is applied to the dimerization expression, we find

$$
\bar{H} - \bar{H}_{00} = \frac{1}{m_0}\{[M]\Delta H_{11}{}^{\circ}\beta_{11}x + [M]^2\Delta H_{20}{}^{\circ}L_{20}(1 + \beta_{21}x + \beta_{22}x^2)
$$

$$
+ [M]^2 L_{20}(\Delta H_{21}{}^{\circ}\beta_{21}x + \Delta H_{22}{}^{\circ}\beta_{22}x^2)\}, \qquad (6.105)
$$

with m_0 given by equation (6.22), and we recognize that the various equilibrium constants without zero superscripts are actually functions of temperature implied here and written out fully in equation (6.103). The specific value of $[M]$ at any given temperature and activity of x is found by solving the conservation-of-mass equation (6.22) at a given subunit concentration m_0.

In a titration calorimetric experiment where we start with the unligated system and add ligand X, the reference enthalpy state $(\bar{H}_0, x = 0)$ is found by letting $x = 0$:

$$\bar{H}_0 - \bar{H}_{00} = \frac{1}{m_0}\{[M_0]^2 \Delta H_{20}{}^{\circ} L_{20}\},\qquad(6.106)$$

and $\bar{H} - \bar{H}_0$ is then given by (6.105) by subtraction of this term. Calorimetric titration curves on such systems are more easily described if there are concurrent measurements of X-ligand activity. If only the amount of X ligand added to the system is known (as is often the case), then a mass-balance expression for free (i.e., x) and bound X using equation (6.21) must be solved at each point during the titration. This procedure greatly increases the sensitivity of the equations to experimental errors.

Another simple calorimetric experiment is to measure the heat of dilution of the macromolecular solution. Solvent (buffer) is added to the biopolymer solution. The moles of subunits (n_2) are assumed fixed, and are calculated from the volume V and the subunit concentration m_0; i.e., $n_2 = m_0 V$. The volume increases with the addition of solvent, from an initial value V' to a value of V''. The heat q is then

$$q = n_2(\bar{H}'' - \bar{H}'),\qquad(6.107)$$

where $\bar{H}''$ and $\bar{H}'$ are given by equation (6.105) with $m''_0 = n_2/V''$ and $m'_0 = n_2/V'$, respectively. Studies of this type can, in principle, measure the enthalpy of dissociation of the dimer to monomer in unligated or fully ligated states.

Temperature-scanning calorimetric experiments offer an alternative method for characterizing the enthalpy changes in associating systems. Briefly, consider an aggregate (M_n) of n subunits in equilibrium with monomers in either of two conformations, folded (M) or unfolded (U). This corresponds to the situation of thermal denaturation of many multi-subunit proteins. We assume here for simplicity that the heats of ligand binding to the various macromolecular forms may be neglected compared to the enthalpy changes of aggregation or denaturation. The reaction scheme is

$$nM \xrightarrow{\ L_n\ } M_n \qquad(6.108)$$
$$\Big\downarrow {\scriptstyle (L_U)^n}$$
$$nU$$

The partition function is expressed as

$$Q = [M]P_M + [M]L_U P_U + [M]^n L_n P_n,\qquad(6.109)$$

where P_M, P_U, and P_n are the ligand-binding polynomials to the native subunit, denatured subunit, and native aggregate. The total monomer concentration,

m_0, is

$$m_0 = [M]P_M + [M]L_U P_U + n[M]^n L_n P_n. \qquad (6.110)$$

The enthalpy of the system relative to the pure monomer is found by applying (6.104).

$$\bar{H} - \bar{H}_0 = \frac{[M]L_U P_U \Delta H_U^o + [M]^n L_n P_n \Delta H_{n1}^o}{m_0}, \qquad (6.111)$$

where ΔH_U^o and ΔH_{n1}^o are the enthalpy changes for the denaturation (per monomer) and aggregation steps. Note that $[M]$ is given by the solution of equation (6.110) at each temperature, with m_0 and the binding polynomials held at fixed values.

The heat-capacity change referred to the native monomer state is given by the temperature derivative of equation (6.111):

$$\bar{C} - \bar{C}_0 = \frac{[M]L_U P_U \dfrac{\Delta H_U^o}{RT^2} \Delta H_U^o + [M]^n L_n P_n \dfrac{\Delta H_{n1}}{RT^2} \Delta H_{n1}^o}{m_0}$$

$$+ \frac{\dfrac{\partial[M]}{\partial T} L_U P_U \Delta H_U^o + \dfrac{\partial[M]}{\partial T} n[M]^{n-1} L_n P_n \Delta H_{n1}^o}{m_0}. \qquad (6.112)$$

The derivative $\partial[M]/\partial T$ must be evaluated from a temperature differentiation of equation (6.110):

$$0 = \frac{\partial[M]}{\partial T} P_M + \frac{\partial[M]}{\partial T} L_U P_U + [M]\frac{L_U P_U \Delta H_U^o}{RT^2}$$

$$+ n^2[M]^{n-1} \frac{\partial[M]}{\partial T} L_n P_n + n[M]^n \frac{L_n P_n \Delta H_{n1}^o}{RT^2}$$

or

$$\frac{\partial[M]}{\partial T} = -\frac{[M]\dfrac{L_U P_U \Delta H_U^o}{RT^2} + n[M]^n \dfrac{L_n P_n \Delta H_{n1}^o}{RT^2}}{P_M + L_U P_U + n^2[M]^{n-1} L_n P_n}. \qquad (6.113)$$

The excess heat capacity as a function of temperature and concentration will, in general, be a complicated curve. If the aggregate is simply a dimer, the solution of (6.110) will be a quadratic expression, and a closed form for either $\bar{H} - \bar{H}_0$ or $\bar{C} - \bar{C}_0$ can be written.

For the purposes of thermal scanning experiments, having to refer to the pure monomer properties is not very useful. The *excess heat capacity* is the appropriate quantity, defined as the heat capacity in excess of the heat capacity of the native state. In arriving at this quantity experimentally, the properties of the native state are extrapolated phenomenologically underneath the denaturational transition region. In order to express the excess heat capacity, we must thus first subtract from the average enthalpy expression [equation (6.111)] the average enthalpy of the native-state species alone. The average enthalpy of the native state, itself relative to that of the pure monomer, is obtained by first writing the partition function for the native state, or, for the present example,

$$Q_{\text{Native}} = [M]P_M + [M]^n L_n P_n. \tag{6.114}$$

The average enthalpy of the native-state species, relative to that of the monomer species, is obtained by differentiation as in equation (6.111), except that the denominator must be the total subunit concentration of the native species alone instead of m_0 (all species). Subtraction of this quantity from the total enthalpy cancels the monomer properties, and we are left with $\bar{H} - \bar{H}_{\text{Native}}$. From the temperature derivative of this we obtain the excess heat capacity. In Figure 6-15 we show the excess heat capacity as a function of temperature for an aggregating system with $n = 4$, assuming no change in enthalpy upon aggregation. The asymmetry evident in this plot is similar to that actually seen for the core protein of the tetrameric lac repressor (Manly et al., 1985).

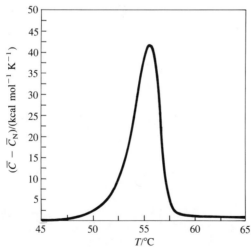

Figure 6-15.
Excess heat capacity as a function of temperature for an aggregating system ($n = 4$) undergoing thermal denaturation. The reaction parameters used were as follows: $L_4 = 10^{+12}$ and $\Delta H = 0$ for the process $4\,M \rightarrow M_4$; $M \rightarrow D$ has $T_m = 50°\text{C}$, $\Delta H_D = 136$ kcal/mol, and $\Delta C_p = 1.0$ kcal/deg-mol; subunit concentration = 10^{-4} M.

6.11 SUMMARY

Comparison of the analysis developed in this chapter with that of the preceding chapters shows that the basic difference between aggregating and simple allosteric systems lies in the concentration dependence of aggregating systems. This is a direct consequence of the application of the mass law where the number of reaction species changes in the reaction; otherwise everything remains basically the same. The aggregation partition function can be formulated as a sum of species concentrations. The heat or volume change of binding can be deduced. The detailed results are more complex because of the general concentration dependence, but the principles are the same as in nondissociating systems. In a broad sense, linkage in aggregating systems brings the activity of the solvent water into play in a direct way that is not present in nondissociating systems. But it all comes back to the mass law that determines the distribution of species under various conditions.

Ligand Linkage Between 7
Macromolecular Phases

The control of aggregation processes by ligands has been developed in detailed theoretical terms in the preceding chapter. The biological relevance of such phenomena in the formation of large macromolecular structures, such as viruses, nucleosomes, and microtubules, is apparent. In such structures, the aggregated molecules are considered to remain soluble; i.e., only a single solution phase is involved in the description of the ligand-linked processes. When the extent of aggregation is sufficiently large, a new phase, usually as a solid gel phase, occurs. This phase exists in equilibrium with a solution of dissolved macromolecules. For example, within cells called cyanoblasts, which produce hemocyanin in *Limulus polyphemus*, Fahrenbach (1970) has observed the formation of extensive crystalline arrays as shown in Figure 7-1. These cells produce hemocyanin molecules, which consist of many protein subunits (MW about two million) with oxygen-containing binding sites. They form crystals that continue to grow until the cell is virtually filled with crystals in contact with a small amount of solution. Rupture of the cell disperses the hemocyanin crystals, which then dissolve rather slowly into the blood of the animal.

The formation of microcrystalline arrays of sickle-cell hemoglobin is the classic example of how a ligand (in this case, oxygen) can control the formation of a solid phase. The removal of oxygen from the hemoglobin converts the macromolecule to a shape in which extensive aggregation occurs. The first large structures that appear are twisted cylinders made of the HbS tetramers (Figure 7-2). These tubes with protein walls interact to form larger arrays of a "solid" phase, as indicated in Figure 7-3. The extent of solid and solution is controlled by factors such as the oxygen partial pressure, the amount of

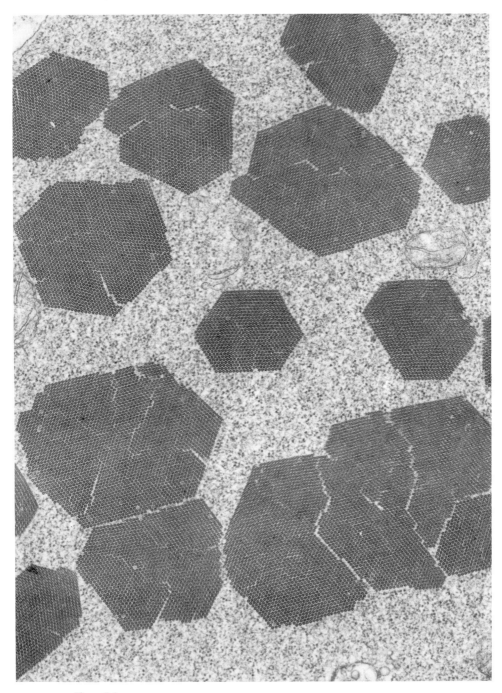

Figure 7-1.
Electron micrograph of an advanced cyanoblast, showing crystals of hemocyanin from *Limulus* (Fahrenbach, 1970).

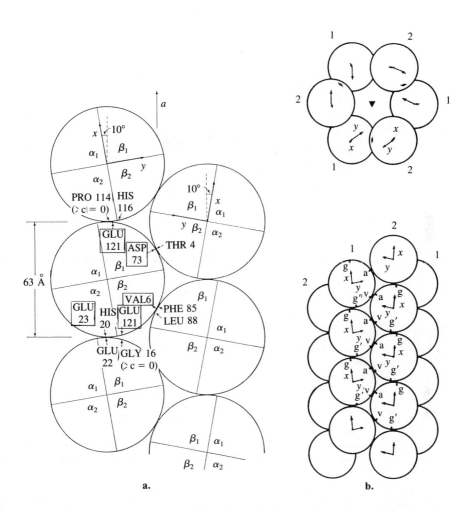

Figure 7-2.
Structural contacts between HbS tetramers found in deoxyhemoglobin HbS crystals
(a) and a possible model (b) for the tubules formed in sickled cells (Wishner *et al.*,
1975). The diagram (a) shows the double strand of tetramers found in the crystal
along with the residues, enclosed in boxes, believed to be involved in sickling interactions. A possible tubule model (b) for deoxy HbS fibers, based upon three pairs of
the strands found in the crystal. The top view is down the fiber axis. The symbols v,
a, g and g' indicate the approximate positions of the pertinent amino acid residues,
Val6β_2, Asp73β_1, Glu121β_1, and Glu121β_2, which are involved in intermolecular
contacts.

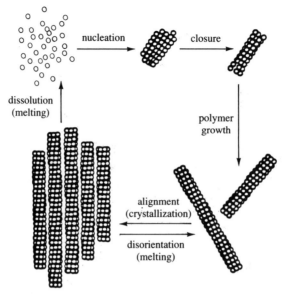

Figure 7-3.
Polymerization of sickle-cell hemoglobin (HbS) from single molecules to random linear array, and finally to an ordered "solid" phase (Hofrichter *et al.*, 1976a).

macromolecule, and the amount of water. Interestingly, an increase in temperature favors the formation of the aggregated phase, implying that heat is absorbed during aggregation.

Hemoglobin crystals have been found within rat erythrocytes, and presumably might function to control the level of oxygen transport (Condo *et al.*, 1981). The formation of such a highly organized structure is regulated by specific control ligands, such as chloride and oxygen.* The presence of a concentrated phase of oxygen-carrying hemoglobin molecules offers the potential of greatly increasing both the oxygen-carrying capacity and the response, i.e., cooperativity, of the system to deliver oxygen.

Since many biological systems and structures occur in highly concentrated and compact forms, it seems quite likely that their formation is governed by the general rules of thermodynamics of ligand-controlled phase formation. Little is known about the control reactions that must play a key role in the creation of new phases. One can even imagine that ligand regulation of

---

* The solubility of human hemoglobin crystals differs greatly between deoxygenated and fully oxygenated states. For example, Jope and O'Brien (1949) found that the solubility of human hemoglobin changed from 0.02 gm/ml under deoxy conditions to 0.13 gm/ml in the fully oxygenated state (in 0.6 M phosphate buffer, 20°C).

aggregation states, or microphase formation, within lipid bilayers of nerve endings or within the brain itself, could provide the molecular basis for specific sensory or memory events. In order to unravel the mysteries of such processes it is useful to have a clear understanding of the fundamentals of how ligands affect aggregation and phase formation.

7.1   EFFECT OF A LIGAND ON THE SOLUBILITY OF A MACROMOLECULE

The essential thermodynamic relations between ligand binding and solubility in macromolecular systems have been described (Wyman, 1964) and used to interpret the properties of oxygenated and deoxygenated hemoglobin crystals. A macromolecular solution in equilibrium with its crystals has a certain solubility determined by temperature, pressure, and added solutes, or ligands. As ligand is increased in the system, then, depending on the affinity of binding to sites in the solution or solid phase, the solubility will be either enhanced or depressed. The solubility is enhanced when the dissolved molecule binds the ligand more strongly.

In order to put these ideas in the context of the binding partition function, let us first consider the situation where the ligand does not bind to the solid. The equilibrium is described as

$$
\begin{array}{ccc}
M(s) & \rightarrow & M(l) \\
 & & \downarrow \\
 & & MX(l) \\
 & & \downarrow \\
 & & MX_2(l) \\
 & & \downarrow \\
 & & \text{etc.}
\end{array}
\qquad (7.1)
$$

where $M(s)$ represents the unliganded macromolecule in the solid phase, $M(l)$ represents the unliganded form in the liquid phase, and $MX(l)$, etc., represent the liganded forms in the liquid phase. The condition of equilibrium requires that the chemical potential of the unliganded macromolecule, μ_M, be the same in both phases:

$$
\mu_M{}^s = \mu_M{}^l. \qquad (7.2)
$$

The superscripts denote the phases solid (s) and liquid (l). Since the solid phase is assumed here to be unliganded, its chemical potential is independent of ligand activity, and may be represented by $\mu_M{}^{os}$. The liquid-phase macromolecular chemical potential for an ideal solution is given by (6.97); so we have

$$\mu_M{}^{os} = \mu_M{}^{ol} + RT \ln [M]_T - RT \ln P^l. \tag{7.3}$$

Here $[M]_T$ represents the total dissolved macromolecule concentration, i.e., its solubility, and P^l is the X-binding polynomial for the dissolved macromolecule. In the absence of ligand, $P^l = 1$, and $[M]_T = [M]_T^o$, the solubility in the absence of ligand; so the reference-state chemical potentials are related by

$$\mu_M{}^{os} = \mu_M{}^{ol} + RT \ln [M]_T^o. \tag{7.4}$$

Thus the difference in reference chemical potentials is determined by the solubility of the macromolecule at zero ligand activity. Combining (7.4) and (7.3) gives the fundamental relation between the solubility $[M]_T^o$ and its binding polynomial P^l in the liquid phase:

$$[M]_T = [M]_T^o P^l. \tag{7.5}$$

The same result could have also been obtained from the general linkage relation of the effect of ligands on the equilibrium constant of a reaction. The equilibrium constant for the solubility process, K, is given by the total solubility, i.e., $[M]_T$. Then K_0 is the solubility $[M]_T^o$ at the reference state, i.e., with no ligand present, and when this is multiplied by the ligand-phase binding polynomial, we obtain the preceding ligand-linked solubility expression.

Next, consider the more general case where the solid phase also binds ligand. The relevant equilibria of species between solid and solution are given as

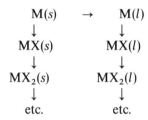

The solid-phase binding polynomial, P^s, describes the formation of different ligated species in the solid phase. The chemical potential of the macromolecule in this phase is then given as

$$\mu_M{}^{s} = \mu_M{}^{os} - RT \ln P^s, \tag{7.6}$$

and the equilibrium between dissolved and solid macromolecule* is found
to be

$$[M]_T = [M]_T^o \frac{P^l}{P^s}. \tag{7.7}$$

This result, as expected, is a simple expression of the effect of ligand linkage
on the solubility constant. It could have been written directly from the
preceding array of equilibrium species, as we have done many times before.
The effects of additional ligands, as well as temperature and pressure, can be
incorporated into these expressions as well, if desired. The result of equation (7.7) shows that the solubility is controlled by the ratio of the liquid-state
binding polynomial to the solid-state binding polynomial. If the macromolecule in the liquid has a higher ligand affinity than that in the solid, the
solubility is enhanced with increasing ligand activity, and if the solid phase has
a higher affinity than the liquid phase, then just the opposite occurs. Or put
another way, if the solution has more ligand bound than the solid at a given
ligand activity, then the solubility increases with ligand activity.

The solubility of a fully ligated solid phase, or more precisely when the
ligand activity is infinite, will be designated by $[M]_T^\infty$, and its relation to the
unligated solubility is found by considering the ratio of the largest terms of
the binding polynomials in (7.7), that is, $\beta_t^l x^t / \beta_t^s x^t$ as x becomes infinite. Thus,
for a macromolecule with t binding sites,

$$[M]_T^\infty = [M]_T^o \frac{\beta_t^l}{\beta_t^s}. \tag{7.8}$$

Then, if desired, the solubility may be expressed in terms of the fully ligated
state by

$$[M]_T = [M^\infty]_T \frac{\beta_t^s}{\beta_t^l} \frac{P^l}{P^s}. \tag{7.9}$$

---

* We are here ignoring for simplicity any effect of solvent ligand upon the chemical potential
μ_M^s. Solvent effects are considered in Section 7.4. Frequent use is made of the assumption
that a solid phase is unaffected by ligands or solvent conditions, for example, in studies of the
solubilities of amino acids in salt solutions. However, this assumption will be unjustified when
there are significant changes of composition within a given phase, for example, by ligation to
proteins. The use of a binding polynomial for the solid assumes that a finite number of liganded
states, such as stoichiometrically ligated states, apply to the macromolecule in the crystal.
Interaction with surrounding molecules is assumed to be absorbed into the binding constants
of P^s.

These results depend on the appropriateness of the use of binding polynomials to describe the influence of ligand on the macromolecular chemical potential. They are thus based on the idea that the mass-action law can be used to describe the various species in both phases, and that activity coefficients for ligated species within a given phase are canceled in the mass-action laws of the form given by equation (3.2). For the liquid phase, we may include activity coefficients in the terms expressing concentrations, i.e., $[M]_T$, to account for nonideal solution effects at high concentrations, and thereby improve the precision of (7.7) and (7.9). However, the key features can be most easily seen in terms of the idealized concentration expressions.

The relation between solubility and ligand-binding polynomials is expressed conveniently in the logarithmic form of (7.7), providing the most direct correlation between solubility and ligand-binding curves:

$$\ln[M]_T = \ln[M]_T^o + \ln P^l - \ln P^s. \tag{7.10}$$

Recall that $\ln P^l$ or $\ln P^s$ represents the area under the binding curve to $\ln x$. Thus $\ln P^l - \ln P^s$ describes the difference in area between the binding curves for liquid and solid phases. We illustrate this for a situation (shown in Figure 7-4) where X binding is noncooperative in both phases. As seen in this figure, when the ligand affinities of the phases are reversed, then the solubility dependence on the activity x is reversed.

An alternative, but less informative, way of plotting solubility data is to make the plots against the degree of ligation in one phase or the other, such as the liquid phase, $\bar{X}^{liq}$. This normalizes the abscissa to a limit of 1. The left example shown in Figure 7-4 is plotted in this form in Figure 7-5.

A striking example of the influence of ligand activity on the solubility of a macromolecule is afforded by the beautiful studies of Sorensen and Sorensen (1933) and Green (1931) on the effect of pH on the solubility of horse carbonylhemoglobin. Their results have been depicted by Rupley (1968) in Figure 7-6. Rupley (1968) interpreted these data, along with direct pH titration measurements of proton binding to crystals and dissolved horse hemoglobin, to conclude that crystallization affects approximately nine ionizable groups (out of 130 with pK's less than 9). Furthermore, the crystal phase change at pH 5.9 is accompanied by an uptake of about two protons in going from the A to the B form. The pH at which both crystalline forms exist in equilibrium with solution may be described as a *triple point*, and conforms to the crystallographic phase change observed by Perutz (1946, 1965). In the following sections we shall develop the thermodynamic expressions that can be applied to interpret such observations.

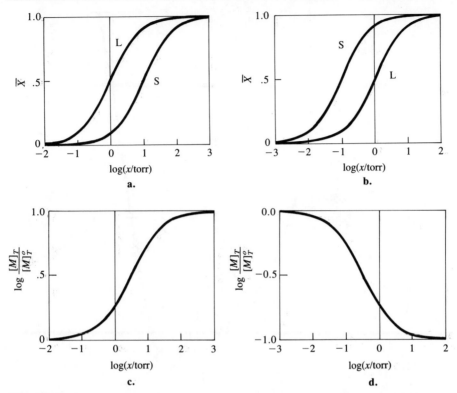

Figure 7-4.
Diagrams relating single-site ligand binding curves (top) to liquid (L) and solid (S) phases to logarithm of the solubility (bottom) as a function of logarithmic values of the ligand activity x under different conditions of ligand affinity within the solid phase. The degree of binding is $\bar{X}$ and the solubility is denoted by $[M]_T$ in the presence of ligand and $[M]_T^o$ in the absence of ligand. (a) and (c) are drawn with liquid and solid phase affinity constants 1 and 0.1 torr^{-1}, while (b) and (d) are drawn with affinity constants of 1 torr^{-1} and 10 torr^{-1}, respectively.

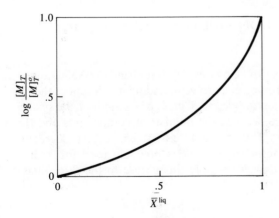

Figure 7-5.
Relative solubilities for different ligand affinities to solid and liquid phases plotted against degree of ligation in the liquid phase ($K^l = 1, K^s = 10^{-1}$). The reference solubility is that of the unliganded state ($[M]_T^o$).

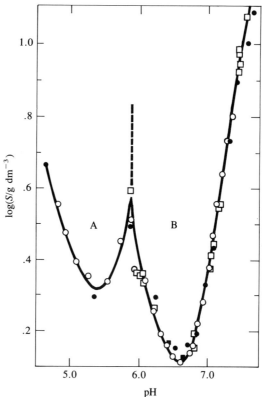

Figure 7-6.
Log solubility versus pH for horse CO hemoglobin: ○, ●, data
of Sorensen and Sorensen (1933), 2.2 M-ammonium sulfate;
□, data of Green (1931), 25°C, range of ionic strength of potassium
phosphate between 0.8 and 2 M. Note that regions A and B represent
different solid phases. Figure taken from Rupley (1968).

7.2   EFFECT OF LIGAND ON MULTIPLE-PHASE EQUILIBRIA: TRIPLE POINT

Consider a system composed of three phases (one liquid and two solid) and at
least three components, macromolecule, solvent, and ligand. Suppose that T
and p are fixed. Then by the phase rule the degrees of freedom of the system
will be given by the difference between the number of components and the
number of phases: $3 - 3 = 0$. This is therefore a system of zero degree of
freedom, and although the term *triple point* is precisely used for a one-
component system, it is customary to apply this phrase to the three-phase

macromolecular situation as well. The condition arises when the concentration of the partially ligated macromolecular solution, in contact with a solid phase, reaches a point where a new solid phase, possibly fully ligated, begins to precipitate. This would lead to the presence of three phases, two solid and one liquid. Further addition of ligand beyond this triple-point state increases the solid fraction that is fully ligated, and the solubility then decreases. Thus the dependence of solubility on ligand activity depends on the difference between the amount of bound ligand in the two phases. The quantitative aspects of this situation can be outlined by extension of the preceding discussion.

Call the two distinct solid phases A and B, each with its different binding curve. Then the triple point will occur at a particular ligand activity where the solubility is the same for each solid. The solubility of each form (A or B) is governed by its binding polynomial and by the solubility at the boundary conditions of either zero or infinite ligand activity. To illustrate this, we take the example of Figure 7-4 (a for A, b for B), and suppose the limiting solubilities of A and B are $[M]_{TA}^o = 1$ and $[M]_{TB}^o = 50$. Then using equation (7.10) to express $\ln[M]_T$ for each phase as a function of X ligand activity, we obtain the two curves (plotted with abscissa representing $\ln x$) shown in Figure 7-7; there is a solubility crossover point where the logarithm of ligand activity is about 1. The curves will be shifted vertically if solubilities in the unliganded states differ from each other. Thus if $[M]_{TB}^o > 50$, the B curve

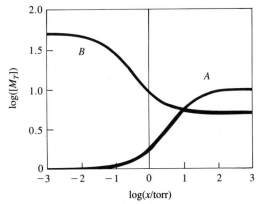

Figure 7-7.
Solubility functions of two solids (A and B) with affinities $K_A^s = 10^{-1}$, $K_B^s = 10$, $K^l = 1$, $[M]_{TA}^o = 1$, and $[M]_{TB}^o = 50$. Crossover occurs at triple-point value of x at 9.8 torr. At any given ligand activity the form with lower solubility is the stable form; so at low activities the A curve is followed to the triple point, and then the B curve applies. This is indicated by the extra-heavy lines.

is raised and the triple point is shifted to higher values of x, and if the limiting solubility at high ligand activity of B exceeds that of A, then, of course, a triple point would not be observed. The binding curve of the solid phases for this example follows the heavier line in Figure 7-8. In the next section we will see why this path is followed. At the triple point the system is infinitely cooperative, with a Hill slope of infinity.

The difference in the amount of X ligand bound per mole of macromolecule between the liquid and solid phases at any given ligand activity may be computed from the slope of the solubility curve with respect to $\ln x$. This is seen by differentiating equation (7.10) with respect to $\ln x$, and recognizing that

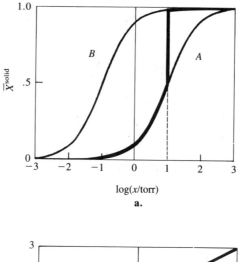

a.

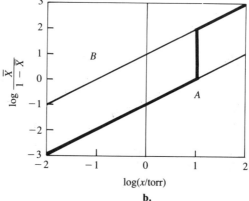

b.

Figure 7-8.
Solid-state binding curve and Hill plot for the example of Figure 7-7. Heavier line is predicted binding behavior, first following the lower soluble A form until the triple point ($x = 9.8$ torr) is reached, where conversion to B form occurs.

$\bar{X}^l = \partial \ln P^l / \partial \ln x$ and $\bar{X}^s = \partial \ln P^s / \partial \ln x$:

$$\frac{\partial \ln [M]_T}{\partial \ln x} = \bar{X}^l - \bar{X}^s. \tag{7.11}$$

This result is similar to the results found for the linkage effect of second ligands on the equilibrium binding constant of a primary ligand, as derived for Bohr and DPG effects on the oxygen-binding properties of hemoglobin. It was derived by Wyman (1964).

For the example given in Figures 7-4, 7-7, and 7-8, we find that the slope given by (7.11) is equal to $K^l x / (1 + K^l x) - K^s x / (1 + K^s x)$, where K^s is either $K_A{}^s$ or $K_B{}^s$, depending on whether we are on the A or B solid side of the triple point. The nature of this function is illustrated in Figure 7-9. At low activities, where A solid is most stable, there is more X bound in the liquid phase. At the triple point, a shift occurs: the B form, now the most stable, has more X bound than the liquid phase.

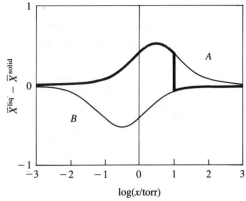

Figure 7-9.
The difference in binding between dissolved and solid state macromolecule as a function of ligand activity for the example illustrated in Figure 7-8.

7.3   MACROMOLECULAR CHEMICAL POTENTIAL OF SOLID PHASES

The fundamental basis of the effect of ligation upon the solubility of a macromolecule is given by chemical potential in the solid and liquid phases. Within a solid phase formed by a macromolecule we cannot change the concentration of the macromolecular species by dilution with solvent. We can still change the effective concentration or mole fraction of the unligated form of a macromolecule, say, A, by either diluting the solid phase with other macromolecules, such as B, as occurs in alloy formation, or diluting the unligated macromolecule A, by converting A to ligated forms. In this way, the chemical potential of the macromolecule in the solid phase can be altered by ligation. For the situation of a pure solid A in which ligand binding occurs, the macromolecular chemical potential of the solid is

$$\mu_{M,A}{}^s = \mu_{M,A}^{os} - RT \ln P_A^s, \tag{7.12}$$

where $\mu_{M,A}^{os}$ is the macromolecular chemical potential in the unliganded solid A form, and P_A^s is the binding polynomial to macromolecules A in the solid form. Similar equations will apply to other distinct solid phases.

We may use this result to illustrate the influence of a ligand X on the chemical potentials of two solid forms, A and B, which have distinct physical properties and different ligand-binding properties. We suppose they can form a triple point where both chemical potentials will be equal. For each solid phase we consider a simple single-site binding polynomial, and obtain

$$\mu_{M,A}{}^s = \mu_{M,A}^{os} - RT \ln (1 + \kappa_A{}^s x), \tag{7.13}$$

$$\mu_{M,B}{}^s = \mu_{M,B}^{os} - RT \ln (1 + \kappa_B{}^s x). \tag{7.14}$$

At the triple point $(x = x_T)$,

$$\mu_{M,B}{}^s = \mu_{M,A}{}^s,$$

which thus determines the difference

$$\mu_{M,B}^{os} - \mu_{M,A}^{os} = RT \ln \left(\frac{1 + \kappa_B{}^s x_T}{1 + \kappa_A{}^s x_T} \right). \tag{7.15}$$

For convenience we choose $\mu_{M,A}^{os} = 0$, and express all chemical potentials relative to this value as

$$\mu_{M,A}{}^s = -RT \ln (1 + \kappa_A{}^s x), \tag{7.16}$$

$$\mu_{M,B}{}^s = RT \ln \left(\frac{1 + \kappa_B{}^s x_T}{1 + \kappa_A{}^s x_T} \right) - RT \ln (1 + \kappa_B{}^s x). \tag{7.17}$$

A plot of these functions for $\kappa_B{}^s = 10$ torr^{-1} and $\kappa_A{}^s = .1$ torr^{-1}, if the unliganded solubilities are 50 and 1, respectively, is shown in Figure 7-10. The triple point for this situation is at $x = 9.8$ torr. From the location of these curves, the chemical potential of solid A is lower than B at low X activities, so the A phase is the stable phase under those conditions. The reverse occurs above the triple point. This gives the thermodynamic explanation of why only

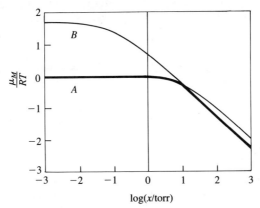

Figure 7-10.
Macromolecular chemical potentials for A and B solid phases with properties
given in Figure 7-7, as a function of X-ligand activity (25°C). The triple point is at
9.8 torr. The heavier line corresponds to the paths shown in Figures 7.7
through 7.9.

certain portions of the two individual solid-phase binding curves shown in
Figures 7.7 and 7.8 are physically accessible.

To conclude this section, we wish to point out two things. First, although we
have discussed the features of ligand-linked phase equilibria by using a specific
simple situation of single-site noncooperative binding, the idea is easily
extended to more complex binding polynomials. Second, when studying
liquid/solid systems, we must often work at high concentrations, and so must
use activities to describe the concentration behavior of the chemical potentials. Ross and Minton (1977) have shown how a simple hard-sphere model
can be used to describe the activity coefficients of hemoglobin solutions to
very high concentrations.

7.4   GENERAL EFFECT OF SEVERAL LIGANDS ON PHASE
EQUILIBRIA OF MACROMOLECULES

The concepts introduced in the preceding section on the influence of a ligand
on solubility of macromolecules can be developed in a more general manner to
encompass effects of several ligands on macromolecular equilibria between
several phases. The phases can also be either solids or liquids or combinations
of these. As we have seen, the control of the equilibrium between different
phases containing macromolecules is affected by specific binding of ligands to
the macromolecule. This type of control has been described as *polyphasic*

linkage (Wyman and Gill, 1980) and is a logical extension of *allosteric linkage* (Wyman, 1967; Monod *et al.*, 1965) and *polysteric linkage* (Colosimo *et al.*, 1976) as discussed in Chapter 6. In all of these situations, ligand binding causes a redistribution of forms, aggregates, or phases of macromolecules.

Perhaps the best-known example of polyphasic linkage in nature is that of sickle-cell anemia. Sickle-cell anemia occurs through oxygen-controlled aggregation and phase formation (Pauling *et al.*, 1949). It has been quantitatively described by many studies (Minton, 1977; Hofrichter *et al.*, 1976b; Gill *et al.*, 1979, 1980; Sunshine *et al.*, 1979, 1982; Benedict *et al.*, 1981b). The aggregation process of sickle-cell hemoglobin (HbS) is controlled by the oxygen concentration in the blood, and below critical values leads to extensive fiber or gel formation. This may be characterized as the formation of a solid phase in equilibrium with a liquid phase of hemoglobin molecules within the blood cell. An electron micrograph of the gel-fiber structure is shown in Figure 7-11. Our goal in this section is to formulate a general thermodynamic description of such polyphasic phenomena, i.e., the equilibria between several phases in the presence of ligand-binding reactions.

We start by recognizing that the chemical potentials between phases of all components must be equal. Furthermore, they must all respond equally when subjected to changes in temperature, pressure, and concentration of various components. The changes of the intensive variables in a given phase are described by the Gibbs-Duhem equation, as follows:

$$0 = S\,dT - V\,dp + n_W\,d\mu_W + n_M\,d\mu_M + n_X\,d\mu_X + n_Y\,d\mu_Y + \cdots, \quad (7.18)$$

where S and V are the entropy and volume of the phase; $n_W, n_M, n_X, n_Y, \ldots$ are the moles of solvent, macromolecule, ligand X, ligand Y, etc.; T and p are the temperature and pressure; and $\mu_W, \mu_M, \mu_X, \mu_Y, \ldots$ are the chemical potentials of solvent, macromolecule, ligand X, ligand Y, etc., in the given phase.

Since we are primarily interested in the thermodynamic properties of the macromolecule, we solve equation (7.18) in terms of the macromolecular chemical potential, μ_M. We first divide by the total moles of macromolecules n_M. We shall abbreviate the resulting terms in (7.18) by using a tilde ($\sim$) to represent such macromolecular molar normalization. Then $\tilde{X} = n_X/n_M$, etc. The change in macromolecular chemical potential at given T and p is thus expressed by

$$-d\mu_M = \tilde{W}\,d\mu_W + \tilde{X}\,d\mu_X + \tilde{Y}\,d\mu_Y. \quad (7.19)$$

In writing this equation we must realize that a term like $\tilde{X}$ includes all moles of X, whether bound or free, per mole of macromolecule in a given phase, and is not to be confused with $\bar{X}$, which refers only to bound X.

At constant T and p, when there are two phases, α and β, each phase will be represented by an equation of the form of (7.19). The chemical potentials and any change in chemical potentials must be equal for equilibrium to hold

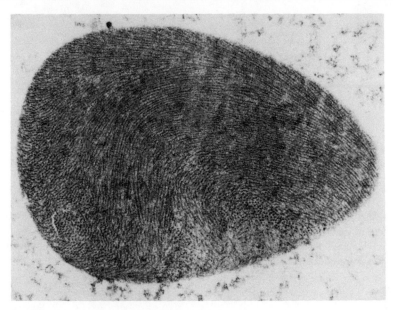

Figure 7-11.
Thin section of sickled erythrocyte viewed in the electron microscope. Rod-like
polymers are approximately 170 Å in diameter (White and Heagan, 1973).

between the phases. Put another way, the macromolecular chemical potentials
in each phase are described by a surface with variables μ_W, μ_X, and μ_Y. For the
phases to be in equilibrium, there will be a line of intersection between the two
surfaces. We may now define the equation of this equilibrium line as follows
(using superscripts α and β to designate the two phases):

$$d\mu_M{}^\alpha = d\mu_M{}^\beta, \tag{7.20}$$

$$\tilde{W}^\alpha\, d\mu_W + \tilde{X}^\alpha\, d\mu_X + \tilde{Y}^\alpha\, d\mu_Y = \tilde{W}^\beta\, d\mu_W + \tilde{X}^\beta\, d\mu_X + \tilde{Y}^\beta\, d\mu_Y. \tag{7.21}$$

The changes in the chemical potentials are equal in the two phases, and do not
need superscript designation. Several simple derivative rules follow from this
expression. For example, at fixed μ_Y we can write

$$\left(\frac{\partial \mu_W}{\partial \mu_X}\right)_{\mu_Y} = -\frac{\tilde{X}^\alpha - \tilde{X}^\beta}{\tilde{W}^\alpha - \tilde{W}^\beta}. \tag{7.22}$$

This equation defines one of the derivative properties of the equilibrium line
of intersection of the macromolecular chemical potentials for the two phases,
as indicated in Figure 7-12.

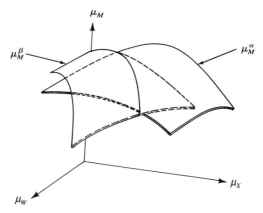

Figure 7-12.
Surfaces of macromolecular chemical potentials for phases α and β in terms of species chemical potentials μ_W and μ_X. Line of intersection determines equilibrium conditions for coexistence of the two phases.

In general the values of $\tilde{X}$ and $\tilde{W}$ for each phase will be a function of both μ_X and μ_W. Integration of (7.22) ultimately gives μ_W as a function of μ_X for each phase. This equation is the exact counterpart of the Clausius-Clapeyron equation $(dp/dT = \Delta S/\Delta V)$, which describes the variation of vapor pressure with temperature for a single substance in terms of entropy and volume changes. The integration is simplified if there is no W–X linkage in either phase, so the variables are separable. But whether they are or not, we know that the integral must exist; for each phase, the macromolecular potentials by which $\tilde{X}$ and $\tilde{W}$ are determined in that phase will be a single-valued function of μ_X and μ_W*.

When there are three phases, α, β, and γ, and three components (M, W, and X), then a triple point, representing equilibrium among the three phases, is

---

* We need not assume that T and p are held constant. For example, if T is a variable with μ_X, then we obtain, holding p, μ_W, etc., constant,

$$\left(\frac{d\mu_X}{dT}\right)_{p,\mu_W} = -\frac{\tilde{S}^\alpha - \tilde{S}^\beta}{\tilde{X}^\alpha - \tilde{X}^\beta}.$$

Since we are examining the phases at equilibrium,

$$\tilde{S}^\alpha - \tilde{S}^\beta = (\tilde{H}^\alpha - \tilde{H}^\beta)/T,$$

where $\tilde{H}$ is the enthalpy per mole of macromolecule, and the difference is measurable by the heat per mole of macromolecule transferred between phases.

given by the intersection of three nonparallel surfaces, one for each phase. Any such point corresponds to a unique pair of μ_X and μ_W. This argument may be extended to additional components (Wyman and Gill, 1980) which will in general affect the location of the triple point, or more precisely the *multiple point*, of the system.

An illustration of these ideas is shown for the influence of oxygen pressure on the solubility (or water activity) of HbS. The solubility of HbS (Gill *et al.*, 1980) determines the water activity, which gives the measure of the chemical potential of the solvent water. The slope of the plot of $\ln a_W$ versus $\ln p_{O_2}$ as given by equation (7.22) determines $-(\tilde{O}_2^l - \tilde{O}_2^s)/(\tilde{W}^l - \tilde{W}^s)$. As seen in Figure 7-13, the slope of this curve is everywhere negative, indicating that more oxygen is bound to the dissolved hemoglobin than to the solid at these partial pressures. The increasing negative slope means that more oxygen is absorbed in the solution phase than in the solid phase with increasing oxygen pressure. If any three of the four quantities $\tilde{O}_2^l$, $\tilde{O}_2^s$, $\tilde{W}^l$, $\tilde{W}^s$ are known, the other may be determined from the slope of a plot like that in Figure 7-13. The easiest quantities to measure are $\tilde{O}_2^l$, $\tilde{W}^l$, and $\tilde{W}^s$; so we can find $\tilde{O}_2^s$, which is a measure of the oxygen-binding curve in the solid phase.

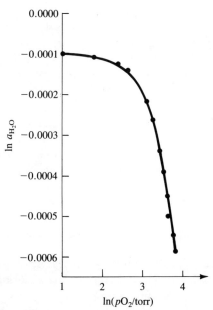

Figure 7-13.
Solubility data (Gill *et al.*, 1980) for HbS at 25°C, pH 7.4, in terms of the logarithm of solvent water activity, a_{H_2O} (or a_W), and the logarithm of oxygen partial pressurre p_{O_2}.

From what has been discussed so far, we can see that a new solid phase with different binding properties could in theory be part of this system. If such a new phase is stable at a higher oxygen pressure, then another line relating $\ln a_{H_2O}$ and $\ln p_{O_2}$ must be included in Figure 7-13. Such a line has not yet been found experimentally for the HbS system, but if it were to occur, then the intersection with the preceding known equilibrium line would define the triple point. (Note, however, that the solubility studies examined in detail in Section 7.6 indicate where the triple point might occur.)

7.5   INFLUENCE OF SPECIFIC BINDING OF LIGANDS ON PHASE EQUILIBRIA

The analysis of the influence of ligand and solvent chemical potentials on the equilibrium state of two (or more) phases has been expressed in general terms in the preceding section. There we have seen that the molar properties such as $\tilde{X}$ and $\tilde{W}$ for the various phases influence the coexistence curve between phases. The quantities $\tilde{X}$ and $\tilde{W}$ give the total amount of X and W per mole of macromolecule in a specific phase. One part of $\tilde{X}$ may be regarded as specifically bound to the macromolecule, and subject to equations of mass action. The other part may then be considered free, and in this sense sets the chemical potential of X in the phase. Our analysis of the influence of ligand binding on the formation of different phases will be enlarged by incorporation of the ideas of mass action, and in this section we wish to formulate these ideas from this more general thermodynamic argument. In doing this, we shall see the very special role that the solvent water plays in these processes.

We first will address some aspects of notation. We have used a bar over a specific ligand symbol, $\bar{X}$, to represent specific ligand binding governed by mass-action laws which can be formulated in terms of binding polynomials. $\bar{X}$ represents moles of ligand specifically bound per mole of macromolecule. The free amount of X per mole of macromolecule is determined by the X ligand activity (in concentration units) divided by the total macromolecular concentration. We denote the free amount per mole of macromolecule by $\hat{X}$, and then the total amount of X in the system per mole of macromolecule is the sum of the free and bound contributions in a given phase:

$$\tilde{X} = \bar{X} + \hat{X}. \tag{7.23}$$

There is no experimental problem in accurately describing $\tilde{X}$, say, by quantitative analysis. The real problem comes in measuring either $\bar{X}$ or $\hat{X}$. We shall assume that the specifically bound component can be measured from spectroscopic or dialysis techniques, and characterized by suitable binding polynomials or binding partition functions; i.e., $\bar{X} = \partial \ln P / \partial \ln x$. The difference between $\tilde{X}$ and $\bar{X}$ gives $\hat{X}$. We note that $\hat{X}$ is also calculated by dividing the free ligand concentration x by the macromolecular concentration.

Mass-action laws, when applicable, provide relations between $\bar{X}$ and $\hat{X}$, as we have seen in detail in the preceding chapters.

Since it is the state of the macromolecule that is our primary concern, we wish to examine the properties of the chemical potential of the macromolecule itself. For practical reasons, the measurement of the chemical potential of a macromolecule depends on studies of its thermodynamic properties in solution. The chemical potential μ_M of a nondissociating macromolecule in liquid solution (l) may be defined at given T and p by equation (6.97) in terms of its total concentration, or more precisely by its activity a_T, and its binding polynomial P^l. In differential form at constant T and P, we have

$$d\mu_M = RT\,d\ln a_T - RT\,d\ln P^l. \tag{7.24}$$

Then in terms of specific ligand-binding parameters $\bar{X}$ and $\bar{Y}$, etc., this may be expressed as

$$d\mu_M = RT\,d\ln a_T - \bar{X}^l\,d\mu_X - \bar{Y}^l\,d\mu_Y\ldots. \tag{7.25}$$

This expression specifically indicates (1) how the bound amounts of ligands X and Y affect μ_M, and (2) how the influence of solvent, or total macromolecular concentration, is lumped into the activity term a_T. As shown in the next chapter, a careful analysis of osmotic equilibrium provides the means for practical evaluation of all the terms in this equation.

We now wish to connect the operational definitions of the macromolecular chemical potential given by (7.25) with general results for phase equilibria. This will enable us to introduce the properties of specific and nonspecific ligand binding, and to evaluate their influence on phase formation.

Equation (7.19) may be normalized to the amount of solvent by dividing by $\tilde{W}$ and rearranging as

$$-\frac{1}{\tilde{W}}d\mu_M = d\mu_W + \frac{\tilde{X}}{\tilde{W}}d\mu_X + \frac{\tilde{Y}}{\tilde{W}}d\mu_Y + \cdots. \tag{7.26}$$

The result applies to any phase. When applied to a liquid (l) phase in equilibrium with another phase denoted by α, subtraction of the two equations gives

$$-\left(\frac{1}{\tilde{W}^l} - \frac{1}{\tilde{W}^\alpha}\right)d\mu_M = \left(\frac{\tilde{X}^l}{\tilde{W}^l} - \frac{\tilde{X}^\alpha}{\tilde{W}^\alpha}\right)d\mu_X + \left(\frac{\tilde{Y}^l}{\tilde{W}^l} - \frac{\tilde{Y}^\alpha}{\tilde{W}^\alpha}\right)d\mu_Y + \cdots, \tag{7.27}$$

where the superscripts denote the mole-ratio properties in a given phase. Inserting the operational form given by (7.25) for $d\mu_M$, using equation (7.23) to express the free and specifically bound ligands, and letting the chemical potentials of X and Y be described by their activities, i.e., $d\mu_X = RT\,d\ln x$, etc., we obtain

$$d \ln a_T = \frac{(\bar{X}^l - \bar{X}^\alpha) + \tilde{W}^\alpha \left[\dfrac{\hat{X}^l}{\tilde{W}^l} - \dfrac{\hat{X}^\alpha}{\tilde{W}^\alpha} \right]}{1 - \dfrac{\tilde{W}^\alpha}{\tilde{W}^l}} d \ln x$$

$$+ \frac{(\bar{Y}^l - \bar{Y}^\alpha) + \tilde{W}^\alpha \left[\dfrac{\hat{Y}^l}{\tilde{W}^l} - \dfrac{\hat{Y}^\alpha}{\tilde{W}^\alpha} \right]}{1 - \dfrac{\tilde{W}^\alpha}{\tilde{W}^l}} d \ln y + \cdots. \tag{7.28}$$

In writing this result, we have assumed that the ligands X and Y have specific binding properties, whereas the solvent W has been treated in general terms of the total amount in each phase. If there were no solvent in the α phase, i.e., $\tilde{W}^\alpha = 0$, then we would obtain the same result as given by (7.11), but generally this will not be true in biological systems.

There are special cases that lead to some simplification. If the X and Y ligands are small, and the free amounts are distributed equally within the solvent in both phases, then cancellation occurs within the bracketed terms [ ] of (7.28), and we have

$$d \ln a_T - \frac{\tilde{W}^\alpha}{\tilde{W}^l} d \ln a_T = (\bar{X}^l - \bar{X}^\alpha) d \ln x + (\bar{Y}^l - \bar{Y}^\alpha) d \ln y. \tag{7.29}$$

It is convenient here to define the macromolecular activity a_T in terms of an effective solvent activity a_W, by

$$\frac{1}{\tilde{W}^l} d \ln a_T = -d \ln a_W, \tag{7.30}$$

which is obtained by considering the Gibbs-Duhem relation between the macromolecular concentration activity and water activity. If this result is used with (7.29), and $\tilde{W}^\alpha$ is assumed constant, we can easily obtain an integrated form given as

$$\ln \frac{a_T}{a_T{}^o} = -\tilde{W}^\alpha \ln \frac{a_W}{a_W{}^o} + \ln \frac{P^l}{P^\alpha}. \tag{7.31}$$

The superscript ^{o} denotes unliganded conditions, and the relation between the ligand-binding polynomials and the specific binding properties of the respective phases has been taken into account.

The ideas behind equation (7.31) have been quantitatively explored in studies of sickle-cell hemoglobin oxygen-linked phase formation (Gill *et al.*,

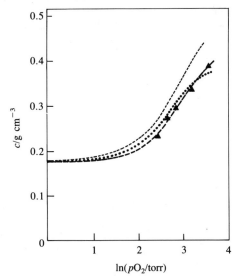

Figure 7-14.
Comparison of calculated solubility lines using equation (7.31) and assuming no oxygen binding to solid (---), noncooperative binding to solid (– – –), and cooperative binding to solid (• • •) with experimental solubility measurements for HbS at different oxygen activities (Gill *et al.*, 1980).

1980; Benedict *et al.*, 1981b). Experimental measurements of the solubility c (gm HbS/ml) are given in Figure 7-14. The computation of the theoretical curve depends on the terms in (7.31). The hemoglobin activity (a_T) in the liquid phase is the product of the concentration (c) and activity coefficient (γ). Ross and Minton (1977) have given equations for both γ and the effective water activity a_W. The activity coefficient depends on concentration at high concentrations of hemoglobin. Sunshine *et al.* (1979) calculated the water content $(\tilde{W}^\alpha)$ of solid HbS as 2,400 moles water/mole HbS, and the solubility of deoxy HbS under the buffer conditions of these experiments is 0.19 g/ml (Sunshine *et al.*, 1982). The binding polynomial for oxygen binding in the liquid phase is given from Adair constants as calculated in separate experiments. Thus we have all the information we need to predict the solubility as a function of oxygen pressure, provided we assume a solid-phase oxygen-binding polynomial. A noncooperative solid binding curve with an affinity constant of .010 torr^{-1} fits the data (see Figure 7-14) as well as we might think possible in view of both experimental and theoretical limitations. The assumption that there is no oxygen binding to the solid form seems quite out of line with experimental results.

A direct measurement of the oxygen binding to the solid phase of HbS has been achieved by use of changes in linear dichroism upon oxygen ligation of microcrystalline regions of HbS gel (Sunshine *et al.*, 1982). The pertinent results, shown in a Hill plot (Figure 7-15), cover only a limited range of oxygen

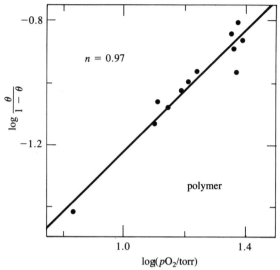

Figure 7-15.
Hill plot of oxygen binding to polymer HbS (Sunshine *et al.*, 1982). Binding constant equals .0059 ± .0015 torr^{-1} and p_{50} equals 170 ± 40 torr.

saturation to the polymer (0.04 to 0.14), but clearly indicate noncooperative binding with a single affinity constant of .006 torr^{-1}. In view of the experimental difficulty of measuring the binding directly, and the complex evaluation of the solid-state binding properties from solubility determinations, the general agreement between the different approaches is quite satisfactory. Finding nearly the same binding constant in the solid as K_1 in the liquid supports the idea of a simple MWC allosteric mechanism. Since the solid at low oxygen pressures is in the T form, its binding constant should then be nearly the same as κ_T in solution provided lattice forces have an insignificant perturbation on the binding affinity. This suggestion is supported further by solubility studies of crystals of HbA and HbC (the $\beta6$ glu → lys mutant) to be discussed in the next section.

That lattice forces do not affect binding constants has been demonstrated in other studies of substrate binding to enzymes in either the crystalline or dissolved state. Butler and Rupley (1967) showed by direct analysis that N-acetylglucosamine binds with equal affinity to either crystals or dissolved lysozyme. They also showed that the solubility of lysozyme was unaffected by the saccharide concentration, and since the solubility is directly influenced by the difference in the binding properties of the protein in the two phases, the affinities are the same in both. Direct measurements of substrate binding in crystalline proteins have also been made using single-crystal spectrophotometric techniques (Mozzarelli *et al.*, 1979). They show that the binding properties of various substrates (1-glutamate, 2-oxoglutarate, 1-aspartate, and oxaloacetate) are comparable within a factor of two for the enzyme in crystal or solution states.

An important application of equation (7.31) is in the quantitative analysis of how an antisickling agent, such as butyl urea, affects the solubility of sickle-cell hemoglobin (Benedict *et al.*, 1981a). This can be studied in terms of solubility as a function of oxygen pressure, but the significant effect can be examined by noting the type of butyl urea binding polynomial ratio that describes the deoxygenated solubility of HbS. The antisickling effect is brought about through the second term of (7.31), i.e., the ratio of binding polynomials. Experimentally this ratio is $P_{BU}^l/P_{BU}^s = 1 + 5[BU] + 40[BU]^2$, where $[BU]$ is the molar concentration of butyl urea. The quadratic nature of this expression implies that there are at least two butyl urea binding sites present on the hemoglobin in the liquid phase that are not present in the gel phase. Further, this expression cannot be factored into positive linear factors; so the binding of butyl urea must be cooperative in the phase-linked second site. This might indicate that when one such ligand is bound, a site of enhanced affinity is formed.

7.6 TRIPLE-POINT BEHAVIOR OF HUMAN HEMOGLOBIN

Crystals of hemoglobin exist in different forms, depending on whether they are oxygenated or not (Perutz, 1976). The fully ligated heme form is designated as the R form, and the completely unligated heme form is the T form. The ligand-binding properties of these crystalline forms are still largely unknown, although the observation by Haurowitz (1938) that unligated crystal shattered upon exposure to oxygen clearly suggests that the two forms have different stabilities that depend on oxygen pressure.

We have seen in the preceding sections that the phase behavior, i.e., the solubility (or water chemical potential) in the liquid phase is regulated by the oxygen and water "binding" properties in the solid and liquid phases. The solubility [see equation (7.31)] is expressed in terms of the water content in the solid phase, $\tilde{W}^s$, the effective water activity, a_W, and the ratio of the oxygen-binding polynomials in liquid and solid phases. We shall write this in terms of concentration c of dissolved hemoglobin with an activity coefficient γ as

$$\ln\frac{\gamma c}{\gamma^o c^o} = -\tilde{W}^s \ln\frac{a_W}{a_W^o} + \ln\frac{P^l}{P^s}, \tag{7.32}$$

where the superscript ^{o} refers to the deoxygenated reference state. A fully ligated state reference condition is achieved at $\gamma^\infty c^\infty$ by letting the ligand activity take on a very large value. Then from (7.32) we have

$$\ln\frac{\gamma^\infty c^\infty}{\gamma^o c^o} = -\tilde{W}^s \ln\frac{a_W^\infty}{a_W^o} + \ln\frac{\beta_t^l}{\beta_t^s}, \tag{7.33}$$

where c^∞ stands for the solubility when the system is fully oxygenated, and only the last Adair coefficient of the binding polynomials survives. The approximations used in arriving at (7.33) depend on the constancy of the water content of the crystals, i.e., $\tilde{W}^s$, and the assumption that the oxygen binding is described by mass-action-law terms contained in a binding polynomial. Direct binding measurements have so far eluded experimental study on multisite crystals, although Sunshine et al. (1982) have found oxygen-binding curves on HbS fibers over a limited range of pressures, as was discussed in the preceding section.

Conditions of very low solubility may be produced in the presence of high salt or polyethylene glycol (PEG) concentrations. Equations (7.32) and (7.33) are greatly simplified, since all the activity coefficients are equal to the first approximation, $\gamma = \gamma^o = \gamma^\infty$, and $a_W = a_W{}^o = a_W{}^\infty$.

$$\ln\frac{c}{c^o} = \ln\frac{P^l}{P^s} \tag{7.34}$$

or

$$\ln\frac{c}{c^\infty} = \ln\frac{P^l/\beta_t^l}{P^s/\beta_t^s}, \tag{7.35}$$

for the expressions of the solubility curves referred to either the unligated or the fully ligated state. The solubility of a given form will then depend on c^o (or c^∞), P^l, and P^s for that form.

In general, when two distinct solid phases occur, we expect to have two different solubility curves. Each will be described by either (7.34) or (7.35) with the appropriate binding polynomial for the particular solid phase. For hemoglobin, we could have solid crystals in either the T or the R form; their binding properties will then be governed by the respective polynomials $P^{s,T}$ and $P^{s,R}$. An early observation by Perutz, cited by Wyman (1964), noted that such behavior probably occurs with human hemoglobin crystals. As we have already noted, the point where both forms have the same solubility is the triple point. Precise solubility measurements by Haire et al. (1981) of HbA, HbC, and HbS under low solubility conditions and as a function of oxygen pressure, or equivalently expressed as oxygen binding in the liquid phase, are shown in Figure 7-16. The oxygen-binding curve of HbA in the liquid phase is shown in Figure 7-17 for the same high polyethylene glycol condition (17.5 percent) used in these studies.

The predicted solubilities are governed by equations (7.34) and (7.35), where P^l is found from the liquid phase with data given by Figure 7.17, and P^s depends on the nature of the solid phase. The assumption was made that the two solid phases behave toward oxygen binding as noncooperative T or R binding states similar to those calculated from the liquid-state binding curves.

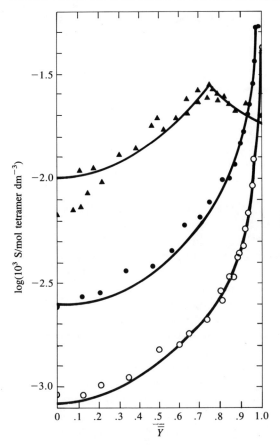

Figure 7-16.
Solubility of HbA ●, HbC ▲, and HbS ○ as a function of liquid-phase fractional oxygen saturation in the presence of 17.5 percent PEG. Theoretical curves are generated from equations (7.34) and (7.35) using MWC constants obtained from liquid-phase binding curves like that shown in Figure 7-17 for HbA (Haire *et al.*, 1981).

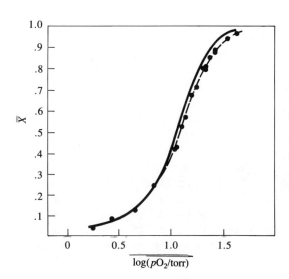

Figure 7-17.
Oxygen binding curve of HbA in the presence (– – –) and absence (——) of 17.5 percent polyethylene glycol. Theoretical line (– – –) generated from MWC binding polynomial with $L = 3 \times 10^{10}$, $\kappa_T = 0.026$ torr^{-1}, and $\kappa_R = 39$ torr^{-1} (Haire *et al.*, 1981).

The relevant binding polynomials are described by

$$P^l = \frac{1}{1 + L}(1 + \kappa_R x)^4 + \frac{L}{1 + L}(1 + \kappa_T x)^4, \tag{7.36}$$

$$P^{s,R} = (1 + \kappa_R x)^4, \tag{7.37}$$

$$P^{s,T} = (1 + \kappa_T x)^4. \tag{7.38}$$

With these binding polynomials, and $\beta_4^{s,R} = (\kappa_R)^4$, $\beta_4^l = (L\kappa_T^4 + \kappa_R^4)/(1 + L)$, we obtain the theoretical lines of Figure 7-16. As seen, the theoretical lines agree with the experimental results as well as can be expected. One of the striking features of these calculations is that the solubility of all three hemoglobins, HbA, HbS, and HbC, can be predicted by the same binding polynomial, derived from liquid-phase data on HbA. The satisfactory application of the liquid-state intrinsic affinities κ_R and κ_T to the solid-phase binding behavior suggests that the crystal lattice does not affect the affinity of a given form, although the lattice prevents conversion from T to R until sufficient oxygen pressure is reached. These solubility studies show that the T solid form dominates the picture until relatively high oxygen pressure (or degree of liquid-phase oxygen saturation) is present. This is especially true for HbA and HbS. We can hardly see the slight dependence of the oxygen pressure on the solubility of the R solid form and the intersection of the two curves at the triple point in Figure 7-16 for these materials, since the very high solubility at full ligation obscures the intersection point. However, for HbC, with its lower fully-ligated solubility, the intersection of the two solubility curves is displaced to much lower pressures, and is more clearly identified in these studies.

It would be desirable to have further confirmation of the presence of the triple-point behavior for hemoglobin, or for that matter other allosteric molecules, in order to establish better the importance of major conformational states of these molecules. Interestingly, a recent discovery by Brzozowski et al. (1984) sheds further light on this phenomenon in a quite unexpected way. They found that T-form crystals of HbA could be prepared from PEG solutions exposed to air, and these crystals are essentially half-oxygenated. As shown in Figure 7-18, the α chains are oxygenated, and the β chains are deoxygenated.

An explanation in terms of triple-point properties was given by Gill and Richey (1984), who suggested that the half-oxygenated crystals were probably formed under triple-point conditions. The reasoning goes as follows. The binding-curve data of the liquid-phase HbA give R and T binding constants that are assumed to be applicable to the solid phases. The triple-point oxygen pressure occurs where the solubilities of R and T forms are equal. From

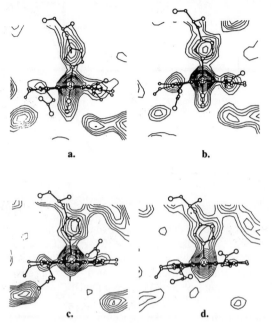

Figure 7-18.
The heme and proximal histidine viewed edge-on. The section of the electron density through the Fe and proximal histidine shows oxygen binding to the α hémes (in a and b), but not to the β hemes (c and d) (Brzozowski *et al.*, 1984).

(7.34) and (7.35) this is given by

$$\frac{c^{oT}}{c^{\infty R}} = \frac{P^{s,T}_{\text{triple}}/\beta_t^l}{P^{s,R}_{\text{triple}}/\beta_t^{s,R}}, \qquad (7.39)$$

where P_{triple} indicates the value of the relevant solid-state binding polynomial at the triple point. Using the observed limiting solubilities and various binding constants given by Figure 7-17, we find that the triple-point pressure is 55 torr oxygen. At this point the T form is 58 percent oxygen-saturated, and this fractional saturation agrees quite well with the half-saturation value found in the crystals of Brzozowski. There are some additional features suggested from these calculations.

The binding curves predicted for the solid R and T forms are shown by dotted lines in Figure 7-19. The predicted binding curve for solid hemoglobin A is shown in this figure by the course of the solid line. Starting with the more stable but lower-affinity T form, we proceed to the triple point, where nearly saturated R-form crystals precipitate with further addition of oxygen until all

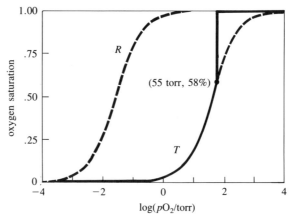

Figure 7-19.
Broken lines show proposed binding curves for oxygen to human hemoglobin in R and T solid forms ($\kappa_T = .026$ torr^{-1} and $\kappa_R = 39$ torr^{-1}). Triple point occurs at 55 torr for HbA, 108 torr for HbS, and 33 torr for HbC. The HbA T form is 58 percent saturated, and R form is 99.8 percent saturated. The respective saturation for T solid forms is 74 percent for HbS and 33 percent for HbC.

the solid is in the R form. Then the oxygen pressure can be increased further. There is a large range of oxygen saturation where both R and T crystals coexist at the triple point; this fact might help explain why Brzozowski obtained half-saturated T crystals without paying special attention to the exact partial-pressure conditions. The reason why the T-form crystals are more stable than the R below the triple point is indicated by the macromolecular chemical potentials for the R and T forms, calculated by equation (7.12) using the appropriate solid binding polynomials. These are indicated in Figure 7-20. The R form has a higher chemical potential than the T form at low oxygen pressures; the T form is more stable under such conditions. The reverse is true at pressures above the triple point.

The preceding analysis, based on a combination of solubility and liquid-phase binding curves, does not account for the observation by Brzozowski that only the α chains appear to be ligated. This result suggests that a more detailed binding polynomial, which distinguishes binding to the α from binding to the β chain, is operating in these molecules. This is not unexpected, but with the necessary assumptions and accuracy of existing experiments, the preceding thermodynamic analysis alone could not verify the need for such a more elaborate binding polynomial. What their results suggest is that the β chains in the T form have a much lower affinity than the α chains in this form. A MWC binding polynomial (liquid) which recognizes this fact is then

$$P = \frac{1}{1+L}(1 + \kappa_R{}^\alpha x)^2 (1 + \kappa_R{}^\beta x)^2 + \frac{L}{1+L}(1 + \kappa_T{}^\alpha x)^2, \qquad (7.40)$$

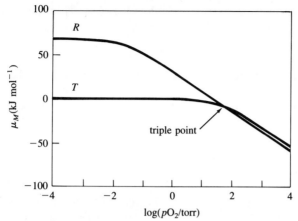

Figure 7-20.
The macromolecular chemical potentials of the T and R solid forms of hemoglobin HbA or HbS as a function of oxygen pressure. The reference chemical potential of the unliganded T form is taken as zero.

where κ_T^{β} is assumed to be zero. This equation has four parameters in place of the usual three for the simple MWC model.

A recent oxygen-binding study of concentrated HbA_0 by means of differential measurements (Gill et al., 1987) has shown that the third-degree term in the binding polynomial is small to negligible. An allosteric model that also includes cooperative interaction between the binding processes of the α chains in the T form has been found to represent these recent oxygen-binding measurements to concentrated human hemoglobin (Di Cera et al., 1987a). An unanswered question is whether the solid forms really follow the T and R portions of this polynomial. What is needed to answer this are high-precision solid-state binding curves. With such information available, we can assess the influence of the crystal lattice and the nature of cooperativity, if any, in the solid state. This approach appears to be of particular value in examining the applicability of MWC or KNF models to oxygen binding in hemoglobin. If the binding behavior in the solid is of zero or negative cooperativity, then the MWC model provides a ready explanation. If the cooperativity in the solid is much the same as that for the liquid, then a KNF model, in which each increment of X ligation produces a new allosteric form within the crystal lattice, would seem more appropriate. It remains to be seen if such studies can enlarge our understanding of allosteric systems.

The extension of the preceding examination of ligand-linked phase phenomena to other systems of biological importance must await detailed studies of ligand-induced phase changes. One of the striking features that we have noticed in the few available examples is the potentially high degree of cooperativity that can be exhibited by multiple-phase systems in the triple-point region. Such high cooperativity may be useful in several ways. One would be to provide an extremely high buffer capacity for a particular ligand species. This might be useful in delivery systems where a constant ligand activity is required in the system. Another feature of triple-point situations is the possibility of information storage by ligand conversion of microcrystalline aggregates of one form to another. The two forms represent stable entities that could possess uniquely different enzymatic or ligand-binding properties. Such a macromolecular system has many of the elements needed for a long-term memory system.

7.7 OVERVIEW

In this chapter, the underlying effect of a ligand on equilibrium between phases has been developed as an extension of the concepts used for allosteric and polysteric systems. In a sense the situation is actually simpler in the polyphasic case, since we can see and sample the extent of phase formation as a function of ligand activity. A triple point or multiple point represents a unique situation where three or more phases coexist. An infinitely sharp transition, implying infinite cooperativity, occurs at such points.

The Thermodynamics of 8
Macromolecules

Thermodynamics is a phenomenological subject, as contrasted with statistical mechanics, which is postulational. Of itself thermodynamics provides no model. On the other hand, it leads to relations applicable to any model, and consequently serves as a touchstone for any proposed mechanism for a physical situation. This makes it particularly suitable for the study of macromolecules, which are usually far too complicated to allow detailed formulation of the partition function of statistical mechanics.

As we have seen in previous chapters, the behavior of biological macromolecules, as exemplified by the functional chemistry of the respiratory proteins, particularly hemoglobin, is a subject of great complexity. However, the macroscopic principles of thermodynamics always apply. In this chapter we will consider these broad principles, and present the essential elements of thermodynamics as they bear on phenomena described in previous chapters. In doing this we adopt the approach developed by Gibbs before the turn of the century (Gibbs, *Collected Works*, 1928).

8.1 THE FIRST AND SECOND LAWS OF THERMODYNAMICS

The first and second laws of thermodynamics are two existence theorems based on universal experience. The *first law* tells us that there always exists a function, the energy E, which is subject to conservation in any isolated system, and is uniquely determined by the state of the system. The state is defined by macroscopic quantities such as temperature, pressure, volume, and chemical composition. The *second law* tells us that there also exists another function, the entropy S, likewise uniquely determined by the state of the system, which always either increases or remains constant during any process which the system, when isolated, may undergo. Constancy corresponds to reversibility; increase, to irreversibility.

Combination of these two theorems leads to an equation applicable to any physiochemical system that undergoes a reversible change in which the only work done is pressure-volume work:*

$$dE = T\,dS - p\,dV + \sum_{1}^{c} \mu_i\,dn_i. \tag{8.1}$$

Here T is the thermodynamic temperature, operationally defined on the basis of the two theorems in terms of entropy and heat, p and V are pressure and volume, n_i is the total amount of component i present in the system of all c components, and μ_i is the chemical potential of component i. Since by the first law dE is a perfect differential, equation (8.1) shows that we may identify T with $\partial E/\partial S$, p with $-\partial E/\partial V$, and μ_i with $\partial E/\partial n_i$.

It is also a matter of observation that the energy is a first-order homogeneous function of its variables S, V, and all n_i. That is, if each variable is multiplied by a factor a, then the function itself is multiplied by the same factor: i.e., $E(aS, aV, an_1, \ldots) \equiv aE(S, V, n_1, \ldots)^\dagger$.

The principles of homogeneous functions are applicable to the energy E when it is expressed in terms of the extensive variables S and V, and the n_i's. Extensive variables are recognized by the physical fact that, for example, when the system is doubled in amount of material, these variables are doubled. Hence we may apply Theorem I in Appendix 8.1 for a homogeneous function of first order to obtain the expression for the energy E, as

$$E = TS - pV + \sum \mu_i n_i. \tag{8.2}$$

---

* If other variables come into play, additional terms must be added. For example, electric work is governed by the electrostatic potential and charge, and surface work is determined by the surface tension and surface area.

† A function is said to be n-order homogeneous when each independent variable, multiplied by the factor a, gives the function itself multiplied by a^n. Thus, if F is a function in r variables, $x_1, x_2, \ldots, x_r$,

$$F(ax_1, ax_2, \ldots, ax_r) \equiv a^n F(x_1, x_2 \ldots x_r).$$

For example,

$$F = x_1 + x_2 + x_3 \quad \text{is order 1;}$$

$$F = x_1^4 + x_2^4 \quad \text{is order 4;}$$

$$F = \frac{x_1^2}{x_2 x_3} + \frac{x_2^2}{x_1^2} \quad \text{is order 0.}$$

Equation (8.2) can be regarded as the embodiment of the two laws of thermodynamics in integral form, and equation (8.1) that in differential form. Since E is first-order homogeneous in terms of the variables $S, V, n_1, \ldots$, the first partial derivatives $\partial E/\partial S$, $\partial E/\partial V$, and $\partial E/\partial n_i$ are zero order. The second derivatives are of order -1, and so on. These results follow from the general properties of homogeneous functions (see Theorem III in Appendix 8.1 for details).

The first derivatives of the energy, namely, T, p, and the μ_i, are zero order and they are called *intensive* variables. The general relations between the pairs of extensive and intensive quantities (S and T, V and p, n_i and μ_i) form the subject of chemical thermodynamics, or, we might say, *functional* chemistry, in particular, for our interests, the *functional chemistry* of biological systems.

If we had *a priori* analytical knowledge of E as a function of its variables, we would know everything about the thermodynamics of a system. The development of functional chemistry would then be reduced to mere differentiation of the energy function. Actually, of course, we have no such knowledge—functional chemistry, like all chemistry, is an experimental subject, and E can be obtained only by observation of its derivatives. If we were able experimentally to measure all the intensive quantities as functions of the extensive ones, then, to be sure, we could, by integration (graphical or analytical), obtain E subject to a constant, which, owing to its first-order homogeneous property, could be set equal to zero.

Of the variables involved in equations (8.1) and (8.2), T, p, V, and the amounts n_i are all susceptible to direct measurement. The entropy S, on the other hand, is known to us only in terms of its changes, being given by the heat Q absorbed during a reversible process that takes the system from an arbitrarily chosen state 1 to state 2. The value of $S_2 - S_1 = \int_1^2 dQ/T$, and is independent of the path. Thus S, as known to us experimentally, is, at any given temperature, subject to an unknown constant*. Similarly, each chemical potential μ_i, being given by the work done in taking the component in question from an arbitrarily chosen standard state to another state, is thus subject to an arbitrary constant, namely, its value in the standard state.

The aim of functional chemistry is to establish relations between the extensive and intensive variables of a system, for example, the binding curve of a macromolecule. There are some general conditions that always apply here. The total number of variables (extensive and intensive) is $4 + 2c$, i.e., S, T, V, p, and c pairs of terms n_i, μ_i. Of these, a number t are independent—half of the total. In practice we deal with relations involving first-order and higher-order partial derivatives of the energy. The second-order derivatives are of greatest interest, since they reveal the interdependence of the different functions of a macromolecule. The influence of pH on the oxygen binding of respiratory

---

* This takes no account of the Third Law of Thermodynamics, which states that the entropy of a perfect crystal at absolute zero is zero. This has been of great importance in dealing with simple molecules that can form perfect crystals, or crystals with calculable randomness. Protein crystals, which contain significant amounts of water and other components, have thus far not yielded crystals suitable for application of Third-Law principles.

proteins such as hemoglobin is an example. The second-order derivatives are homogeneous functions of -1 order in the extensive variables (S, V, and the n_i), and fall into two classes, which describe *homotropic* and *heterotropic* effects.

The *homotropic* derivatives are $\partial V/\partial p$, $\partial S/\partial T$, and $\partial n_i/\partial \mu_i$, and involve conjugate variables, i.e., (p, V), (T, S), and $(\mu, n.)$. The derivatives represent the compressibility $[\beta = -1/V(\partial V/\partial p)]$, the heat capacity $[C = T(\partial S/\partial T)]$, and the slope of the binding-curve, or the binding capacity $[\text{Б} = 1/n_M(\partial n_x/\partial \mu_x)]$, where n_M denotes the moles of macromolecule in the system. The binding capacity Б can be considered the chemical parallel of the heat capacity (Di Cera *et al.*, 1988b). The number of homotropic derivatives is $2 + c = t$, two for the ever present physical variables (T, S, p, V), and c for the chemical terms. The *heterotropic* derivatives involve nonconjugate variables. They are $\partial T/\partial V$, $\partial p/\partial S$, $\partial \mu_i/\partial n_j$, etc. Since each of the independent variables has $t - 1$ nonconjugate variables, there are $t(t - 1)$ heterotropic derivatives. However, only half of these are independent, because of the existence of relations, like the Maxwell equations, that arise from second derivatives of the energy functions:

$$\frac{\partial^2 E}{\partial S \, \partial V} = \frac{\partial^2 E}{\partial V \, \partial S} \quad \text{or} \quad \frac{\partial T}{\partial V} = -\frac{\partial p}{\partial S} \tag{8.3}$$

and

$$\frac{\partial^2 E}{\partial n_2 \partial n_1} = \frac{\partial^2 E}{\partial n_1 \partial n_2} \quad \text{or} \quad \frac{\partial \mu_1}{\partial n_2} = \frac{\partial \mu_2}{\partial n_1}. \tag{8.4}$$

Hence the number of independent heterotropic derivatives is $t(t - 1)/2$. These equations define what may be called linkage of the first order. Finally, since there are t independent homotropic derivatives and $t(t - 1)/2$ independent heterotropic derivatives, we have a total of $t + t(t - 1)/2 = t(t + 1)/2$ independent derivatives that describe any given system.

In practical terms, the extent to which we can implement the ideas concerning the functional properties described by homotropic and heterotropic derivatives depends on our ability (1) to measure them (whether or not absolutely) and (2) to fix the values of the various extensive and intensive variables of a system. For pressure, volume, and moles of various components, this usually presents no problem. For the others (especially chemical potentials), it generally calls for the introduction of auxiliary phases in equilibrium with the system under consideration.

Consider, for example, the specification of the temperature T of a system. The operational definition of the absolute value of T, in spite of the unknown constants involved in S and E, is one of the triumphs of nineteenth-century physics. It is a deduction of thermodynamics that in any polyphase system at equilibrium, the value of each intensive variable must be the same in all the phases. A thermometer, whether it be a gas or an ordinary mercury thermometer, is itself, after all, a phase, and when we place it in the system under observation, we are in fact introducing an additional phase. To be sure, this phase may be made so small that it does not appreciably alter the state of the system to which it is applied, but it remains nevertheless an unavoidable additional phase. In measuring entropy changes, we measure the change in our system by keeping it in contact with a heat reservoir as it undergoes a reversible change. The heat reservoir is itself another phase. For the chemical potential μ_i, its measurement is accomplished (a) by exposing the system to a vapor phase in which the ith component has a measurable partial pressure, (b) by introducing a suitable electrode, or (c) by introducing a semipermeable membrane, as in osmotic-pressure determination. In all of these measurements an instrument, another phase, is used to measure a specific property of the system.

8.2   THERMODYNAMIC POTENTIALS AND THE LEGENDRE TRANSFORMATION

Starting from the energy, we can obtain a whole set of additional functions or potentials, by use of the Legendre transformation*. Gibbs in effect used this procedure to obtain the familiar potentials enthalpy (H), Helmholtz free energy (A), and the Gibbs free energy (G). We shall show that there are additional ones of special use. The Legendre transformation by its specific properties allows us to obtain these various potentials starting from any one.

We shall start with the energy E for a one-component system. The energy differential is then expressed by

$$dE = T\,dS - p\,dV + \mu\,dn, \tag{8.5}$$

and the following partial derivatives determine the temperature, pressure, and chemical potential of the system:

$$T = \left(\frac{\partial E}{\partial S}\right)_{V,n}, \tag{8.6}$$

$$-p = \left(\frac{\partial E}{\partial V}\right)_{S,n}, \tag{8.7}$$

$$\mu = \left(\frac{\partial E}{\partial n}\right)_{S,V}. \tag{8.8}$$

---

* The Legendre transformation may be formally defined as follows. Let ϕ be a function of t variables $x_1, x_2 \cdots x_t$, and let $\xi_i = \partial\phi/\partial x_i$. Suppose that ϕ, together with its first derivatives ξ_i, is continuous. Define a new function ϕ' as $\phi' = \phi - x_i\xi_i$. Then ϕ' has the property that $\partial\phi'/\partial x_j = \xi_j$ for $j \neq i$ and $\partial\phi'/\partial\xi_i = -x_i$. The transformation of ϕ to ϕ' is the Legendre transformation. In the new function ϕ', the variable x_i is replaced with the new independent variable ξ_i.

We now perform a Legendre transformation with respect to p and V to obtain a new thermodynamic function, the enthalpy. The procedure is to take the original function, and subtract from it the derivative of E with respect to the concerned variable, here the volume, multiplied by the variable itself: $E - (\partial E/\partial V)V = E - (-p)(V)$. This gives the enthalpy $H = E + pV$. The derivative of H is $dH = dE + p\,dV + V\,dp$, and substitution of dE gives the differential relation of H in terms of the variables S, p, and n:

$$dH = T\,dS + V\,dp + \mu\,dn. \tag{8.9}$$

In this particular Legendre transformation, we have passed to a new function (H) in which one of the extensive variables, specifically, V, has been replaced by the conjugate intensive one, $-p$. The partial derivatives of H with respect to any one of its variables determine characteristic properties of the system:

$$T = \left(\frac{\partial H}{\partial S}\right)_{p,n}, \tag{8.10}$$

$$V = \left(\frac{\partial H}{\partial p}\right)_{S,n}, \tag{8.11}$$

$$\mu = \left(\frac{\partial H}{\partial n}\right)_{p,S}. \tag{8.12}$$

Another Legendre transformation applied to E with respect to the variable S leads to $E - TS = A$, known as the Helmholtz potential. Differentiation gives

$$dA = -S\,dT - p\,dV + \mu\,dn, \tag{8.13}$$

and we note the variables are T, V, and n. Applying the Legendre transformation to E with respect to both V and S gives $E + pV - TS = G$, known as the Gibbs potential or Gibbs free energy. Differentiation of this gives

$$dG = -S\,dT + V\,dp + \mu\,dn, \tag{8.14}$$

in which the variables are now T, p, and n. A fifth transformation, in which E is transformed with respect to n, gives $E_I = E - \mu n$, which has no special name, but defines a potential with variables S, V, and μ. Likewise, a sixth transformation, found with respect to V and n, gives $H_I = E + pV - \mu n$, with variables T, V, and μ. A seventh transformation is obtained with respect to S and n, and yields $A_I = E - TS - \mu n$. Finally, we find the eighth and last transformation, in which E is transformed with respect to all three variables, V, S, and n, giving $E + pV - TS - \mu n = 0$, which, as indicated, vanishes identically. Differentiation and substitution of dE give

$$0 = S\,dT - V\,dp + n\,d\mu. \qquad (8.15)$$

This is the Gibbs-Duhem equation. A summary of these Legendre transformations that determine the different linkage potentials, with their specified independent variables, is shown in Table 8.1. Each of these transformations,

Table 8.1
Thermodynamic potentials derived from E by Legendre transformation to a single-component system

Potential	Legendre transformation	Derivative	Independent variable
E		$dE = T\,dS - p\,dV + \mu\,dn$	S, V, n
H	$E - \dfrac{\partial E}{\partial V}V = E + pV$	$dH = T\,dS + V\,dp + \mu\,dn$	S, p, n
A	$E - \dfrac{\partial E}{\partial S}S = E - TS$	$dA = -S\,dT - p\,dV + \mu\,dn$	T, V, n
G	$E - \dfrac{\partial E}{\partial V}V - \dfrac{\partial E}{\partial S}S = E + pV - TS$	$dG = -S\,dT + V\,dp + \mu\,dn$	T, p, n
E_I	$E - \dfrac{\partial E}{\partial n}n = E - \mu n$	$dE_I = T\,dS - p\,dV - n\,d\mu$	S, V, μ
H_I	$E - \dfrac{\partial E}{\partial V}V - \dfrac{\partial E}{\partial n}n = E + pV - \mu n$	$dH_I = T\,dS + V\,dp - n\,d\mu$	S, p, n
A_I	$E - \dfrac{\partial E}{\partial S}S - \dfrac{\partial E}{\partial n}n = E - TS - \mu n$	$dA_I = -S\,dT - p\,dV - n\,d\mu$	T, V, μ
0	$E - \dfrac{\partial E}{\partial V}V - \dfrac{\partial E}{\partial S}S - \dfrac{\partial E}{\partial n}n = E + pV - TS - \mu n$	$0 = -S\,dT + V\,dp - n\,d\mu$	T, p, μ

except the last, gives a useful set of heterotropic linkage relations as given by equations (8.3) and (8.4). These are obtained either by equating second-order heterotropic derivatives of the potential or by equating appropriate cross derivatives of each potential. The results are given in detail in Table 8.2.

There is no potential defined by the last transformation, and therefore no linkage relations can be based on it. This corresponds to the fact that we cannot describe the amount of a system by specifying only the intensive variables T, p, and μ. We note that, corresponding to any one potential, there are three linkage relations, and with seven potentials there are 21 linkage relations.

Table 8.2
Linkage relations for various potentials for a single-component system

Potential	Linkage relations		
E	$\left(\dfrac{\partial T}{\partial V}\right)_{S,n} = -\left(\dfrac{\partial p}{\partial S}\right)_{V,n};$	$\left(\dfrac{\partial T}{\partial n}\right)_{S,V} = \left(\dfrac{\partial \mu}{\partial S}\right)_{n,V};$	$-\left(\dfrac{\partial p}{\partial n}\right)_{V,S} = \left(\dfrac{\partial \mu}{\partial V}\right)_{n,S}$
H	$\left(\dfrac{\partial T}{\partial p}\right)_{S,n} = \left(\dfrac{\partial V}{\partial S}\right)_{T,n};$	$\left(\dfrac{\partial T}{\partial n}\right)_{S,p} = \left(\dfrac{\partial \mu}{\partial S}\right)_{p,n};$	$\left(\dfrac{\partial \mu}{\partial p}\right)_{S,n} = \left(\dfrac{\partial V}{\partial n}\right)_{S,p}$
A	$\left(\dfrac{\partial S}{\partial V}\right)_{T,n} = \left(\dfrac{\partial p}{\partial T}\right)_{V,n};$	$-\left(\dfrac{\partial S}{\partial n}\right)_{T,V} = \left(\dfrac{\partial \mu}{\partial T}\right)_{V,n};$	$-\left(\dfrac{\partial p}{\partial n}\right)_{V,T} = \left(\dfrac{\partial \mu}{\partial V}\right)_{T,n}$
G	$-\left(\dfrac{\partial S}{\partial p}\right)_{T,n} = \left(\dfrac{\partial V}{\partial T}\right)_{p,n};$	$-\left(\dfrac{\partial S}{\partial n}\right)_{T,p} = \left(\dfrac{\partial \mu}{\partial T}\right)_{n,p};$	$\left(\dfrac{\partial V}{\partial n}\right)_{T,p} = \left(\dfrac{\partial \mu}{\partial p}\right)_{T,n}$
E_I	$\left(\dfrac{\partial T}{\partial V}\right)_{S,\mu} = -\left(\dfrac{\partial p}{\partial S}\right)_{V,\mu};$	$\left(\dfrac{\partial T}{\partial \mu}\right)_{S,V} = -\left(\dfrac{\partial n}{\partial S}\right)_{\mu,V};$	$\left(\dfrac{\partial p}{\partial \mu}\right)_{V,S} = \left(\dfrac{\partial n}{\partial V}\right)_{\mu,S}$
H_I	$\left(\dfrac{\partial T}{\partial p}\right)_{S,\mu} = \left(\dfrac{\partial V}{\partial S}\right)_{p,\mu};$	$\left(\dfrac{\partial T}{\partial \mu}\right)_{S,p} = -\left(\dfrac{\partial n}{\partial S}\right)_{\mu,p};$	$\left(\dfrac{\partial V}{\partial \mu}\right)_{p,S} = -\left(\dfrac{\partial n}{\partial p}\right)_{\mu,S}$
A_I	$\left(\dfrac{\partial S}{\partial V}\right)_{T,\mu} = \left(\dfrac{\partial p}{\partial T}\right)_{V,\mu};$	$\left(\dfrac{\partial S}{\partial \mu}\right)_{T,V} = \left(\dfrac{\partial n}{\partial T}\right)_{\mu,V};$	$\left(\dfrac{\partial p}{\partial \mu}\right)_{V,T} = \left(\dfrac{\partial n}{\partial V}\right)_{\mu,T}$

8.3   THE LINKAGE POTENTIALS

In most practical terms the functional chemistry of a system is determined not by its absolute size, but rather by its intensive properties. The composition may be described in relative terms, and the appropriate intensive variables are T, p, and μ_i. Thus the usual set of potentials, E, H, A, G, etc., that we defined through the Legendre transformation, and which depend on the extent of the system, may not be the most appropriate to characterize the interactions and interrelationships between different thermodynamic properties of the system. What we want are thermodynamic potentials, which are independent of the size of the system. These potentials can be obtained by the procedure of *normalization* (Wyman, 1965), and are called linkage potentials (Wyman, 1975a).

The normalization is accomplished by dividing through the regular potentials by the amount of one component, chosen as the reference component. Since we are primarily concerned with the properties of the macromolecular components, the usual normalizing quantity is the moles of macromolecule, and for this purpose we shall write the normalized potentials with a tilde ($\sim$) over the potential symbol. Thus if there are n moles of macromolecule, the normalized energy $\tilde{E}$ is defined by

$$\tilde{E} = \frac{E}{n}. \tag{8.16}$$

Likewise, normalized entropy and volume are indicated by $\tilde{S}$ and $\tilde{V}$. The operation of normalizing $E(S, V, n)$ by n moles is equivalent to dividing each extensive variable by n. In functional form, this is given as

$$\tilde{E} = \tilde{E}(\tilde{S}, \tilde{V}, 1). \tag{8.17}$$

This is the same as removing n as a variable by setting $n = 1$. The normalized function then describes the thermodynamics of the system per mole of macromolecule. The presence of the constant, i.e., 1, in equation (8.17), destroys the mathematical homogeneity of this function. (See Theorem V in Appendix 8.1 for a detailed proof.) This normalization is a fundamental point having significant consequences, because all Legendre transformations of nonhomogeneous (or normalized) functions are nonzero; i.e., they all exist. In contrast, we have just shown that for a first-order homogeneous function, such as the energy, one transformation gives a zero result, and thus does not give a potential function. In the following sections we apply these concepts to the formulation of linkage potentials where the normalizing component is the moles of macromolecule in the system. Here the macromolecule drops out of the picture, and plays the role of an observer. Clearly, any component may be chosen as the reference component, and each choice will correspond to a different observer.

We start with the normalized energy $\tilde{E}$. From equation (8.5) with n at a fixed value of one mole, we may write $d\tilde{E} = T\,d\tilde{S} - p\,d\tilde{V}$. From this we can proceed to obtain all other potentials by Legendre transformation, i.e., $\tilde{H} = \tilde{E} + p\tilde{V}$, $\tilde{A} = \tilde{E} - T\tilde{S}$, and $\tilde{G} = \tilde{E} + p\tilde{V} - T\tilde{S}$. (Had we normalized with respect to $V = 1$, then we would have obtained a different group of four normalized potentials, where $\mu\tilde{n}$ replaces $-p\tilde{V}$.) The derivatives of the normalized potentials are

$$d\tilde{E} = T\,d\tilde{S} - p\,d\tilde{V}, \tag{8.18}$$

$$d\tilde{H} = T\,d\tilde{S} + \tilde{V}\,dp, \tag{8.19}$$

$$d\tilde{A} = -\tilde{S}\,dT - p\,d\tilde{V}, \tag{8.20}$$

$$d\tilde{G} = -\tilde{S}\,dT + \tilde{V}\,dp. \tag{8.21}$$

This is a subgroup of the homogeneous function E, for which one of the variables, namely, n, has been eliminated, and is complete without the disappearance of any member. Here there are two variables, and the Legendre transformation gives rise to three new potentials, making a total of four. There is one linkage relation for each potential, giving a total of $1 \times 4 = 4$. These are the first members of the familiar Maxwell relations.

We next show how normalization affects the potentials for a two-component system by normalizing with respect to the moles (n_2) of a second component. The results are summarized in Table 8.3.

Table 8.3

Normalized potential of a two-component system with respect to moles of second component ($\tilde{E} = E/n_2$, $\tilde{S} = S/n_2$, etc.)

Potential	Variables	Legendre transform	Derivative function
$\tilde{E}$	$\tilde{S}, \tilde{V}, \tilde{n}_1$		$d\tilde{E} = T\,d\tilde{S} - p\,d\tilde{V} + \mu_1\,d\tilde{n}_1$
$\tilde{H}$	$\tilde{S}, p, \tilde{n}_1$	$\tilde{E} + p\tilde{V}$	$d\tilde{H} = T\,d\tilde{S} + \tilde{V}\,dp + \mu_1\,d\tilde{n}_1$
$\tilde{A}$	$T, \tilde{V}, \tilde{n}_1$	$\tilde{E} - T\tilde{S}$	$d\tilde{A} = -\tilde{S}\,dT - p\,d\tilde{V} + \mu_1\,d\tilde{n}_1$
$\tilde{G}$	$T, p, \tilde{n}_1$	$\tilde{E} + p\tilde{V} - T\tilde{S}$	$d\tilde{G} = -\tilde{S}\,dT + \tilde{V}\,dp + \mu_1\,d\tilde{n}_1$
$\tilde{E}_I$	$\tilde{S}, \tilde{V}, \mu_1$	$\tilde{E} - \mu_1\tilde{n}_1$	$d\tilde{E}_I = T\,d\tilde{S} - p\,d\tilde{V} - \tilde{n}_1\,d\mu_1$
$\tilde{H}_I$	$\tilde{S}, p, \mu_1$	$\tilde{H} - \mu_1\tilde{n}_1$	$d\tilde{H}_I = T\,d\tilde{S} + \tilde{V}\,dp - \tilde{n}_1\,d\mu_1$
$\tilde{A}_I$	$T, \tilde{V}, \mu_1$	$\tilde{A} - \mu_1\tilde{n}_1$	$d\tilde{A}_I = -\tilde{S}\,dT - p\,d\tilde{V} - \tilde{n}_1\,d\mu_1$
$\tilde{G}_I$	T, p, μ_1	$\tilde{G} - \mu_1\tilde{n}_1$	$d\tilde{G}_I = -\tilde{S}\,dT + \tilde{V}\,dp - \tilde{n}_1\,d\mu_1$

Table 8.3 shows that all the normalized potentials are realized by the Legendre transform. This was not the case when the nonnormalized function E was subject to Legendre transform (see Table 8.1), where one of the potentials was zero. As noted, a complete set of potentials can be obtained by this process because of the zero-order homogeneous nature of the linkage potential. Furthermore, the full set of linkage relations between the various normalized parameters and the intensive properties of the system can be obtained.

The last of the expressions in Table 8.3 is related to the Gibbs-Duhem equation. For a two-component system, we have

$$0 = -S\,dT + V\,dp - n_1\,d\mu_1 - n_2\,d\mu_2. \tag{8.22}$$

When we normalize this by dividing by n_2, we obtain, upon rearrangement,

$$d\mu_2 = -\tilde{S}\,dT + \tilde{V}\,dp - \tilde{n}_1\,d\mu_1. \tag{8.23}$$

Thus the linkage potential $\tilde{G}_I$ is the same as the chemical potential of the reference component.

Generalization to a three-component system is straightforward. We first normalize with respect to the moles of component three, i.e., n_3. Then $\tilde{E}$ is expressed as a function of $\tilde{S}, \tilde{V}, \tilde{n}_1$, and $\tilde{n}_2$. The Legendre transformation with respect to the normalized molar variables $\tilde{n}_1$ and $\tilde{n}_2$ then gives three new potentials in addition to the original potential for each set. For example, the $\tilde{E}$ potentials with the pertinent variables written in parentheses are

$$\tilde{E} \qquad\qquad (\tilde{S}, \tilde{V}, \tilde{n}_1, \tilde{n}_2),$$

$$\tilde{E}_1 = \tilde{E} - \tilde{n}_1 \mu_1 \qquad (\tilde{S}, \tilde{V}, \mu_1, \tilde{n}_2), \qquad (8.24)$$

$$\tilde{E}_2 = \tilde{E} - \tilde{n}_2 \mu_2 \qquad (\tilde{S}, \tilde{V}, \tilde{n}_1, \mu_2), \qquad (8.25)$$

$$\tilde{E}_{12} = \tilde{E} - \tilde{n}_1 \mu_1 - \tilde{n}_2 \mu_2 \qquad (\tilde{S}, \tilde{V}, \mu_1, \mu_2). \qquad (8.26)$$

The new potentials $(\tilde{E}_i)$ are specified by the subscript, which indicates the chemical ligand variables involved in the transformation. This procedure yields 2^4 normalized potentials when all four potentials E, H, A, and G are used for a three-component system.

A system of special practical interest occurs when the physical variables are T and p, and are held fixed. The relevant potentials are then the G functions. For example, suppose a biological macromolecule (M) is present, along with water (W), and added ligands X and Y, which might be salts, buffers, oxygen, and so forth. Then the functional properties of the G function for this four-component case are shown in Table 8.4.

Table 8.4

Properties of the $\tilde{G}$ potentials at constant T, p for a four-component system: macromolecule(M), water (W), and ligands (X, Y).

Function	Variables	Differential expression
$\tilde{G}$	$\tilde{W}, \tilde{X}, \tilde{Y}$	$d\tilde{G} = \mu_W\, d\tilde{W} + \mu_X\, d\tilde{X} + \mu_Y\, d\tilde{Y}$
$\tilde{G}_W = \tilde{G} - \tilde{W}\mu_W$	$\mu_W, \tilde{X}, \tilde{Y}$	$d\tilde{G}_W = -\tilde{W}\, d\mu_W + \mu_X\, d\tilde{X} + \mu_Y\, d\tilde{Y}$
$\tilde{G}_X = \tilde{G} - \tilde{X}\mu_X$	$\tilde{W}, \mu_X, \tilde{Y}$	$d\tilde{G}_X = \mu_W\, d\tilde{W} - \tilde{X}\, d\mu_X + \mu_Y\, d\tilde{Y}$
$\tilde{G}_Y = \tilde{G} - \tilde{Y}\mu_X$	$\tilde{W}, \tilde{X}, \mu_Y$	$d\tilde{G}_Y = \mu_W\, d\tilde{W} + \mu_X\, d\tilde{X} - \tilde{Y}\, d\mu_Y$
$\tilde{G}_{WX} = \tilde{G}_W - \tilde{X}\mu_X$	$\mu_W, \mu_X, \tilde{Y}$	$d\tilde{G}_{WX} = -\tilde{W}\, d\mu_W - \tilde{X}\, d\mu_X + \mu_Y\, d\tilde{Y}$
$\tilde{G}_{WY} = \tilde{G}_W - \tilde{Y}\mu_Y$	$\mu_W, \tilde{X}, \mu_Y$	$d\tilde{G}_{WY} = -\tilde{W}\, d\mu_W + \mu_X\, d\tilde{X} - \tilde{Y}\, d\mu_Y$
$\tilde{G}_{XY} = \tilde{G}_X - \tilde{Y}\mu_Y$	$\tilde{W}, \mu_X, \mu_Y$	$d\tilde{G}_{XY} = \mu_W\, d\tilde{W} - \tilde{X}\, d\mu_X - \tilde{Y}\, d\mu_Y$
$\tilde{G}_{WXY} = \tilde{G}_{WX} - \tilde{Y}\mu_Y$	μ_W, μ_X, μ_Y	$d\tilde{G}_{WXY} = -\tilde{W}\, d\mu_W - \tilde{X}\, d\mu_X - \tilde{Y}\, d\mu_Y$

The last of the generalized $\tilde{G}$ functions represented in Table 8.4 correspond, except for sign, to the binding potential, which was originally denoted by Π (Wyman, 1965). The identity is $\Pi = -\tilde{G}_{WXY}$. The normalized total amount of ligand bound (such as $\tilde{X}$)* is seen to be given by the partial derivative $\partial\Pi/\partial\mu_X$

---

* It should be emphasized that the tilde represents the total (or thermodynamic) binding as distinct from the free and chemically bound in accordance with the mass law. The free is noted by $\hat{X}$, and the chemically bound by $\bar{X}$: $(\tilde{X} = \bar{X} + \hat{X})$. In favorable situations $\bar{X}$ can be determined by spectroscopic means.

at constant T, p. The sign of Π was chosen so that the partial derivative of Π with respect to μ_X gives $+\tilde{X}$. By the Gibbs-Duhem equation $\tilde{G}_{WXY}$ is identical to the chemical potential of the macromolecule μ_M, and thus $\Pi = -\mu_M$. Since the activity of the macromolecule is equal to $\exp[(\mu_M - \mu_M{}^o)/RT]$, where $\mu_M{}^o$ represents the standard-state value, this result is of fundamental importance in subsequent development involving use of the mass-action law for reactions between macromolecules, as occurs in the allosteric models used throughout this book.

As we go on adding more components (c) to the system, the number of different (normalized) potentials will increase by a factor of 2 for each new component, to make a total of $2^t = 4$, 8, 16, etc., for one, two, or three components where $t = 2 + (c - 1)$. For any one of these potentials, there will be $t(t - 1)/2$ linkage relations, or, 1, 3, 6, etc., and thus the total number of linkage relations is $2^t \cdot (t - 1)/2$ or 4, 24, 96, etc., for one-, two-, or three-component systems.* Obviously we will not formulate all of them. For a given physical situation corresponding to $\tilde{E}$, $\tilde{H}$, $\tilde{A}$, or $\tilde{G}$ defined by the physical variables T or $\tilde{S}$, p or $\tilde{V}$, we have 2^{c-1} subpotentials. The physical variables most easily controlled in experiments are p and T. Thus the most appropriate subpotential is $\tilde{G}$, and this can be defined in 2^{c-1} different ways, depending on the particular way of choosing the independent variable from μ_i and $\tilde{n}_i$ (Wyman, 1984).

8.4   GROUP IDEAS ABOUT POTENTIALS

The behavior of the system in terms of linkage phenomena can be deduced from the set of linkage potentials. In this section we wish to show that the Legendre transformations applied to the linkage potentials form a complete mathematical *group*.

The existence of a group requires (1) that successive application of any two transformations gives rise to a transformation which is a member of the group, (2) that each transformation has an inverse or opposite which restores the original function, and (3) that there is an identity transformation which leaves the function unchanged. When the order of these transformations makes no difference, the group is said to be Abelian. Rigorously, it is the operations themselves which form a group, but as is often done (for example, by crystallographers in assigning crystals to space groups), we may speak of the normalized potentials themselves as a group, isomorphic with the group of transformations. In this sense the normalized potentials themselves form a closed group or a complete set. The order of the group, i.e., the number of its elements, is 2^t, where t is the number of variables $[2 + (c - 1)]$, the -1 representing the result of normalization to one component.

---

* In principle, the linkage relations apply to the total thermodynamic variable, i.e., for ligand X this is given by $\tilde{X}$. However, $\tilde{X} = \bar{X} + \hat{X}$, and if $\hat{X}$ is assumed to be unlinked, only then can the linkage relation become applicable to mass-law binding ($\bar{X}$).

The observed properties of the Legendre transformation of the linkage potentials suggest that they form a group. We first note that any two transformations, each involving a single variable, are equivalent to a single double transformation, e.g., if $\phi_1 = \phi - x_1 \xi_1$ and $\phi_{12} = \phi_1 - x_2 \xi_2$, then $\phi_{12} = \phi - x_1 \xi_1 - x_2 \xi_2$. The same principle holds for successive applications of double or higher-order transformations. Next, we observe that two successive applications of the same transformation restore the function to itself; e.g., if $\phi_1 = \phi - x_1 \xi_1$, then, since $\partial \phi_1 / \partial \xi_1 = -x_1$, we have the transformation of ϕ_1 given by $\phi_1 - \xi_1 (\partial \phi_1 / \partial \xi_1) = \phi_1 + \xi_1 x_1 = \phi$. From these two considerations, it is apparent that the transformations do indeed form a group, the product of any two elements being itself an element, and each being its own inverse. The identity element simply consists in leaving the function unchanged.

These ideas can be illustrated in thermodynamic terminology by considering a one-component system. Starting with the normalized potential $\tilde{E}(\tilde{S}, \tilde{V})$, we obtain, by the Legendre transformation with respect to $\tilde{V}$,

$$\tilde{H} = \tilde{E} - (\partial \tilde{E} / \partial \tilde{V}) \tilde{V} = \tilde{E} + p\tilde{V},$$

in which now $\tilde{H} = \tilde{H}(\tilde{S}, p)$. If we next perform the Legendre transformation on $\tilde{H}$ with regard to p, we obtain $\tilde{H} - (\partial \tilde{H} / \partial p)p = \tilde{H} - p\tilde{V} = \tilde{E}$, showing that each transformation has its own inverse. We may continue these operations by including the $T\tilde{S}$ transformation, and finally the double transformation, $p\tilde{V} + T\tilde{S}$, and so on. The results of these operations are summarized in Table 8.5.

Table 8.5
Legendre transformations applied to $\tilde{E}$ (one component)

	←	Transformation	→	
	1	$p\tilde{V}$	$T\tilde{S}$	$p\tilde{V} + T\tilde{S}$
1	$\tilde{E}$	$\tilde{H}$	$\tilde{A}$	$\tilde{G}$
$p\tilde{V}$	$\tilde{H}$	$\tilde{E}$	$\tilde{G}$	$\tilde{A}$
$T\tilde{S}$	$\tilde{A}$	$\tilde{G}$	$\tilde{E}$	$\tilde{H}$
$p\tilde{V} + T\tilde{S}$	$\tilde{G}$	$\tilde{A}$	$\tilde{H}$	$\tilde{E}$

Table 8.5 shows that all members of the group of normalized potentials exist, reflecting the fact that the normalized potentials are no longer first-order homogeneous. Thus for normalized potentials the Legendre transformation forms a group, in fact, an Abelian group. The symmetry properties of this group are those of a two-dimensional rectangle. The results summarized in Table 8.5 correspond to a multiplication table showing the operations as they

might be applied to any system, for example, symmetry operations applicable to a two-dimensional rectangle. In general terms, if we let a and b represent any two transformations, the general two-dimensional group multiplication table becomes that shown in Table 8.6.*

Table 8.6
Multiplication table for the two-dimensional group

	1	a	b	ab
1	1	a	b	ab
a	a	1	ab	b
b	b	ab	1	a
ab	ab	b	a	1

8.5 LINKAGE GRAPHS

Any linkage potential may be represented by a multidimensional surface in terms of the coordinates of the variables of the potential. Thus if we had an expression for the normalized energy $\tilde{E}$ as a function of $\tilde{V}$, $\tilde{S}$, and $\tilde{n}_i$, we could construct such a surface. The other potentials, such as $\tilde{H}$, $\tilde{A}$, and $\tilde{G}$, can be described in terms of the appropriate variables by application of the Legendre transformation. In practice, the potentials are known to us only in terms of their derivatives, which are found by experiment, and expressed graphically. Thus the integrated form can in general only be deduced from such graphs. Transformations to other potentials can in general be made only by graphical procedures.

To put these concepts in more concrete terms, consider the binding of oxygen and protons to hemoglobin at fixed concentration $\tilde{W}$, and T and p. The four pertinent subpotentials (see Table 8.4) are $\tilde{G}$, $\tilde{G}_X$, $\tilde{G}_Y$, and $\tilde{G}_{XY}$. With sufficient knowledge about any one, we can find the others by Legendre transformation. It is necessary to have experimental methods for simultaneous measurement of all four variables, μ_X, $\tilde{X}$, μ_Y, and $\tilde{Y}$, and we may describe the relevant information between these variables by pairs of graphs, each describing a term in the particular potential. For example, since $d\tilde{G}_{XY} = -\tilde{X} d\mu_X - \tilde{Y} d\mu_Y$, the important graphical information is contained in plots of $\tilde{X}$ versus μ_X at constant μ_Y and of $\tilde{Y}$ versus μ_Y at constant μ_X. Likewise, $\tilde{G}_Y$ is described graphically by $\tilde{X}$ versus μ_X (constant μ_Y) and $\tilde{Y}$ versus μ_Y (constant $\tilde{X}$). Such pairs of graphs are shown in Figure 8-1. In this figure

---

* This procedure can obviously be extended to include transformations involving multiple-component systems of c components. The order of the group is then 2^t, where $t = 2 + (c - 1)$, and such a group has the symmetries of a higher-dimensional rectangle (Wyman, 1975a).

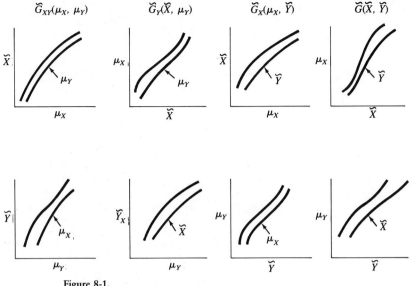

$\tilde{G}_{XY}(\mu_X, \mu_Y)$ $\tilde{G}_Y(\tilde{X}, \mu_Y)$ $\tilde{G}_X(\mu_X, \tilde{Y})$ $\tilde{G}(\tilde{X}, \tilde{Y})$

Figure 8-1.
Binding graphs for linkage potentials $\tilde{G}_{XY}$, $\tilde{G}_Y$, $\tilde{G}_X$, and $\tilde{G}$.

we have drawn only two curves (on each graph) chosen from the whole field. From properly chosen pairs of such plots, we may construct any other pair. This construction is equivalent to performing the Legendre transformation. The proper choice of suitable pairs is dictated by the requirement that between the pair all four variables, $\tilde{X}$, μ_X, $\tilde{Y}$, and μ_Y, must be represented. This excludes certain pairs of graphs. Graphs of this type are called linkage graphs (Wyman, 1984).

Each graph is also accompanied by the equation that relates the second-order derivatives that may be read from it. For example, the top left graph gives from its slope $(\partial\tilde{X}/\partial\mu_X)_{\mu_Y}$. The partial derivatives $(\partial\mu_Y/\partial\tilde{X})_{\mu_X}$ and $(\partial\mu_X/\partial\mu_Y)_{\tilde{x}}$ may be found from changes of the parameters (measured either vertically or horizontally) between closely spaced lines, as shown in Figure 8-2. Any two such partial derivatives determine the third from the general cyclic relation

$$\left(\frac{\partial\tilde{X}}{\partial\mu_X}\right)_{\mu_Y}\left(\frac{\partial\mu_Y}{\partial\tilde{X}}\right)_{\mu_X}\left(\frac{\partial\mu_X}{\partial\mu_Y}\right)_{\tilde{x}} = -1. \qquad (8.27)$$

Of course, graphs having their axes interchanged yield identical information concerning their partial derivatives; so we see that half of these, or four, are equivalent for that purpose. Thus we can find $3 \times 4 = 12$ partial derivatives from these graphs; four are homotropic, eight are heterotropic, and four of the latter are equivalent, because of linkage identities.

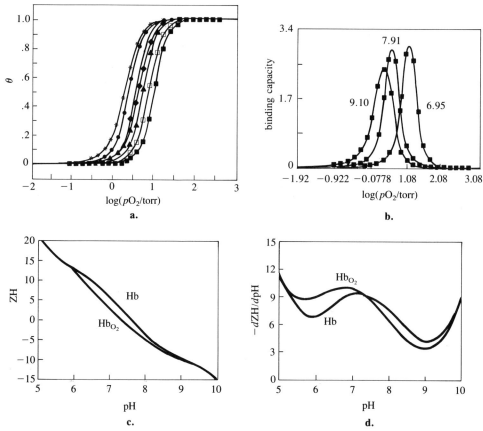

Figure 8-2.

Linkage graphs for hemoglobin in the presence of oxygen and protons. (a) Oxygen binding curves of HbA_0 at various pH values are depicted in this figure as binding curves. The pH values are: 6.95 (■), 7.27 (□), 7.51 (▲), 7.71 (△), 7.91 (*), 8.50 (◇), and 9.10 (◆) (Di Cera *et al.*, 1988a). (b) Oxygen-binding-capacity plot for hemoglobin for selected pH values (binding capacity = $\partial \bar{X} / \partial \ln p_{O2}$. (c) Proton-binding curve for oxygenated and deoxygenated human hemoglobin as a function of pH (taken from Janssen *et al.*, 1970). Note ZH is equivalent to $\tilde{n}_H$. (d) Proton-binding capacity as a function of pH.

For each graph in Figure 8-1 there are relevant equations that relate the first-order derivatives of the descriptive variables for each graph. Each of these are described by one homotropic derivative and two heterotropic ones. The number of independent second-order derivatives associated with *each* potential is $t(t + 1)/2$. In this case, where $t = 2$, there are three. Of these, two are homotropic, and one is heterotropic. Since we can transform any one potential to another, the number of independent second-order derivatives must be the same for each. However, the *total* number of second derivatives associated with any one potential is $t + t(t - 1) = t^2$, and the total for the whole subgroup is $t^2 \cdot 2^t$. For $t = 2$, there are 16. It follows that all 16 derivatives may be expressed in terms of three, of which two are homotropic and one is heterotropic.

Bridgman (1914) showed how all possible second-order derivatives involving the physical variables T, $\tilde{S}$, p, and $\tilde{V}$, and the four normalized potentials $\tilde{E}$, $\tilde{H}$, $\tilde{A}$, and $\tilde{G}$, could be expressed in terms of three chosen independent second-order derivatives. The chosen three were specific heat at constant pressure, compressibility at constant temperature, both homotropic, and the coefficient of thermal expansion, which is heterotropic. His tables are immediately transferable to the situation of $\tilde{X}$ and $\tilde{Y}$, considering just ligands, or to the mixed situation, such as $\tilde{S}$ and $\tilde{X}$, by noting the correspondence with appropriate independent second-order partial derivatives.*

8.6   APPLICATION OF LINKAGE GRAPHS

Suppose we are interested in the linkage relations, homotropic and heterotropic, of oxygen and proton binding to human hemoglobin at constant temperature and pressure. As we have shown, any two of the eight linkage graphs of Figure 8-1, which involve between them all four variables $\tilde{n}_{O_2}$, μ_{O_2}, $\tilde{n}_H$, μ_H, will then suffice to give a complete picture. Four representative graphs are shown in Figure 8-2.

The first graph gives us $\tilde{n}_{O_2}$ as a function of $\ln p_{O_2}$ at any given pH. Construction of the second graph involves carrying out a pH-titration curve of the protein (necessarily without buffer) either at constant $\tilde{n}_{O_2}$ or constant μ_{O_2}. Although this sounds simple, it is in fact difficult to do except when $\tilde{n}_{O_2} = 0$ or anyplace where the oxygen-binding curve shows a plateau over a range of values of μ_{O_2}. We are thus left in ignorance of the shape of the pH-titration curve at intermediate values of $\tilde{n}_{O_2}$ (or μ_{O_2}). We should make a large number of scattered measurements in the complete absence of buffer, measuring all four quantities, μ_{O_2}, $\tilde{n}_{O_2}$, μ_H, $\tilde{n}_H$, simultaneously, i.e., on aliquots of the same sample. From such data we could, with the aid of small interpolations, construct both graphs, and have a complete picture of oxygen and proton binding to human hemoglobin.

In any case, we must not forget that the two linkage graphs, however obtained and however precise, are for the whole system, and apply to the total amounts (corresponding to the tilde) of the ligands present, including both the amounts chemically bound and the amounts present in solution. Thus the picture they give, though it may be enough for the physiologist, will hardly

---

* In general, a theorem can be proven that the independent second derivatives associated with any one linkage potential are necessary and sufficient to express all second derivatives and, also, any given partial derivative that contains thermodynamic quantities as independent variables (Di Cera *et al.*, 1988c).

satisfy the molecular biologist's interest in the operation of the macromolecule as a physicochemical machine. His concern will usually center on the amounts of ligand chemically bound in accordance with the mass-action law. In general, it is very difficult to distinguish between the two kinds of binding, and it is only when fortune or ingenuity provides us with some special technique, some special pair of "spectacles," as it were, that we can separate them.

As another specific example, we consider measurements of CO_2 linkage to oxygen binding in human hemoglobin. Oxygen-binding curves were determined at various values of final CO_2 partial pressures, as shown in Figure 8-3 (Doyle et al., 1987). The analysis of these results in terms of the mass law involves four CO_2 oxygen-linked binding sites and two allosteric forms, R and T (the T form binds O_2 only to the α chains).

The linkage between CO_2 bound and O_2 bound at fixed values of CO_2 partial pressure is shown in Figure 8-4a. Here one clearly sees the negative linkage between O_2 and CO_2 binding, and the linkage is nearly constant over the entire range of oxygen binding for a given CO_2 pressure. This feature corresponds to the close parallelism seen in the oxygen-binding curves at different fixed CO_2 pressures and is a direct manifestation of the linkage relation

$$\left(\frac{\partial \bar{Y}}{\partial \bar{X}}\right)_{\ln y} = -\left(\frac{\partial \ln x}{\partial \ln y}\right)_{\bar{X}}. \tag{8.28}$$

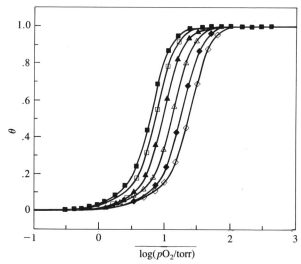

Figure 8-3.
Oxygen-binding curves for HbA_0 (30°C, pH 7.38) at fixed CO_2 pressures in torr: 0 (■), 10.6 (□), 27.2 (▲), 71.6 (△), 192 (◆), and 510 (◇). Curves are drawn using parameters given by Doyle et al., 1987.

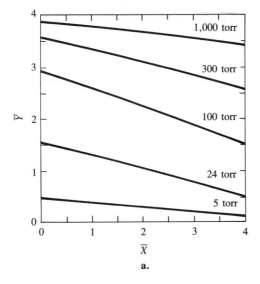
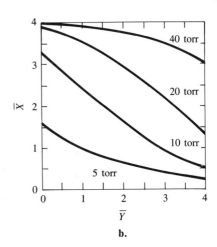

a.

b.

Figure 8-4.
(a) Linkage graph of CO_2 molecules bound $(\bar{Y})$ per hemoglobin molecule at various fixed CO_2 partial pressures as a function of number of O_2 molecules bound $(\bar{X})$.
(b) Number of O_2 molecules bound $(\bar{X})$ per hemoglobin molecule at various fixed O_2 partial pressures (in torr), as a function of the number of CO_2 molecules bound $(\bar{Y})$. Doyle et al., 1987. The slope of these curves determines

$$\left(\frac{\partial \bar{Y}}{\partial \bar{X}}\right)_{\ln y} \quad \text{and} \quad \left(\frac{\partial \bar{X}}{\partial \bar{Y}}\right)_{\ln x}.$$

The derivative on the left reflects the properties of Figure 8-4a, and the derivative on the right those of Figure 8-3.

Other linkage graphs can be constructed for this system from appropriate derivatives of the binding polynomial. The pair shown in Figure 8-5 represents the derivative properties of $\bar{G}(\mu_{O_2}, \mu_{CO_2})$.

Finally we show the CO_2 binding curve as a function of CO_2 partial pressure at fixed O_2 pressures (Figure 8-6). The corresponding linkage graph of bound oxygen versus bound CO_2 at fixed O_2 pressures (Figure 8-4b) is markedly different from its counterpart given in Figure 8-4a. The linkage between $\bar{X}$ and $\bar{Y}$ is not constant at given O_2 pressures, and the CO_2 binding curves are thus not parallel to each other. In fact, at intermediate oxygen fixed pressures, the CO_2 binding shows cooperativity. The cooperativity can be seen by plotting either the slope of the CO_2 binding curve or the calculated Hill slope, shown in Figure 8-7 as a function of CO_2 and oxygen pressure. The derivative of the binding curve is the *binding capacity*, discussed in Section 8.8.

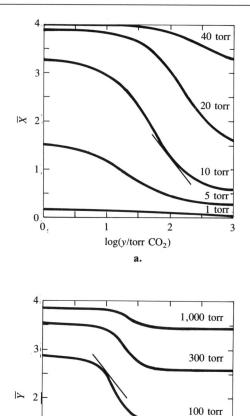

Figure 8-5.
(a) Number of O_2 molecules bound ($\bar{X}$) per hemoglobin as a function of the logarithm of CO_2 partial pressure (y) at given oxygen partial pressures.
(b) Number of CO_2 molecules bound ($\bar{Y}$) per hemoglobin as a function of logarithm of O_2 partial pressure (x), at given CO_2 partial pressures. The designated slopes illustrate the linkage-equation equality requirement,

$$\left(\frac{\partial \bar{X}}{\partial \ln y}\right)_{\ln x} = \left(\frac{\partial \bar{Y}}{\partial \ln x}\right)_{\ln y}.$$

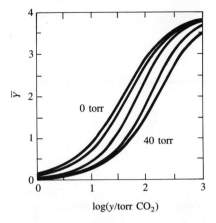

Figure 8-6.
Binding curve of CO_2 per mole of hemoglobin ($\bar{Y}$) versus logarithm of CO_2 partial pressure (torr) at fixed oxygen partial pressures (from left to right, 0, 5, 10, 20, and 40 torr) (Doyle *et al.*, 1987).

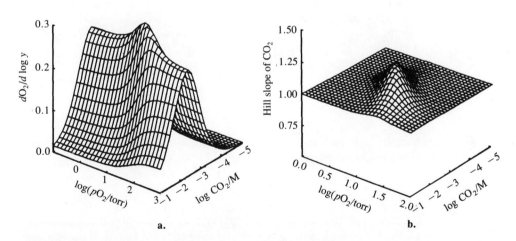

Figure 8-7.
(a) Binding capacity of carbon dioxide linked to oxygen binding as a function of the logarithm of oxygen partial pressure and carbon dioxide molarity. (b) Carbon dioxide Hill slope as a function of oxygen and carbon dioxide. Graphs constructed from data of Doyle *et al.* (1987).

8.7 PSEUDOLINKAGE

The binding potential (Л) contains the basic information about the functional properties and linkage exerted by the macromolecule through its ligands. When the binding potential is given by the sum of potentials, one for each ligand,

$$Л(\mu_W, \mu_X, \mu_Y) = Л(\mu_W) + Л(\mu_X) + Л(\mu_Y), \qquad (8.29)$$

there is no "true" linkage between any of the ligands. The macromolecule binds its ligands independently. For mass-law binding this leads to complete factorability of the binding polynomial if the system is expressible in this form.

We describe "true" linkage through the intensive properties that define the state of the system, i.e., the chemical potentials of the ligands. If the binding potential breaks down into functions such as

$$Л(\mu_W, \mu_X, \mu_Y) = Л(\mu_W, \mu_X) + Л(\mu_W, \mu_Y), \qquad (8.30)$$

then we have true linkage between W and X and between W and Y, but none between X and Y. These two situations may be depicted by the maps shown in Figure 8-8.

a.   **b.**

Figure 8-8.
Topological linkage map representation of (a) independent linkage group and (b) linkage of groups X and W, Y and W, but not X and Y. More complex situations obviously can be envisaged.

The nature of the linkage in a given system depends on the independent variables. When we pass from a description in terms of chemical potentials of all components to one of amounts of a given species, then we find that the linkage relations change, and situations which are unlinked in the "true" linkage description in terms of the binding potential become linked in terms of the variables of a different potential. This is termed *pseudolinkage*. For such situations the linkage relation, which is zero in terms of the intensive variables, becomes finite in terms of the new set of variables.

8.8 THE BINDING CAPACITY

Previous discussion has brought out a formal identity of physical (S and V) and chemical ligands (X and Y) within the linkage potentials. Given the linkage potential, then its first derivative yields $\partial \Pi/\partial \mu_x = \tilde{X}$, $\partial \Pi/\partial T = \tilde{S}$, and $\partial \Pi/\partial p = -\tilde{V}$. Likewise, the second homotropic derivatives are $\partial \tilde{X}/\partial \mu_x$, $\partial \tilde{S}/\partial T$, and $-\partial \tilde{V}/\partial p$; the last two determine the heat capacity and the compressibility. The first of these is the *binding capacity* Б . All three represent what we may call a generalized binding capacity, whether for physical or chemical ligands. For chemical binding, this is a measure of cooperativity. By the same analogy, the reciprocal of the derivative gives a generalized measure of buffering. Explicitly,

$$\text{Б}_X = \frac{\partial \tilde{X}}{\partial \mu_x}, \quad \text{Б}_S = \frac{\partial \tilde{S}}{\partial T}, \quad \text{Б}_V = \frac{\partial \tilde{V}}{\partial p}. \tag{8.31}$$

Each of the homotropic binding capacities will, in general, be a function of the external conditions, in terms of intensive or extensive variables. As a general principle, the binding capacity with fixed intensive variables will always be greater than that with fixed extensive variables, i.e.,

$$\text{Б}_\omega \geq \text{Б}_\Omega, \tag{8.32}$$

where Ω is an extensive quantity and ω its conjugate, intensive one. The general inequality (8.32) includes the familiar inequalities of heat capacity and compressibility; $C_p \geq C_V$ and $\beta_T \geq \beta_S$. For chemical binding it states that the cooperativity (or binding capacity) is always greater when all linked ligands are kept at constant chemical potentials. These alternative conditions (constancy of Ω or ω) distinguish "open" and "closed" systems. Inequality (8.32) represents a general property of the binding capacity for a thermodynamic system at equilibrium (Di Cera *et al.*, 1988b). It is a consequence of thermodynamic stability and can be extended to the heterotropic derivatives of the linkage potentials (Di Cera *et al.*, 1988c) as well.

8.9 SPECIFIC BINDING AND MODELS

The thermodynamic treatment given in the preceding sections points out the necessary relationships and describes properties of a macromolecular thermodynamic system in terms of measurable intensive and extensive variables. This description is of little use in understanding the chemical nature of the system unless the results can be interpreted in terms of some simplifying model. For example, the ideal gas law is an important model against which all gases can be interpreted in terms of correspondence or deviation. This model leads to formulation of the ideal-gas thermometer for measuring temperature, or to the ideal-gas chemical potential expression for measurement of chemical potentials. Deviation from these expressions, indicating nonideal corrections, gives activity coefficients to handle real systems exactly. The employment of model systems gives us the essential features of the system, and aids our intuitive understanding of complex phenomena.

In describing macromolecular systems in the presence of solvent and various ligands, we are faced with the need to formulate simple limiting model cases that contain key features of these complex systems. At one extreme we can think of the system as obeying ideal solution laws, applicable at high dilutions of all components. At another extreme we can consider that the amounts of ligands, X and Y, bind to the macromolecule according to ideal mass-action laws expressed in terms of concentrations of the various reactants.

As was indicated by the notation introduced in Chapter 7, the amount of ligand X bound per mole of macromolecule is represented by $\bar{X}$, and the amount that remains free or unbound per mole of macromolecule by $\hat{X}$. The total amount, which is the analyzable quantity, is $\tilde{X}$, and is, of course, given by the sum of $\bar{X}$ and $\hat{X}$:

$$\tilde{X} = \bar{X} + \hat{X}. \tag{8.33}$$

The fundamental thermodynamic quantity is $\tilde{X}$. The division of $\tilde{X}$ into $\bar{X}$ and $\hat{X}$ requires some type of operational procedure, such as spectroscopic or dialysis equilibrium determinations. The validity of this division is contingent on the ability of the model to describe the properties of $\bar{X}$ in terms of $\hat{X}$. Specific binding reactions between macromolecules and ligands adequately describe many biological reactions. To a first approximation these reactions seem appropriate for simple mass-action-law formulation. Reactions between macromolecules themselves can be expressed in terms of such ideal mass-action constants, but nonideal effects often complicate the real picture.

For the situation of specific ideal binding of X and Y ligands to a non-dissociating macromolecule, the amount of ligand bound per mole of macromolecule is given, as we have seen, by the derivatives of the partition function:

$$\bar{X} = \frac{\partial \ln Q}{\partial \ln x} = \frac{RT \partial \ln Q}{\partial \mu_x}, \quad \bar{Y} = \frac{\partial \ln Q}{\partial \ln y} = \frac{RT \partial \ln Q}{\partial \mu_y}, \tag{8.34}$$

where Q is the binding partition function (or binding polynomial). The basic linkage equations apply to the total amount of ligand, i.e., $\tilde{X}$ and $\tilde{Y}$. As an example, we can express a typical linkage relation as

$$\frac{\partial \bar{X}}{\partial \mu_Y} + \frac{\partial \hat{X}}{\partial \mu_Y} = \frac{\partial \bar{Y}}{\partial \mu_X} + \frac{\partial \hat{Y}}{\partial \mu_X}. \tag{8.35}$$

If there is no linkage involving the amounts *not* specifically bound, i.e., the $\hat{X}$ and $\hat{Y}$ terms, then $\partial \hat{X}/\partial \mu_Y = \partial \hat{Y}/\partial \mu_X = 0$, and the experimentally determined linkage relation based on measurements of *total* amounts gives the linkage for the amounts specifically bound:

$$\frac{\partial \bar{X}}{\partial \mu_Y} = \frac{\partial \bar{Y}}{\partial \mu_X}. \tag{8.36}$$

Under these conditions, we may relate the binding potential $\Pi \, (-\tilde{G}_{WYZ})$ for a given value of μ_Y and μ_X to $\ln Q$ as follows. The basic thermodynamic relation is the derivative of Π with respect to μ_X, which gives $\tilde{X}$:

$$\tilde{X} = \frac{\partial \Pi}{\partial \mu_X}. \tag{8.37}$$

However, the linkage derivative for $\bar{X}$ is given in terms of the binding partition function as

$$\frac{\partial \bar{X}}{\partial \mu_Y} = RT \frac{\partial^2 \ln Q}{\partial \mu_Y \, \partial \mu_X}. \tag{8.38}$$

If the free ligand ($\hat{X}$) is unlinked to μ_Y, then from (8.37) it follows that

$$\frac{\partial \bar{X}}{\partial \mu_Y} = \frac{\partial^2 \Pi}{\partial \mu_Y \, \partial \mu_X}. \tag{8.39}$$

Comparison of these last two equations shows that, except for a constant depending on the choice of standard states,

$$\Pi = RT \ln Q. \tag{8.40}$$

This is the mass-action-law model for Π, and corresponds to attributing all the linkage of the system to mass-action laws. It is this model which has formed the basis of the treatment developed in the previous chapters.

8.10 LINKAGE IN SOLUTIONS

The mass-action approach just described results from the neglect of the nonspecific binding. Alternatively, we may suppose mass-action binding is negligible in comparison to nonspecific binding. This leads to a consideration of linkage in ideal solutions.

Consider an ideal solution containing $r + 1$ components in the amounts $n_0, n_1, \ldots n_r$, and held at constant temperature and pressure. Then, since by definition an ideal solution is one in which the activity of each component is proportional to its mole fraction, we can write

$$a_i = \gamma_i \frac{n_i}{n_0 + n_1 + \cdots + n_r} = \gamma_i \frac{\hat{n}_i}{1 + \sum\limits_1^r \hat{n}_i}, \tag{8.41}$$

where each γ_i is a constant at any given temperature and pressure, and the second expression results from normalization by n_0; i.e., $\hat{n}_i = n_i/n_0$. If the activity a_i is expressed as the solution mole fraction, then $\gamma_i = 1$, and if the activity is expressed as a vapor pressure, then γ_i is the pure ith-component vapor pressure. [Note that the same formal expression also applies to dilute solutions, where Henry's law applies and where γ_i takes on the value of the Henry's law constant for the ith component.] There are r-linked equations between the a_i's and $\hat{n}_i$'s.

The derivative of the binding potential with respect to $\ln a_i$ yields $\hat{n}_i$:

$$\frac{1}{RT} \frac{\partial \Pi}{\partial \ln a_i} = \hat{n}_i. \tag{8.42}$$

In order to integrate this expression, we need to express $\hat{n}_i$ in terms of a_i. We note the mole fraction f_i is given by

$$f_i = \frac{\hat{n}_i}{1 + \sum \hat{n}_i}, \qquad i = 1, 2 \ldots r. \tag{8.43}$$

It follows that $\hat{n}_i = f_i/f_0$. Here $f_0 = 1 - \sum f_i$, and the summation is taken from 1 to r. Thus we may write

$$\hat{n}_i = \frac{f_i}{1 - \sum f_i}. \tag{8.44}$$

From (8.41), $a_i = \gamma_i f_i$, and we thus obtain

$$\hat{n}_i = \frac{a_i/\gamma_i}{1 - \sum a_i/\gamma_i}. \tag{8.45}$$

Substitution into and integration of equation (8.42) then yields the expression of Π for an ideal solution:

$$\Pi = -RT \ln\left(1 - \sum_1^r a_i/\gamma_i\right). \tag{8.46}$$

The activity a_i may be expressed in terms of the chemical potential of species i,

μ_i, as

$$a_i = e^{\ln(\mu_i - \mu_i^o)/RT}.$$ (8.47)

It will be recalled that $Л$ is minus the chemical potential of the reference component, the zeroth species.

When there are only two components, the ideal solution binding potential reduces to

$$Л = -RT \ln (1 - a_1/\gamma_1)$$ (8.48)

and

$$\hat{n}_1' = \frac{a_1/\gamma_1}{1 - a_1/\gamma_1}.$$ (8.49)

The graph of this equation is a rectangular hyperbola with asymptotes $a_1 = \gamma_1$ and $\hat{n}_1 = -1$, as shown in Figure 8-9. We are, of course, interested in only that

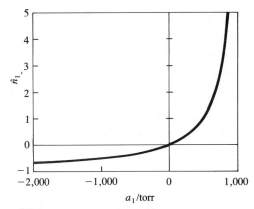

Figure 8-9.
Solvent (1) binding curve ($\hat{n}_1$, moles solvent/mole solute) as a function of activity (a_1) for an ideal solution with pure solvent vapor pressure, $\gamma_1 = 1,000$ torr.

part of the graph which lies in the first quadrant, and if γ_1, which may be identified with the vapor pressure of the pure component, is greater than the total applied pressure, the physically realizable part of it will be limited to that of the applied pressure.

This graph for solution-binding behavior may be compared with that for the simplest case of mass-law binding when there is a single site, and where the binding potential is $Л = RT \ln (1 + Kx)$, where K is the equilibrium constant, and x the activity of X. As we have seen before,

$$\bar{X} = \frac{Kx}{1 + Kx}. \tag{8.50}$$

This too corresponds to a rectangular hyperbola, but one with different asymptotes, namely, $\bar{X} = 1$ and $x = -1/K$, as shown in Figure 8-10. Again,

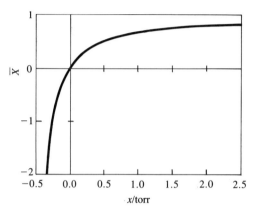

Figure 8-10.
Specific binding to single site with $K = 2$ torr^{-1} showing asymptotes at $-1/K$ and 1.

we are interested only in the portion of the graph which lies in the first quadrant, and again the value of x is limited by the total applied pressure.

In both cases we have assumed the "binding" to be ideal, as defined above. For mass-law binding, departures from ideality, representing cooperativity or anticooperativity, are clearly represented in a Hill plot. For solution binding they are best seen in a double reciprocal plot as departures from the straight line corresponding to the equation

$$\frac{1}{\hat{n}_1} = \frac{\gamma_1}{a_1} - 1. \tag{8.51}$$

Such a plot is shown in Figure 8-11.

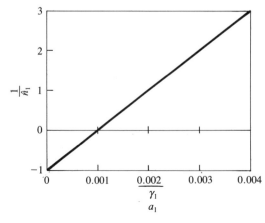

Figure 8-11.
Behavior of a perfect two-component solution represented in terms of a double reciprocal plot for situation shown in Figure 8-9.

It is apparent from Figure 8-10 that only if the observed binding curve of a two-component system (or, in fact, a system of any number of components) has an upper asymptote can we rule out the presence of "solution binding." However, because of the operational limitation imposed by the necessarily finite value of the total activity, this can never be established with certainty. Suppose we assume, as a working hypothesis (or model), that both types of binding are present, and that they are additive. What form for the binding curve may be expected? There are three cases to consider: if $K \gg 1/\gamma$, then specific binding dominates; if $K \approx 1/\gamma$, then both specific binding and solution binding occur; if $K \ll 1/\gamma$, then solution binding dominates. We have denoted specific binding by $\overline{X}$, nonspecific ideal binding by $\hat{X}$, and the presence of both by $\tilde{X}$. The ligand activity is x. These three cases are shown in Figure 8-12. These three graphs might describe a two-component system of macromolecules and ligand. It is evident that our assumptions allow for a

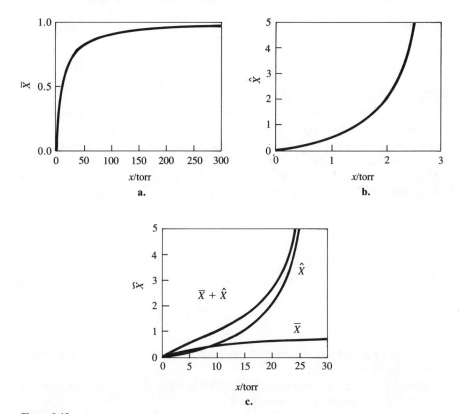

Figure 8-12.
Binding of X in a two-component idealized system: (a) specific binding; $\overline{X}$ vs. activity x, $K \gg 1/\gamma$. (b) nonspecific ideal solution; $\tilde{X}$ vs. x, $K \ll 1/\gamma$; (c) combination; $\tilde{X} = \overline{X} + \hat{X}$ vs. x, where $1/3\gamma = 1/K$. Cases shown are for $K = .1$, and $\gamma = 300$ (a), 3 (b), 30 (c).

wide variety of overall binding curves, each representing a combination of solution binding and mass-law binding in different proportions. If the observed curve is of type 8-12a, we conclude that the binding is essentially mass-law binding; if of type 8-12b, that it is essentially solution binding; if of type 8.12c, then it represents a combination of both kinds of binding in roughly equal proportions. If, further, we allow for the possibility of imperfect solution binding, or imperfect mass-law binding, or both, we can explain any overall binding curve. This raises the question of whether the distinction between the two types of binding is really meaningful. Indeed, were it not for phenomena which are encountered when one or more additional components are present, our assumption of two kinds of binding might be regarded as artificial. Before we go into this, however, there is another matter to be considered, namely, that of a three-component system (macromolecule, solvent, and ligand).

For a three-component system with dilute solution properties, we have

$$\hat{X} = \frac{x/\gamma_x}{1 - w/\gamma_w - x/\gamma_x}, \tag{8.52}$$

where γ_x is the activity coefficient (typically Henry's law coefficient for a gaseous ligand X) and γ_w is the activity coefficient for the solvent W (typically the vapor presence of pure solvent, taken for example as water). The terms x and w represent the ligand and water activities. It will be seen that in solutions there is always a heterotropic linkage between all components, since changing the mole ratio of any one component affects that of all the others. This represents a fundamental difference between solution "binding" and mass-law binding. In the latter, heterotropic linkage is no longer mandatory. [Relating to the discussion in Section 8.9, we now see that strictly equation (8.36) is only applicable when there is an excess amount of solvent, and heterotropic solution linkage between X and Y can approach zero.]

Specific binding to a single molecule is determined by (8.50), and the overall binding function ($\tilde{X} = \bar{X} + \hat{X}$) is then

$$\tilde{X} = \frac{Kx}{1 + Kx} + \frac{x/\gamma_x}{1 - w/\gamma_w - x/\gamma_x}. \tag{8.53}$$

The importance of the solvent activity ($w/\gamma_w = f_w \cong 1$) is clearly seen in the second term on the right in (8.53). Thus $\tilde{X}$ is very sensitive to the solvent concentration. This term originates from (8.53) because of the unbound species with a binding potential denoted by $\hat{\Pi}$.

8.11   THE MACROMOLECULAR CHEMICAL POTENTIAL

The differential of the complete macromolecular chemical potential ($\mu_M = -\tilde{\Pi}$) is given by the sum of the contributions from specific binding and solution binding:

$$d\mu_M = -d\tilde{\hat{\Pi}} = -d\bar{\Pi} - d\hat{\Pi}, \tag{8.54}$$

which from the Gibbs-Duhem equation at constant T and p may be expressed for a solution of macromolecule in water with ligand X as

$$d\mu_M = RT(-\tilde{W}d\ln w - \tilde{X}\,d\ln x). \tag{8.55}$$

The solution portion of the chemical potential of the macromolecule may be described by an activity denoted by a_M. The differential of $\hat{\Pi}$ is defined by

$$d\hat{\Pi} = -RT\,d\ln a_M, \tag{8.56}$$

which is also expressed by

$$d\hat{\Pi} = RT[\hat{X}\,d\ln x + \hat{W}\,d\ln w]. \tag{8.57}$$

Using the preceding set of equations, we obtain the practical expression

$$d\mu_M = RT[d\ln a_M - \bar{W}\,d\ln w - \bar{X}\,d\ln x]. \tag{8.58}$$

The determination of specific binding of solvent ($\bar{W}$) to the macromolecule requires some type of spectroscopic or dialysis method for its detection, and in dilute solutions the term $\bar{W}\,d\ln w$ may be neglected in comparison to the large contribution ($\hat{W}\,d\ln w$), which is effectively represented by $RT\,d\ln a_M$.

For two or more ligands, X and Y, with a macromolecular solution in which the solvent is present in large amount, we arrive at the operational equations (constant T and p)

$$d\hat{\Pi} = -RT[d\ln a_M - \bar{X}\,d\ln x - \bar{Y}\,d\ln y] \tag{8.59}$$

or

$$d\mu_M = RT[d\ln a_M - \bar{X}\,d\ln x - \bar{Y}\,d\ln y]. \tag{8.60}$$

These results depend on our being able to find values for $\bar{X}$ and $\bar{Y}$, as well as for the variables a_M, x, and y, by experiment.

8.12   THE MEASUREMENT OF μ_M BY OSMOTIC DIALYSIS

The macromolecular chemical potential, μ_M, is dependent, as we have seen, on the ligand chemical potentials (including the solvent), the pressure, the temperature, and the quantities of ligand specially bound for a given system. The practical thermodynamic method for achieving this measurement is the osmotic-dialysis technique, which has been analyzed by Scatchard (1946) and Eisenberg (1976). Here we analyze this problem from a somewhat different point of view that emphasizes the binding properties of the system.

The system consists of two phases: in one phase there are the macromolecule, M, the solvent W, and ligands X and Y; in the other phase there are the solvent and ligands alone. The system is maintained at equilibrium by application of an excess pressure, the osmotic pressure, π, imposed on the macromolecular solution side. The two phases are separated by a membrane permeable to solvent and the ligands, but not to the macromolecule. A schematic representation of the situation is shown in Figure 8-13. The diffusible components have equal chemical potential in both phases at equilibrium, whereas the volume of each phase is subject to different pressures. The solution and the dialysate, indicated by a prime superscript, are equivalent to two phases subject to the conditions of equilibrium given by Gibbs. At constant temperature the chemical potentials of the diffusible species must then obey these conditions:

$$\mu_W = \mu_W', \mu_X = \mu_X', \text{ and } \mu_Y = \mu_Y'. \tag{8.61}$$

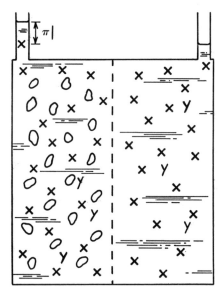

Figure 8-13.
Osmotic-pressure system consisting of two liquid regions, one containing the macromolecular species, and the other the solvent, separated by an impermeable membrane. Diffusible components (solvent W and ligands X and Y) are permeable to the membrane.

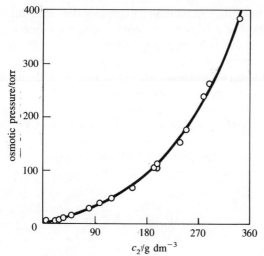

Figure 8-14.
Sheep-hemoglobin osmotic pressure (0°C) as a function of concentration c_2, as determined by Adair (1928), and represented by a simple hard-sphere model (———) developed by Ross and Minton (1977).

We may suppose that these chemical potentials are fixed initially at some specified values, determined by the dialysate alone. We then examine the effect of adding the macromolecule to the solution side. The osmotic pressure changes, since the macromolecule cannot penetrate the membrane.*

We first write complete expressions for the dependence of the chemical potential of components, common to both dialysate and solution, on the intensive properties of the system. The Gibbs-Duhem equation is written for the dialysate at fixed T and p:

$$n_W' \, d\mu_W + n_X' \, d\mu_X + n_Y' \, d\mu_Y = 0. \tag{8.62}$$

Similarly, the Gibbs-Duhem equation applied to the macromolecular solution under the osmotic pressure is

$$-(V - n_M V_M) \, d\pi + n_W \, d\mu_W + n_M \, d\mu_M + n_X \, d\mu_X + n_Y \, d\mu_Y = 0. \tag{8.63}$$

---

* The dependence of π typically is expressed in terms of c(gm/ml) as a virial expansion in terms of coefficients B, C, etc. This gives

$$\pi = \frac{cRT}{M}[1 + MBc + MCc^2 + \cdots]$$

where M is the molecular weight.

The second term in the parentheses expresses the effect of pressure on the chemical potential of M through its partial molar volume V_M. Choosing the solvent water as the reference component, we then divide each of these equations by the respective moles of water, and upon subtraction we eliminate $d\mu_W$ between these two expressions. We obtain after designating the ratios $m_i = n_i/n_W$, $\tilde{X} = m_X/m_M$, $\tilde{X}' = m_X'/m_M$, etc.,

$$d\mu_M = (\tilde{V} - \bar{V}_M)\,d\pi - (\tilde{X} - \tilde{X}')\,d\mu_X - (\tilde{Y} - \tilde{Y}')\,d\mu_Y. \qquad (8.64)$$

We thus identify from equation (8.60) the various terms in this equation with activity of the macromolecule, a_M, and the ligand binding parameters, $\bar{X}$ and $\bar{Y}$, as

$$(\tilde{V} - \bar{V}_M)\,d\pi = RT\,d\ln a_M, \qquad (8.65)$$

$$\bar{X} = (\tilde{X} - \tilde{X}') = \frac{1}{m_M}(m_X - m_X'), \qquad (8.66)$$

$$\bar{Y} = (\tilde{Y} - \tilde{Y}') = \frac{1}{m_M}(m_Y - m_Y'). \qquad (8.67)$$

The right-hand terms of these equations are the measurable parameters that are obtainable from the osmotic dialysis experiment. There are no approximations or assumptions of ideality in performing these determinations. They serve to define what is written as $\bar{X}$ and $\bar{Y}$, the binding parameters of X and Y in the most general sense. This avoids the approximation of setting the free ligand equal on both sides.

A particular linkage potential is defined by this result; it might be designated by Π_π, since its measurement depends on osmotic equilibrium:

$$\Pi_\pi = \Pi_\pi(\pi, \mu_X, \mu_Y). \qquad (8.68)$$

The measurable binding parameters are then given by derivatives:

$$\bar{X} = \frac{\partial \Pi_\pi}{\partial \mu_X}, \qquad \bar{Y} = \frac{\partial \Pi_\pi}{\partial \mu_Y}. \qquad (8.69)$$

Likewise, a whole set of linkage relations follows from this function, such as

$$\left(\frac{\partial \bar{X}}{\partial \mu_Y}\right)_{\Pi, \mu_X} = \left(\frac{\partial \bar{Y}}{\partial \mu_X}\right)_{\Pi, \mu_Y} \qquad (8.70)$$

and

$$\left[\frac{\partial(\tilde{V} - \bar{V}_M)}{\partial \mu_X}\right]_{\Pi, \mu_Y} = -\left(\frac{\partial \bar{X}}{\partial \pi}\right)_{\mu_X, \mu_Y}. \qquad (8.71)$$

These are the operational properties of any macromolecular system, and serve to define the functional behavior of the system in these precise terms. The interpretation of results obtained in this way depends, as we have often emphasized, on using simple idealized models to represent key elements of any system.

8.13 SUMMARY

In this chapter we have shown how the dependence of variables of complex macromolecular systems can be formulated in terms of fundamental thermodynamic concepts. The potentials normalized to the amount of a reference component form a complete group, derivable by Legendre transformation, and the potentials give us the complete description of the behavior of the macromolecule in the presence of its ligands. Normalization with respect to the macromolecule makes it possible to identify the macromolecule with a group of potentials. For most practical purposes, the analytical implementation of the Legendre transformation must be replaced by a graphical approach involving pairs of specific experimental results in the form of binding curves. Graphical integration of these curves serves to determine the potentials themselves, subject to reference-state constants. The binding capacity provides a general measure of the homotropic cooperativity of a system. Spectroscopic methods provide ways of delineating the properties of mass-law binding in favorable situations, and in this way extraneous effects can be set aside. The normalized potentials contain all the information necessary to describe the functional chemistry of the macromolecule with its ligands. The state-defining properties of the potentials provide the thermodynamic basis of all linkage relations that the macromolecule is destined to follow. We have also seen how different models, in particular, the mass or the ideal-solution model, can be used to represent the macromolecular binding potential. And we have seen how the osmotic-pressure dialysis experiment provides the information needed to evaluate a thermodynamic potential that gives the amount of ligand specifically bound to a macromolecule.

Water, as the principal ligand and as solvent for the macromolecule itself, enjoys a very special status here. All this raises unanswered, and perhaps even conceptually unanswerable, questions. If some of the water is truly bound, as it is when the protein is in the crystalline state, is it available as solvent for the other ligands? And does the protein crystal, such as hemoglobin, itself have a binding curve for oxygen and other ligands, including water? In the face of these uncertainties, we can only adopt a pragmatic attitude. Our first objective is, of course, to arrive at some plausible physical model. In looking for one, the distinction between two main types of binding, mass-law binding and solution binding, is important. It is the former which, in biological macromolecules, is by far the more important as the basis of cooperativity, linkage, and control. It is there that the marvels of macromolecular evolution disclose themselves.

The division between the two kinds of binding constitutes the Great Divide of functional chemistry.

We have shown that the behavior of a system in true equilibrium is governed by a group of linkage potentials. It may be emphasized, however, that it is the mass-action law as a kinetic, rather than a thermodynamic, principle that is often of concern to the macromolecular biologist, and it is interesting to recall that it is as a kinetic principle that the mass-action law was devised by Guldberg and Waage, who identified an equilibrium constant with the ratio of two opposing velocity constants. The allosteric model has been explored in the steady state as seen in Section 4.5. All this leads us straight into the vast field of nonlinear dynamics, where the equations can often be studied only numerically. Although ignorance of the reality of time is a limitation of equilibrium thermodynamics, we have seen throughout this book that independence from the complexity of time is one source of its power.

APPENDIX 8.1   THE MATHEMATICAL PROPERTIES OF HOMOGENEOUS FUNCTIONS

There are a number of simple theorems applicable to homogeneous functions. In this section we summarize those that are of particular importance for our discussion of thermodynamic properties.

(a)   Theorem I

Given a homogeneous function

$$F(ax_1, ax_2, \ldots, ax_r) = a^n F(x_1, x_2, \ldots, x_r), \tag{A8.1}$$

then

$$nF = x_1 \frac{\partial F}{\partial x_1} + x_2 \frac{\partial F}{\partial x_2} + \cdots + x_r \frac{\partial F}{\partial x_r}. \tag{A8.2}$$

Proof:

$$\frac{\partial F(ax_1, ax_2, \ldots)}{\partial a} = x_1 \frac{\partial F(ax_1, ax_2, \ldots)}{\partial ax_1} + x_2 \frac{\partial F(ax_1, ax_2, \ldots)}{\partial ax_2} + \cdots$$

$$= na^{n-1} F(x_1, x_2, \ldots). \tag{A8.3}$$

This is true for all values of a, and by setting $a = 1$ we obtain the desired result.

(b) Theorem II

Given
$$nF = x_1 \frac{\partial F}{\partial x_1} + x_2 \frac{\partial F}{\partial x_2} + \cdots + x_r \frac{\partial F}{\partial x_r}, \tag{A8.4}$$

then

$$F(ax_1, ax_2, \ldots, ax_r) = a^n F(x_1, x_2, \ldots, x_r). \tag{A8.5}$$

Proof: Replacing $x_1, x_2, \ldots$ by $ax_1, ax_2, \ldots$, and treating F as a function of a, we obtain

$$\frac{\partial F(ax_1, ax_2, \ldots)}{\partial a} = x_1 \frac{\partial F(ax_1, ax_2, \ldots)}{\partial ax_1} + x_2 \frac{\partial F(ax_1, ax_2, \ldots)}{\partial ax_2} + \cdots. \tag{A8.6}$$

Multiplying by a then gives

$$a\frac{\partial F(ax_1, ax_2, \ldots)}{\partial a} = ax_1 \frac{\partial F(ax_1, ax_2, \ldots)}{\partial ax_1}$$

$$+ ax_2 \frac{\partial F(ax_1, ax_2, \ldots)}{\partial ax_2} + \cdots. \tag{A8.7}$$

By Theorem I we may set this equal to $nF(ax_1, ax_2, \ldots)$ and obtain

$$\frac{\partial \ln F(ax_1, ax_2, \ldots)}{\partial \ln a} = n. \tag{A8.8}$$

Upon integration we have

$$\ln F(ax_1, ax_2, \ldots) = \ln a^n + \text{constant}. \tag{A8.9}$$

The constant gives the value of $\ln F$ when $a = 1$. Consequently,

$$F(ax_1, ax_2, \ldots) = a^n F(x_1, x_2, \ldots). \tag{A8.10}$$

(c) Theorem III

If F is n-order homogeneous in $x_1, x_2; \ldots, x_r$, then $\partial F/\partial x_i$ is $(n - 1)$-order homogeneous in the same variables.

Proof: Write
$$nF = x_1 \frac{\partial F}{\partial x_1} + \cdots + x_i \frac{\partial F}{\partial x_i} + \cdots. \tag{A8.11}$$

Differentiating partially with respect to x_i, and noting

$$\frac{\partial^2 F}{\partial x_i \partial x_j} = \frac{\partial^2 F}{\partial x_j \partial x_i},$$ (A8.12)

we obtain

$$n\frac{\partial F}{\partial x_i} = x_1\frac{\partial}{\partial x_1}\left(\frac{\partial F}{\partial x_i}\right) + \cdots + x_i\frac{\partial}{\partial x_i}\left(\frac{\partial F}{\partial x_i}\right) + \cdots + \frac{\partial F}{\partial x_i},$$ (A8.13)

or

$$(n-1)\frac{\partial F}{\partial x_i} = x_1\frac{\partial}{\partial x_1}\left(\frac{\partial F}{\partial x_i}\right) + \cdots + x_i\frac{\partial}{\partial x_i}\left(\frac{\partial F}{\partial x_i}\right) + \cdots + x_r\frac{\partial}{\partial x_r}\left(\frac{\partial F}{\partial x_i}\right).$$ (A8.14)

This shows that the partial derivative $\partial F/\partial x_i$ is of order $n-1$.

(d)   Theorem IV (Converse of Theorem III)

It can also be shown that the converse of Theorem III holds; i.e., if $\partial F/\partial x_i$ is $(n-1)$ order in $x_1, x_2, \ldots, x_r$ for all i, then F is equal to a function which is n-order homogeneous in the same variables plus a constant. The proof is essentially a reversal of that given for Theorem III. Starting with

$$(n-1)\frac{\partial F}{\partial x_i} = x_1\frac{\partial}{\partial x_1}\left(\frac{\partial F}{\partial x_i}\right) + x_2\frac{\partial}{\partial x_2}\left(\frac{\partial F}{\partial x_i}\right) + \cdots + x_r\frac{\partial}{\partial x_r}\left(\frac{\partial F}{\partial x_i}\right),$$ (A8.15)

and reversing the sequence of the previous argument, we pass to

$$n\frac{\partial F}{\partial x_i} = \frac{\partial}{\partial x_i}\left(x_1\frac{\partial F}{\partial x_1} + x_2\frac{\partial F}{\partial x_2} + \cdots + x_r\frac{\partial F}{\partial x_r}\right).$$ (A8.16)

Integration then gives

$$nF = x_1\frac{\partial F}{\partial x_1} + \cdots + x_i\frac{\partial F}{\partial x_i} + x_r\frac{\partial F}{\partial x_r} + \psi,$$ (A8.17)

where ψ is a constant of integration that may be a function of all x's except x_i. Since this procedure holds for all x_i, it is clear that ψ must be a constant. As an example,

$$F = x_1 x_2 + x_3^2 + \psi \qquad \text{(order 2 for } x_1 x_2 + x_3^2\text{)},$$ (A8.18)

$$\frac{\partial F}{\partial x_1} = x_2, \qquad \frac{\partial F}{\partial x_2} = x_1, \qquad \frac{\partial F}{\partial x_3} = 2x_3. \qquad (A8.19)$$

Each derivative is of order $2 - 1 = 1$. As will be seen, not all variables need be represented in each $\partial F/\partial x_i$.

(e)   Theorem V

If F is n-order homogeneous in a set of variables $x_1, x_2, \ldots, x_r$, it cannot be n-order homogeneous in the remaining subset of variables resulting from setting one or more of the variables equal to a constant. This is brought out by the following example. Let

$$F = \frac{x_1}{x_2{}^4} + \frac{x_1}{x_2 x_3{}^3} \quad \text{(order } -3 \text{ homogeneous)}. \qquad (A8.20)$$

Now let us set $x_1 = a$, a constant. The function is then order -4 homogeneous in x_2 and x_3. However, if we set x_2 or x_3 equal to a, then it is no longer homogeneous at all.

A formal proof applicable to the general case is the following. Multiplying each variable by a/x_1, we obtain

$$\frac{a^n}{x_1{}^n} F = F\left(a, a\frac{x_2}{x_1}, \ldots, a\frac{x_r}{x_1}\right). \qquad (A8.21)$$

If this were n-order homogeneous in the new variables $x_2/x_1, \ldots x_r/x_1$, then multiplication of each variable by x_1 would give

$$a^n F = F(a, ax_2, \ldots, ax_r). \qquad (A8.22)$$

But we know $a^n F = F(ax_1, ax_2, \ldots, ax_r)$ for all values of x's. We thus have an inconsistency. Therefore normalization by x_1 (or any x_i) destroys the homogeneous property of the function. It will be seen that setting x_1 equal to a constant is equivalent to normalizing each variable with respect to x_1, i.e., changing the scale of $x_2, \ldots, x_r$. If it should happen that F were first-order homogeneous ($n = 1$), this would also amount to normalizing F with respect to x_1, that is, to making x_1 a reference component, as in the derivation of the binding potential.

APPENDIX 8.2   BINDING POTENTIAL FOR AN ALLOSTERIC SYSTEM

In order to obtain an expression for the binding potential of an allosteric macromolecule which exists in r conformations, we consider the expression for the total amount of ligand X per mole of macromolecule in terms of the contributions from the r forms. This is given by

$$\tilde{X} = \frac{v_0 \tilde{X}_0 + v_1 \tilde{X}_1 + \cdots}{v_0 + v_1 + \cdots}. \tag{A8.23}$$

The mass-law equilibrium between the zeroth and ith forms is $L_i = v_i/v_0$, assuming the v's are proportional to the activities of the various forms. We then recognize that L_i is determined by the difference between the binding potentials for the ith and zeroth form, i.e., $\Pi_i - \Pi_0$, according to

$$L = L_i^o e^{(\Pi_i - \Pi_0)/RT}, \tag{A8.24}$$

where we choose the standard state L_i^o when $\Pi_i = \Pi_0$. Substitution gives

$$\tilde{X} = \frac{\tilde{X}_0 + L_1^o e^{(\Pi_1 - \Pi_0)/RT} \tilde{X}_1 + \cdots}{1 + L_1^o e^{(\Pi_1 - \Pi_0)/RT} + \cdots}$$

or

$$\tilde{X} = RT \frac{\partial}{\partial \mu_X} \{ \ln e^{\Pi_0/RT} + L_1^o e^{\Pi_1/RT} + L_2^o e^{\Pi_2/RT} + \cdots \}.$$

Since $\partial\Pi/\partial\mu_X = \tilde{X}$, we identify the total binding potential Π as

$$\Pi = RT \ln \sum L_i^o e^{\Pi_i/RT}. \tag{A8.25}$$

We need not have restricted this result to the binding potential Π, which is expressed in terms of intensive variables. We could just as well have used any other G potential (T and p are fixed) where the other variables could include the normalized extensive variables of other ligands. The allosteric equilibrium constants would depend on the choice of conditions.

For simple mass-law binding, the binding potential Π_i will be given by the logarithm of the binding polynomial P_i for the ith form, i.e., $\Pi_i = RT \ln P_i$, and thus the total potential for such a system is itself a polynomial given as

$$P = \sum L_i^o P_i. \tag{A8.26}$$

We can also see how this leads to the concept of nesting by assuming that each potential Π_i is itself expressed by a set of allosteric equilibria. This gives a "fly-away" function built on the form of equation (A8.25) and provides the basis for formulating the concept of nested allosteric instruction (Robert et al., 1987).

Epilogue

Throughout this book we have focused on the principles of linkage thermodynamics and their application to polyfunctional macromolecular systems under equilibrium conditions. In this connection we have developed the concept of linkage potentials, and we have applied them to a variety of situations that fall generally into two broad categories: specific binding, described by mass action; and solution binding, described by ideal solution laws. In mass-action law phenomena, the macromolecule can play a special role, by allosteric conformation changes, by polysteric aggregation, or even by polyphasic or phase-forming changes. In all of these the control ligands may be either chemical or physical, and it is through their interaction with a macromolecule that they become linked. A display of this linkage finds expression in the corresponding linkage graphs. The regulation and cooperativity of complex systems are embodied in these graphs, which represent derivative properties of the thermodynamic potentials. A wealth of thermodynamic relationships, direct and reciprocal, is inherent in the complex structure of a multicomponent system, however it may be modeled.

The analysis of the equilibrium picture, theoretically complete and revealing as it is, gives us only one view of the beauty and complexity of a macromolecular system. When we leave the domain of pure thermodynamics, and pass to the world of real events, we bring with us a sense of time and direction. In addition to the first and second laws, the system is governed by a set of simultaneous differential equations embodying the kinetic form of the mass-action law. The existence of the steady state, and all the phenomena associated with it, then hinges on the existence of a globally stable critical point. A general treatment of linkage under nonequilibrium conditions is impossible. However, a useful model here can be found in the "turning wheel"

309

model of Section 4.5. This model or its elaboration provides a simple conceptual picture of energy transduction and linkage at the steady state (see Section 4.5 with regard to allosteric transitions). In this respect it might be used to draw a connection between the principles of linkage thermodynamics and the relations governing the steady state or even the transient approach to it. This aspect takes us then into the realm of nonlinear dynamics.

References

Ackers, G. K. 1979. Linked functions in allosteric proteins: An exact theory for the effect of organic phosphates on oxygen affinity of hemoglobin. *Biochemistry* 15:3372–3380.

Ackers, G. K., and Halvorson, H. R. 1974. The linkage between oxygenation and subunit dissociation in human hemoglobin. *Proc. Natl. Acad. Sci. USA* 71:4312–4316.

Ackers, G. K.; Johnson, A. D.; and Shea, M. A. 1982. Quantitative model for gene regulation by l phage repressor. *Proc. Natl. Acad. Sci. USA* 79:1129–1133.

Ackers, G. K.; Shea, M. A.; and Smith, F. R. 1983. Free energy coupling within macromolecules: The chemical work of ligand binding at the individual sites in cooperative systems. *J. Mol. Biol.* 170:223–242.

Ackers, G. K., and Smith, F. R. 1987. The hemoglobin tetramer: A three-state molecular switch for control of ligand affinity. *Ann. Rev. Biophys. Biophys. Chem.* 16:583–609.

Adair, G. S. 1925a. A critical study of the direct method of measuring the osmotic pressure of haemoglobin. *Proc. Roy. Soc.* (London), Ser. A, 108A:627–637.

Adair, G. S. 1925b. The hemoglobin system, VI. The oxygen dissociation curve of hemoglobin. *J. Biol. Chem.* 63:529–545.

Allen, D. W.; Guthe, K. F.; and Wyman, J. 1950. Further studies on the oxygen equilibrium of hemoglobin. *J. Biol. Chem.* 187:393–410.

Anderson, W. F.; Grütter, M. G.; Remington, S. J.; Weaver, L. H.; and Matthews, B. W. 1981. Crystallographic determination of the mode of binding of oligosaccharides to T4 bacteriophage lysozyme: Implications for the mechanism of catalysis. *J. Mol. Biol.* 147:523–543.

Antonini, E.; Wyman, J.; Brunori, M.; Taylor, J. F.; Rossi-Fanelli, A.; and Caputo, A. 1964. Studies on the oxidation-reduction potentials of heme proteins. *J. Biol. Chem.* 239:907–912.

Antonini, E.; Wyman, J.; Brunori, M.; Fronticelli, C.; Bucci, E.; and Rossi-Fanelli, A. R. 1965. Studies on the relations between molecular and functional properties of hemoglobin, V: The influence of temperature on the Bohr effect in human and in horse hemoglobin. *J. Biol. Chem.* 240:1096–1103.

311

Arisaka, F., and Van Holde, K. E. 1979. Allosteric properties and the association equilibria of hemocyanin from *Callianassa californiensis. J. Mol. Biol.* 134:41–73.

Arnone, A. 1972. X-ray diffraction study of binding of 2,3-diphosphoglycerate to human deoxyhaemoglobin. *Nature* (London) 237:146–149.

Arvidson, D. N.; Bruce, C.; and Gunsalus, R. P. 1986. Interaction of the Escherichia coli trp aporepressor with its ligand., L-Tryptophan. *J. Biol. Chem.* 261:238–243.

Atha, D. H.; Johnson, M. L.; and Riggs, A. F. 1979. The linkage between oxygenation and subunit association in human hemoglobin Kansas. *J. Biol. Chem.* 254:12390–12398.

Baldwin, J., and Chothia, C. 1979. Haemoglobin: The structural changes related to ligand binding and its allosteric mechanism. *J. Mol. Biol.* 129:175–220.

Barakat, R., and Strekas, T. C. 1982. pH variation of midpoint potential for three photosynthetic bacterial cytochromes c'. *Biochim. Biophys. Acta* 679:393–399.

Bardsley, W. G. 1977a. Factorability of the allosteric binding polynomial and graphical manifestations of cooperativity in third degree saturation functions. *J. Theor. Biol.* 67:407–431.

Bardsley, W. G. 1977b. The relationship between cooperativity coefficients, factorability of the allosteric binding polynomial and curve shape. *J. Mol. Biol.* 113:573–578.

Bardsley, W. G., and Waight, R. D. 1978. Factorability of the Hessian of the binding polynomial. The central issue concerning statistical ratios between binding constants, Hill plot slope and positive and negative cooperativity. *J. Theor. Biol.* 72:321–372.

Bardsley, W. G., and Wyman, J. 1978. Concerning the thermodynamic definition and graphical manifestations of positive and negative cooperativity. *J. Theor. Biol.* 72:373–376.

Bardsley, W. G.; Woolfson, R.; and Mazat, J.-P. 1980a. Relationships between the magnitude of Hill plot slopes, apparent binding constants and factorability of binding polynomials and their Hessians. *J. Theor. Biol.* 85:247–284.

Bardsley, W. G.; Woolfson, R.; and Wood, R. M. W. 1980b. Some mathematical results concerning Hessians of binding polynomials and cooperativity coefficients. *J. Theor. Biol.* 85:45–51.

Barisas, B. G., and Gill, S. J. 1979. Thermodynamic analysis of carbon monoxide binding by hemoglobin trout I. *Biophys. Chem.* 9:235–244.

Bartsch, R. G. 1978. In *The Photosynthetic Bacteria.* R. K. Clayton and W. R. Sistrom, eds. Plenum Press, London.

Benedict, R. C.; Fall, L.; Gill, S. J.; and Hedlund, B. 1981a. The effect of non-binding molecules on the gelation of HbS. *Biophysical Chem.* 13:245–252.

Benedict, R. C.; Richey, B.; Fall, L.; Gill, S. J.; Nagel, R. L.; and Wyman, J. 1981b. Thermodynamics of anti-sickling agents with hemoglobin S. *J. Mol. Biol.* 150:423–434.

Benedict, R. C.; Moudrianakis, E. N.; and Ackers, G. K. 1984. Interactions of the nucleosomal core histones: A calorimetric study of octamer assembly. *Biochemistry* 23:1214–1218.

Benesch, R., and Benesch, R. E. 1967. The effect of organic phosphates from the human erythrocyte on the allosteric properties of hemoglobin. *Biochem. Biophys. Res. Commun.* 26:162–174.

Benesch, R. E., and Benesch, R. 1974. The mechanism of interaction of red cell organic phosphate with hemoglobin. *Adv. Protein Chem.* 28:211–237.

Bennett, W. S., and Steitz, T. A. 1978. Glucose-induced conformational change in yeast hexokinase. *Proc. Natl. Acad. Sci. USA* 75:4848–4852.

Bennett, W. S., and Steitz, T. A. 1980. Structure of a complex between yeast hexokinase A and glucose. *J. Mol. Biol.* 140:183–230.

Bianco, P., and Haladjian, J. 1981. Current potential responses for a tetrahemic protein: A method of determining the individual half-wave potentials of cytochrome c_3 from *Desulfovibrio Desulfuricans* strain Norway. *Electrochimica Acta* 26:1001–1004.

Bohr, C.; Hasselbalch, K. A.; and Krogh, A. 1904. Ueber einen in biologischer Beziehung wichtigen Einfluss, den die Kohlensaurespannung des Blutes aufdessen Sauerstoffbindung ubt. *Skand. Arch. Physiol.* 16:402–412.

Bonaventura, J., and Bonaventura, C. 1980. Hemocyanins: Relationships in their structure, function and assembly. *Am. Zool.* 20:7–17.

Bonaventura, C.; Bonaventura, J.; Antonini, E.; Brunori, M.; and Wyman, J. 1973. Carbon monoxide binding by simple heme proteins under photodissociating conditions. *Biochem.* 12:3424–3428.

Boyes-Watson, J.; Davidson, E.; and Perutz, M. F. 1947. An X-ray study of horse methaemoglobin, I. *Proc. Roy. Soc.* (London) A191:83–132.

Brandts, J. F.; Oliveira, R. J.; and Westort, C. 1970. Thermodynamics of protein denaturation: Effect of pressure on the denaturation of ribonuclease A. *Biochemistry* 9:1038–1047.

Bridgman, P. W. 1925. *A Condensed Collection of Thermodynamic Formulas.* Harvard University Press, Cambridge, MA.

Briggs, W. E. 1983. A new measure of cooperativity in protein-ligand binding. *Biophys. Chem.* 18:67–71.

Briggs, W. E. 1984. Cooperativity and extrema of the Hill slope for symmetric protein-ligand binding polynomials. *J. Theor. Biol.* 108:77–83.

Briggs, W. E. 1985a. The relationship between zeros and factors of binding polynomials and cooperativity in protein-ligand binding. *J. Theor. Biol.* 114:605–614.

Briggs, W. E. 1985b. Zeros and factors of polynomials with positive coefficients and protein-ligand binding. *Rocky Mountain J. of Math.* 15:75–89.

Brunori, M. 1975. Molecular adaptation to physiological requirements: The hemoglobin system of trout. *Current Topics in Cellular Regulation* 9:1–39.

Brunori, M.; Bonaventura, J.; Bonaventura, C.; Antonini, E.; and Wyman, J. 1972. Carbon monoxide binding by hemoglobin and myoglobin under photodissociating conditions. *Proc. Natl. Acad. Sci. USA* 69:868–871.

Brunori, M.; Coletta, M.; and Di Cera, E. 1986. A cooperative model for ligand binding to biological macromolecules as applied to oxygen carriers. *Biophys. Chem.* 23:215–222.

Brzozowski, A. A.; Derewenda, Z.; Dodson, E.; Dodson, G.; Grabowski, M.; Liddington, R.; Skarzynski, T.; and Vallely, D. 1984. Bonding of molecular oxygen to T state human haemoglobin. *Nature* 307:74–76.

Buc, H.; Johannes, J. K.; and Hess, B. 1973. Appendix. Allosteric kinetics of pyruvate kinase of *Saccharoyces carlsbergensis*. *J. Mol. Biol.* 76:199–205.

Butler, L. G., and Rupley, J. A. 1967. The binding of saccharide to crystalline and soluble lysozyme measured directly and through solubility studies. *J. Biol. Chem.* 242:1077–1078.

Cantor, C. R., and Schimmel, P. R. 1980. *Biophysical Chemistry, Part 1: The Conformation of Biological Macromolecules.* W. H. Freeman and Company, San Francisco, CA.

Chaires, J. B. 1986. Inhibition of B to Z transition by intercalators. *Biochemistry* 25:8436–8439.

Chanutin, A., and Curnish, R. R. 1967. Effect of organic and inorganic phosphates on the oxygen equilibrium of human erythrocytes. *Arch. Biochem. Biophys.* 121:96–102.

Chiancone, E.; Vecchini, P.; Rosaria, M.; Fanelli, R.; and Antonini, E. 1972. Studies on erythrocruorin, II: Dissociation of earthworm erythrocruorin. *J. Mol. Biol.* 70:73–84.

Chiancone, E.; Norne, J. E.; Forsen, S.; Bonaventura, J.; Brunori, M.; Antonini, E.; and Wyman, J. 1975. Identification of chloride-binding sites in hemoglobin by nuclear-magnetic-resonance quadrupole-relaxation studies of hemoglobin digests. *Eur. J. Biochem.* 55:385–390.

Chu, A. H.; Turner, B. W.; and Ackers, G. K. 1984. Effects of protons on the oxygenation-linked subunit assembly in human hemoglobin. *Biochemistry* 23:604–617.

Clark, A. F.; Gerken, T. A.; and Hogg, R. W. 1982. Proton nuclear magnetic resonance spectroscopy and ligand binding dynamics of the *Escherichia coli* 1-arabinose binding protein. *Biochemistry* 21:2227–2233.

Cohn, E. J., and Edsall, J. T. 1943. *Proteins, Amino Acids, and Peptides*. Reinhold, New York.

Colosimo, A.; Brunori, M.; and Wyman, J. 1974. Concerted changes in an allosteric macromolecule. *Biophys. Chem.* 2:338–344.

Colosimo, A.; Brunori, M.; and Wyman, J. 1976. Polysteric linkage. *J. Mol. Biol.* 100:47–57.

Condo, S. G.; Giardini, B.; Barra, D.; Gill, S. J.; and Brunori, M. 1981. Purification and functional properties of the hemoglobin components from the rat (Wister). *Eur. J. Biochem.*, 116:243–247.

Connelly, P. R.; Robert, C. H.; Briggs, W. E.; and Gill, S. J. 1986. Analysis of zeros of binding polynomials for tetrameric hemoglobins. *Biophys. Chem.* 24:295–309.

Daniels, R. S.; Downie, J. C.; Hay, A. J.; Knossow, M.; Skehel, J. J.; Wang, M. L.; and Wiley, D. C. 1985. Fusion mutants of the influenza virus hemagglutinin glycoprotein. *Cell* 40:431–439.

Debru, C. 1983. *L'esprit des proteins*. Hermann, Paris.

Debru, C. 1987. *Philosophie moleculaire: Monod, Wyman, Changeux*. Libraire Philosophique J. VRIN, Paris.

Decker, H.; Savel, A.; Linzen, B.; and Van Holde, K. E. 1983. A new graphical test for the MWC-model and its application to some hemocyanins. *Life Chem. Reports*, Suppl. 1:251–256.

Decker, H.; Robert, C. H.; and Gill, S. J. 1986. Nesting: An extension of the allosteric model and its application to tarantula hemocyanin. In *Invertebrate Oxygen Carriers*. Springer-Verlag, Berlin. Pp. 383–388.

Decker, H.; Connelly, P. R.; Robert, C. H.; and Gill, S. J. 1988. Nested allosteric interaction in tarantula hemocyanin revealed through the binding of oxygen and carbon monoxide. *Biochemistry* 27:6901–6908.

Di Cera, E.; Robert, C. H.; and Gill, S. J. 1987a. Allosteric interpretation of the oxygen-binding reaction of human hemoglobin tetramers. *Biochemistry* 26:4003–4008.

Di Cera, E.; Doyle, M. L.; Connelly, P. R.; and Gill, S. J. 1987b. Carbon monoxide binding to human hemoglobin A_0. *Biochemistry* 26:6494–6502.

Di Cera, E.; Doyle, M. L.; and Gill, S. J. 1988a. Alkaline Bohr effect of human hemoglobin A_0. *J. Mol. Biol.* 200:593–599.

Di Cera, E.; Gill, S. J.; and Wyman, J. 1988b. Binding capacity: Cooperativity and buffering in biopolymers. *Proc. Natl. Acad. Sci. USA* 85:449–452.

Di Cera, E.; Gill, S. J.; and Wyman, J. 1988c. Canonical formulation of linkage thermodynamics. *Proc. Natl. Acad. Sci. USA* 85:5077–5081.

Di Cera, E.; and Gill, S. J. 1988d. On the determination of species fractions from ligand-binding sites. Application to human hemoglobin. *Biophysical Chemistry* 29:351–356.

Di Cera, E.; Doyle, M. L.; Morgan, M. S.; De Cristofaro, R.; Landolfi, R.; Biozzi, B.; Castagnola, M.; and Gill, S. J. 1989a. Carbon monoxide binding to human hemoglobin F_0. *Biochemistry* 28:2631–2638.

Di Cera, E.; Phillipson, P.; and Wyman, J. 1989b. Limit cycle oscillations and chaos in reaction networks subject to conservation of mass. *Proc. Natl. Acad. Sci. USA* 86:142–146.

Dickerson, R. E., and Geis, I. 1969. *The Structure and Action of Proteins.* W. A. Benjamin, Menlo Park, CA.

Dickerson, R. E., and Geis, I. 1983. *Hemoglobin.* Benjamin/Cummings, Menlo Park, CA. Pp. 40–41.

Doyle, M. L.; Weber, P. C.; and Gill, S. J. 1985. Carbon monoxide binding to *Rhodospirillum molishianum* ferrocytochrome c′. *Biochemistry* 24:1987–1991.

Doyle, M. L.; Gill, S. J.; and Cusanovich, M. A. 1986. Ligand-controlled dissociation of *Chromatium vinosum* cytochrome c′. *Biochemistry* 25:2509–2516.

Doyle, M. L.; Robert, C. H.; Di Cera, E.; and Gill, S. J. 1987. Carbon dioxide and oxygen linkage in human hemoglobin tetramers. *J. Mol. Biol.* 196:927–934.

Edelstein, S. J.; Josephs, R.; Jarosch, H. S.; Crepeau, R. H.; Telford, J. N.; and Dykes, G. 1976. In *Proceedings of the Symposium on Molecular and Cellular Aspects of Sickle Cell Disease.* J. I. Hercules, G. Cottam, M. R. Waterman, and A. N. Schechter, eds. Dept. of HEW. Dallas, TX. Pp. 33–59.

Edsall, J. T. 1972. Blood and hemoglobin: The evolution of knowledge of functional adaptation in a biochemical system, Part 1: The adaptation of chemical structure to function in hemoglobin. *J. Hist. Biol.* 5:205–257.

Edsall, J. T. 1980. Hemoglobin and the origins of the concept of allosterism. *Fed. Proc.* 39:226–234.

Edsall, J. T., and Wyman, J. 1958. *Biophysical Chemistry.* Academic Press. New York. P. 481.

Edsall, J. T., and Gutfreund, H. 1983. *Biothermodynamics: The Study of Biochemical Processes at Equilibrium.* Wiley, New York. Pp. 39–122.

Eftink, M. R.; Anusiem, A. C.; and Biltonen, R. L. 1983. Enthalpy-entropy compensation and heat capacity changes for protein-ligand interactions: General thermodynamic models and data for the binding of nucleotides to ribonuclease A. *Biochemistry* 22:3884–3896.

Eisenberg, H. 1976. *Biological Macromolecules and Polyelectrolytes in Solution.* Clarendon Press, Oxford.

Eisenstein, L., and Frauenfelder, H. 1982. *Biological Events Probed by Ultrafast Laser Spectroscopy.* Academic Press, New York.

Fahrenbach, W. H. 1970. The cyanoblast: Hemocyanin formation in *limulus polyphemus. J. Cell Biol.* 44:445–453.

Fichera, G.; Sneider, M. A.; and Wyman, J. 1977. On the existence of a steady state in a biological system. *Proc. Natl. Acad. Sci. USA* 74:4182–4184.

Filimonov, V.; Privalov, P. L.; Hinz, H-J.; Von der Haar, F.; and Cramer, F. 1976. Calorimetric investigations on thermal stability of tRNA[Lle] (yeast) and tRNA[Ser](yeast). *Eur. J. Biochem.* 70:25–31.

Ford, G. C.; Harrison, P. M.; Rice, D. W.; Smith, J. M. A.; Treffry, A.; White, J. L.; and Yariv, J. 1984. Ferritin: Design and formation of an iron-storage molecule. *Phil. Trans. R. Soc.* (London) B 304:551–565.

Freire, E., and Biltonen, R. L. 1978a. Statistical mechanical deconvolution of thermal transitions in macromolecules, I: Theory and application to homogeneous systems. *Biopolymers* 17:463–479.

Freire, E., and Biltonen, R. L. 1978b. Statistical mechanical deconvolution of thermal transitions in macromolecules, II: General treatment of cooperative phenomena. *Biopolymers* 17:481–494.

Freire, E., and Biltonen, R. L. 1978c. Statistical mechanical deconvolution of thermal transitions in macromolecules, III: Application to double-stranded and to single-stranded transitions of nucleic acids. *Biopolymers* 17:497–510.

Fukada, H.; Sturtevant, J. M.; and Quiocho, F. A. 1983. Thermodynamics of the binding of L-arabinose and of D-galactose to the L-arabinose-binding protein of *Escherichia coli. J. Biol. Chem.* 258:13193–13198.

Gaykema, W. P. J.; Hol, W. G. J.; Vereijken, J. M.; Soeter, N. M.; Bak, H. J.; and Beintema, J. J. 1984. 3.2 Å structure of the copper-containing, oxygen-carrying protein Panulirus interruptus haemocyanin. *Nature* 309:23–29.

Gaykema, W. P. J.; Volbeda, A.; and Hol, W. G. J. 1986. Structure determination of *Panulirus interruptus* haemocyanin at 3.2 Å resolution: Successful phase extension by sixfold density averaging. *J. Mol. Biol.* 187:255–275.

Gerhart, J. C. 1970. A discussion of the regulatory properties of aspartate trans-carbamylase from escherichia coli. *Curr. Top. Cell Regul.* 2:275–325.

Gibbs, J. W. 1928. *The Collected Work of J. Willard Gibbs.* Longmans, Green.

Gibson, Q. H. 1956. An apparatus for flash photolysis and its application to the reactions of myoglobin with gases. *J. Physiol.* 134:112–122.

Gill, S. J. 1979. Ligand binding of gases to haemoglobin. In *Biochemical Thermodynamics.* N. M. Jones, ed. Elsevier, Amsterdam. P. 224.

Gill, S. J. 1981. The use of the macromolecular chemical potential describing ligand-linked phase equilibriums. *Proc. Aust. Thermodyn. Conf.* Pp. 157–168.

Gill, S. J., and Glogovsky, R. L. 1965. Influence of pressure on the reversible unfolding of ribonuclease and poly-γ-benzyl-l-glutamate. *J. Phys. Chem.* 69:1515–1519.

Gill, S. J.; Gaud, H. T.; Wyman, J.; and Barisas, B. G. 1978. Analysis of ligand binding curves in terms of species fractions. *Biophys. Chem.* 8:53–59.

Gill, S. J.; Benedict, R. C.; Fall, L.; Spokane, R.; and Wyman, J. 1979. Oxygen binding to sickle cell hemoglobin. *J. Mol. Biol.* 130:175–189.

Gill, S. J.; Spokane, R.; Benedict, R. C.; Fall, L.; and Wyman, J. 1980. Ligand-linked phase equilibria of sickle cell hemoglobin. *J. Mol. Biol.* 140:299–312.

Gill, S. J., and Richey, B. 1984. Triple-point behaviour of human haemoglobin. *Nature* 310:160–161.

Gill, S. J.; Richey, B.; Bishop, G.; and Wyman, J. 1985. Generalized binding phenomena in an allosteric macromolecule. *Biophys. Chem.* 21:1–14.

Gill, S. J.; Robert, C. H.; Coletta, M.; Di Cera, E.; and Brunori, M. 1986. Cooperative free energies for nested allosteric models as applied to human hemoglobin. *Biophys.* 50:747–752.

Gill, S. J.; Di Cera, E.; Doyle, M. L.; Bishop, G. A.; and Robert, C. H. 1987. Oxygen binding constants for human hemoglobin tetramers. *Biochemistry* 26:3995–4002.

Gill, S. J.; Robert, C. H.; and Wyman, J. 1988. Analysis of allosteric models for macromolecular reactions. In *Biochemical Thermodynamics,* 2d ed. M. N. Jones, ed. Elsevier, Amsterdam. Pp. 145–181.

Gilliland, G. L., and Quiocho, F. A. 1981. Structure of the L-arabinose-binding protein from *Escherichia coli* at 2.4 Å resolution. *J. Mol. Biol.* 146:341–362.

Green, A. A. 1931. Studies in the physical chemistry of the proteins, XI: The effect of electrolytes on the solubility of hemoglobin in solution of varying hydrogen ion activity with a note on the comparable behavior of casein. *J. Biol. Chem.* 93:517–542.

Grütter, M. G.; Gray, T. M.; Weaver, L. H.; Alber, T.; Wilson, K.; and Matthews, B. W. 1987. Structural studies of mutants of the lysozyme of bacteriophage T4. The temperature-sensitive mutant protein Thr157 → Ile, *J. Mol. Biol.* 197:315–329.

Haire, R. N., and Hedlund, B. E. 1977. Thermodynamic aspects of the linkage between binding of chloride and oxygen to human hemoglobin. *Proc. Natl. Acad. Sci. USA* 74:4135–4138.

Haire, R. N.; Tisel, W. A.; Niazi, G.; Rosenberg, A.; Gill, S. J.; and Richey, B. 1981. Hemoglobin solubility as a function of fractional oxygen saturation for hemoglobins in polyethylene glycol: A sickle hemoglobin model. *Biochem. Biophys. Res. Commun.* 101:177–182.

Haldane, J., and Smith, J. L. 1897. The absorption of oxygen by the lungs. *J. Physiol.* (London) 22:231–258.

Haser, R.; Pierrot, M.; Frey, M.; Payan, F.; Astier, J. P.; Bruschi, M.; and Le Gall, J. 1979. Structure and sequence of the multihaem cytochrome c_3. *Nature* 282:806–810.

Haurowitz, F. 1938. Das Gleichgewicht zwischen Haemoglobin und Sauerstoff. *Z. Physiol. Chem.* 254:266–274.

Hawley, S. A. 1971. Reversible pressure-temperature denaturation of chymotrypsinogen. *Biochemistry* 10:2436–2442.

Henderson, L. J. 1913. *The Fitness of the Environment.* Macmillan, New York.

Heremans, K. 1982. High-pressure effects on proteins and other biomolecules. *Ann. Rev. Biophys. Bioeng.* 11:1–21.

Herzfeld, J., and Stanley, H. E. 1974. A general approach to cooperativity and its application to the oxygen equilibrium of hemoglobin and its effectors. *J. Mol. Biol.* 82:231–265.

Hess, V. L., and Szabo, A. 1979. Ligand binding to macromolecules. Allosteric and sequential models of cooperativity. *J. Chem. Ed.* 56:289–293.

Hill, A. V. 1910. The possible effects of the aggregation of the molecules of hemoglobin on the dissociation curves. *J. Physiol.* (London) 40:iv–vii.

Hill, A. V. 1913. The combination of hemoglobin with oxygen and with carbon monoxide. *Biochem. J.* 7:471–480.

Hill, T. L. 1960. *Introduction to Statistical Thermodynamics.* Addison-Wesley, Reading, MA.

Hill, T. L. 1985. *Cooperativity Theory in Biochemistry.* Springer-Verlag, New York.

Hofrichter, J.; Ross, P. D.; and Eaton, W. A. 1976a. In *Proceedings of the Symposium on Molecular and Cellular Aspects of Sickle Cell Disease.* J. I. Hercules, G. Cottam, M. R. Waterman, and A. N. Schechter, eds. Dept. of HEW. Dallas, TX. Pp. 33–59, 185–222.

Hofrichter, J.; Ross, P. D.; and Eaton, W. A. 1976b. Supersaturation in sickle cell hemoglobin solutions. *Proc. Natl. Acad. Sci. USA* 73:3035–3039.

Hofrichter, J.; Sommer, J. H.; Henry, E. R.; and Eaton, W. A. 1983. Nanosecond absorption spectroscopy of hemoglobin: Elementary processes in kinetic cooperativity. *Proc. Natl. Acad. Sci. USA* 80:2235–2239.

Hopfield, J. J.; Schulman, R. G.; and Ogawa, S. 1971. An allosteric model of hemoglobin, I: Kinetics. *J. Mol. Biol.* 61:425–443.

Howlett, G. J., and Schachman, H. K. 1977. Allosteric regulation of aspartate transcarbamoylase: Changes in the sedimentation coefficient promoted by the bisubstrate analogue N-(Phosphonacetyl)-L-aspartate. *Biochemistry* 16:5077–5083.

Hüfner, G., and Gansser, E. 1907. Ueber das Molekular-gewicht des Oxyhaemo-globins. *Arch. Physiol. Anat.* 209–216.

Ikeda-Saito, M.; Yonetani, T.; Chiancone, E.; Ascoli, F.; Verzili, D.; and Antonini, E. 1983. Thermodynamic properties of oxygen equilibria of dimeric and tetrameric hemoglobins from *Scapharca inaequivalvis*. *J. Mol. Biol.* 170:1009–1018.

Imai, K. 1973. Analyses of oxygen equilibria of native and chemically modified human adult hemoglobins on the basis of Adair's stepwise oxygenation theory and the allosteric model of Monod, Wyman, and Changeux. *Biochemistry* 12: 798–808.

Imai, K. 1982. *Allosteric Effects in Haemoglobin.* Cambridge University Press, Cambridge, MA. Pp. 129–137.

Imai, K., and Tyuma, I. 1973. Simulation of biphasic oxygen equilibrium curves of hemoglobin in the presence of small amounts of 2,3-diphosphoglycerate. *Biochim. Biophys. Acta* 293:290–294.

Imai, K., and Yonetani, T. 1975a. Thermodynamical studies of oxygen equilibrium of hemoglobin. *J. Biol. Chem.* 250:7093–7098.

Imai, K., and Yonetani, T. 1975b. pH dependence of the Adair constants of human hemoglobin: Nonuniform contribution of successive oxygen bindings to the alkaline Bohr effect. *J. Biol. Chem.* 250:2227–2231.

Ip, S. H. C.; Johnson, M. L.; and Ackers, G. K. 1976. Kinetics of deoxyhemoglobin subunit dissociation determined by haptoglobin binding: Estimation of the equilibrium constant from forward and reverse rates. *Biochemistry* 15:654–660.

Ip, S. H. C., and Ackers, G. K. 1977. Thermodynamic studies on subunit assembly in human hemoglobin. *J. Biol. Chem.* 252:82–87.

Janssen, L. H. M.; De Bruin, S. H.; and Van Os, G. A. J. 1970. H^+ titration studies of human hemoglobin. *Biochim. Biophys. Acta* 221:214–227.

Johannes, K.-J., and Hess, Benno. 1973. Allosteric kinetics of pyruvate kinase of *Saccharomyces carlsbergensis*. *J. Mol. Biol.* 76:181–205.

Johnson, M. L.; Halvorson, H. R.; and Ackers, G. A. 1976. Oxygen-linked subunit interactions in human hemoglobin: Analysis of linkage functions for constituent energy terms. *Biochemistry* 15:5363–5371.

Johnson, M. L., and Ackers, G. K. 1982. Thermodynamic analysis of human he-moglobins in terms of the Perutz mechanism: Extensions of the Szabo-Karplus model to include subunit assembly. *Biochemistry* 21:201–211.

Jope, H. M., and O'Brien, J. R. P. 1949. *Haemoglobin.* F. J. W. Roughton and J. C. Kendrew, eds. Butterworth, London.

Kantrowitz, E. R., and Lipscomb, W. N. 1988. *Escherichia coli* aspartate trans-carbamylase: The relation between structure and function. *Science* 241:669–674.

Kendrew, J. C.; Watson, H. C.; Standberg, B. E.; Dickerson, R. E.; Phillips, D. C.; and Shore, V. C. 1961. A partial determination by X-ray methods and its correlation with chemical data. *Nature* 190:666–670.

Kim, S.-H. 1978. Three-dimensional structure of transfer RNA and its functional implications. *Advances in Enzymol.* 46:279–316.

King, E. L. 1981. Allosterism: An explanation for cooperativity in zinc(II) cyanide and nickel(II) cyanide complex ion formation. *Inorg. Chem.* 20:2350–2352.

King, E. L. 1956. Unusual kinetic consequences of certain enzyme catalysis mech-anisms. *J. Phys. Chem.* 60:1378–1381.

Klug, A., and Caspar, D. E. D. 1960. Advan. Virus Res. 7:274.

Koshland, D. E., Jr.; Nemethy, G.; and Filmer, D. 1966. Comparison of experimental binding data and theoretical models in proteins containing subunits. *Biochemistry* 5:365–385.

Krause, K. L.; Volz, K. W.; and Lipscomb, W. N. 1985. Structure at 2.9-ÅÅ resolution of aspartate carbamoyltransferase complexed with the bisubstrate analogue N-(phosphonacetyl)-:-aspartate. *Proc. Natl. Acad. Sci. USA* 82:1643–1647.

Kuiper, H. A.; Torensma, R.; and van Bruggen, E. F. J. 1976. Binding of carbon monoxide to α-hemocyanin and β-hemocyanin from *Helix pomatia*. *Eur. J. Biochem.* 68:425–430.

Kuiper, H. A.; Antonini, E.; and Brunori, M. 1977. Kinetic control of cooperativity in the oxygen binding of *panulirus interruptus* hemocyanin. *J. Mol. Biol.* 116:569–576.

Magaldi, A. G.; Ghiretti, F.; Tognon, G.; and Zanotti, G. 1986. The structure of the extracellular hemoglobin of annelids. In *Invertebrate Oxygen Carriers*. Bernt Linzen, ed. Pp. 45–49. Springer-Verlag, Berlin.

Manly, S. P.; Matthews, K. S.; and Sturtevant, J. M. 1985. Thermal denaturation of the core protein of *lac* repressor. *Biochemistry* 24:3842–3846.

Manning, G. 1978. The molecular theory of polyelectrolyte solutions with applications to the electrostatic properties of polynucleotides. *Quart. Rev. Biophys.* 11:179–246.

Mao, B.; Pear, M. R.; McCammon, J. A.; and Quiocho, F. A. 1982. Hinge-bending in L-arabinose-binding protein. *J. Biol. Chem.* 257:1131–1133.

Markl, J.; Decker, H.; Stocker, W.; Savel, A.; Linzen, B.; Schutter, W. G.; and van Bruggen, E. F. J. 1981. On the role of dimeric subunits in the quaternary structure of arthropod hemocyanins. *Hoppe-Seyler's Z. Physiol. Chem.* 362:185–188.

Matthews, B. W., and Remington, S. J. 1974. The three-dimensional structure of the lysozyme from bacteriophage T4. *Proc. Natl. Acad. Sci. USA* 71:4178–4182.

Matthews, J. B.; Friend, S. H.; and Gurd, F. R. N. 1981. Electrostatic effects in hemoglobin: Electrostatic energy associated with allosteric transition and effector binding. *Biochemistry* 20:571–580.

Mills, F. C.; Johnson, M. L.; and Ackers, G. K. 1976. Oxygenation-linked subunit interactions in human hemoglobin: Experimental studies on the concentration dependence of oxygenation curves. *Biochemistry* 15:5350–5362.

Minton, A. P. 1977. Non-ideality and the thermodynamics of sickle-cell hemoglobin gelation. *J. Mol. Biol.* 110:89–103.

Monod, J., and Jacob, F. 1961. General conclusions: Teleonomic mechanisms in cellular metabolism, growth, and differentiation. *Cold Spring Harb. Symp. Quant. Biol.* 26:389–401.

Monod, J.; Changeux, J. P.; and Jacob, F. 1963. Allosteric proteins and cellular control systems. *J. Mol. Biol.* 6:306–329.

Monod, J.; Wyman, J.; and Changeux, J. P. 1965. On the nature of allosteric transitions: A plausible model. *J. Mol. Biol.* 12:88–118.

Morild, E. 1981. The theory of pressure effects on enzymes. *Adv. Protein Chem.* 34:93–166.

Mozzarelli, A.; Ottonello, S.; Rossi, G. L.; and Fasella, P. 1979. Catalytic activity of aspartate aminotransferase in the crystal. Equilibrium and kinetic analysis. *Eur. J. Biochem.* 98:173–179.

Murray, J. D. 1977. *Lectures on Nonlinear Differential-Equation Models in Biology.* Clarendon Press, Oxford.

Murray, J. D., and Wyman, J. 1971. Facilitated diffusion: The case of carbon monoxide. *J. Biol. Chem.* 246:5903–5906.

Newcomer, M. E.; Lewis, B. A.; and Quiocho, F. A. 1981. The radius of gyration of L-arabinose-binding protein decreases upon binding of ligand. *J. Biol. Chem.* 256:13218–13222.

O'Gorman, R. B.; Rosenberg, J. M.; Kallai, O. B.; Dickerson, R. E.; Itakura, K.; Riggs, A. D.; and Matthews, K. S. 1980. Equilibrium binding of inducer to lac repressor-operator DNA complex. *J. Biol. Chem.* 255:10107–10114.

Parody-Morreale, A.; Robert, C. H.; Bishop, G. A.; and Gill, S. J. 1986. Calorimetric analysis of oxygen binding to lobster hemocyanin. In *Invertebrate Oxygen Carriers*. Bernt Linzen, ed. Pp. 389–393. Springer-Verlag, Berlin.

Pauling, L. 1935. The oxygen equilibrium of hemoglobin and its structural interpretation. *Proc. Natl. Acad. Sci. USA* 21:186–191.

Pauling, L.; Itano, H. A.; Singer, S. J.; and Wells, I. C. 1949. Sickle cell anemia: A molecular disease. *Science* 110:543–548.

Peller, L. 1982. Cooperative deoxygenation of haemoglobin: Asymmetry of binding and subunit differences. *Nature* 300:661–662.

Perutz, M. F. 1946. The composition and swelling properties of haemoglobin crystals. *Trans. Faraday Soc.* 46:187–195.

Perutz, M. F. 1965. Structure and function of haemoglobin, I: A tentative atomic model of horse oxyhaemoglobin. *J. Mol. Biol.* 13:646–668.

Perutz, M. F. 1970. Stereochemistry of cooperative effects in haemoglobin. *Nature* (London) 228:726–739.

Perutz, M. F. 1976. Structure and mechanism of haemoglobin. *Br. Med. Bull.* 32:195–208.

Perutz, M. F. 1979. Regulation of oxygen affinity of hemoglobin: Influence of structure of the globin on the heme iron. *Ann. Rev. Biochem.* 48:327–386.

Perutz, M. F.; Rossmann, M. G.; Cullis, A. F.; Muirhead, H.; Will, G.; and North, A. C. T. 1960. Structure of haemoglobin: A three-dimensional Fourier synthesis at 5.5-Å resolution, obtained by X-ray analysis. *Nature* 185:416–422.

Pettigrew, D. W.; Romeo, P. H.; Tsapis, A.; Thillet, J.; Smith, M. L.; Turner, B. W.; and Ackers, G. K. 1982. Probing the energetics of proteins through structural perturbation: Sites of regulatory energy in human hemoglobin. *Proc. Natl. Acad. Sci. USA* 79:1849–1853.

Pfeil, W., and Privalov, P. L. 1976a. Thermodynamic investigations of proteins, I: Standard functions for proteins with lysozyme as an example. *Biophys. Chem.* 4:23–32.

Pfeil, W., and Privalov, P. L. 1976b. Thermodynamic investigations of proteins, II: Calorimetric study of lysozyme denaturation by guanidine hydrochloride. *Biophys. Chem.* 4:33–40.

Pfeil, W., and Privalov, P. L. 1976c. Thermodynamic investigations of proteins, III: Thermodynamic description of lysozyme. *Biophys. Chem.* 4:41–50.

Privalov, P. L. 1976. Thermodynamic investigations of biological macromolecules. *Pure & Appl. Chem.* 47:293–304.

Privalov, P. L. 1979. Stability of proteins: Small globular proteins. *Adv. Protein Chem.* 33:167–241.

Privalov, P. L., and Ptitsyn, O. B. 1969. Determination of stability of the DNA double helix in an aqueous medium. *Biopolymers* 8:559–571.

Privalov, P. L., and Khechinashvili, 1974. A thermodynamic approach to the problem of stabilization of globular protein structure: A calorimetric study. *J. Mol. Biol.* 86:665–684.

Privalov, P. L., and Filimonov, V. V. 1978. Thermodynamic analysis of transfer RNA unfolding. *J. Mol. Biol.* 122:447–464.

Privalov, P. L.; Griko, Yu. V.; Venyaminov, S. Yu.; and Kutyshenko, V. P. 1986. Cold denaturation of myoglobin. *J. Mol. Biol.* 190:487–498.

Rich, A.; Nordheim, A.; and Wang, A. H.-J. 1984. The chemistry and biology of left-handed Z-DNA. *Ann. Rev. Biochem.* 53:791–846.

Richardson, D. E.; Reem, R. C.; and Solomon, E. I. 1983. Cooperativity in oxygen binding to *Lingula reevii* hemerythrin: Spectroscopic comparison to the sipunculid hemerythrin coupled binuclear iron active site. *J. Am. Chem. Soc.* 105:7780–7781.

Richey, B.; Decker, H.; and Gill, S. J. 1985. Binding of oxygen and carbon monoxide to arthropod hemocyanin: An allosteric analysis. *Biochemistry* 24:109–117.

Robert, C. H.; Decker, H.; Richey, B.; Gill, S. J.; and Wyman, J. 1987. Nesting: Hierarchies of allosteric interactions. *Proc. Natl. Acad. Sci. USA* 84:1891–1895.

Robert, C. H.; Gill, S. J.; and Wyman, J. 1988a. Quantitative analysis of linkage in macromolecules when one ligand is present in limited total quantity. *Biochemistry* 27:6829–6835.

Robert, C. H.; Fall, L.; and Gill, S. J. 1988b. Linkage of organic phosphates to oxygen binding in human hemoglobin at high concentrations. *Biochemistry* 27:6835–6843.

Robert, C. H.; Colosimo, A.; and Gill, S. J. 1989. Allosteric formulation of thermal transitions in macromolecules, including effects of ligand binding and oligomerization. *Biopolymers* 28:1705–1729.

Rodkey, F. L., and Ball, E. G. 1950. Oxidation-reduction potentials of the cytochrome c system. *J. Biol. Chem.* 182:17–28.

Ross, P. D., and Minton, A. P. 1977. Analysis of non-ideal behavior in concentrated hemoglobin solutions. *J. Mol. Biol.* 112:437–452.

Rossi-Fanelli, A., and Antonini, E. 1958. Studies on the oxygen and carbon monoxide equilibria of human myoglobin. *Arch. Biochem. Biophys.* 77:478–492.

Roughton, F. J. W., and Lyster, R.L.J. 1965. Some combinations of the Scholander-Roughton syringe capillary and van Slyke's gasometric techniques, and their use in special haemoglobin problems. *Hvaldradets. Skrifter* 48:185–198.

Rupley, J. A. 1968. Comparison of protein structure in the crystal and in solution, IV: Protein solubility. *J. Mol. Biol.* 35:455–476.

Russo, I. M.; Ho, N. T.; and Ho, C. 1982. A proton nuclear magnetic resonance investigation of histidyl residues in human normal adult hemoglobin. *Biochemistry* 21:5031–5043.

Santucci, R.; Chiancone, Em.; and Giardina, B. 1984. Oxygen binding to *octolasium complanatum* erythrocruorin: Modulation of homo- and heterotropic interactions by cations. *J. Mol. Biol.* 179:713–727.

Savel, A. 1984. Dissertation, Ludwig-Maximilians University. Munich. P. 86.

Scatchard, G. 1946. Physical chemistry of protein solutions, I: Derivation of the equations for the osmotic pressure. *J. Am. Chem. Soc.* 68:2315–2319.

Scatchard, G. 1949. The attractions of proteins for small molecules and ions. *Ann. N. Y. Acad. Sci.* 51:660–672.

Schellman, J. A. 1975. Macromolecular binding. *Biopolymers* 14:999–1018.

Scholander, P. F. 1960. Oxygen transport through hemoglobin solutions. *Science* 131:585–590.

Segrè, E. 1980. *From X-Rays to Quarks*. W. H. Freeman and Co., San Francisco, CA. P. 63.

Shea, M. A., and Ackers, G. K. 1985. The O_r control system of bacteriophage lambda: A physical-chemical model for gene regulation. *J. Mol. Biol.* 181:211–230.

Sheriff, S.; Hendrickson, W. A.; and Smith, J. L. 1983. Structure of the active center of hemerythrins. *Life Chem. Reports* 1:305–308.

Smith, F. R., and Ackers, G. K. 1985. Experimental resolution of cooperative free energies for the ten ligation states of human hemoglobin. *Proc. Natl. Acad. Sci. USA* 82:5347–5351.

Sorensen, S. P. L., and Sorensen, M. 1933. Ueber die Loslichkeit und Dissoziationstendenz des Kohlenoxyd-Haemoglobins in Ammoniumsulfatlosungen. *Biochem. Z.* 258:16.

Sunshine, H. R.; Hofrichter, J.; and Eaton, W. A. 1979. Gelation of sickle cell hemoglobin in mixtures with normal adult and fetal hemoglobins. *J. Mol. Biol.* 133:435–467.

Sunshine, H. R.; Hofrichter, J.; Ferrone, F. A.; and Eaton, W. A. 1982. Oxygen binding by sickle cell hemoglobin polymers. *J. Mol. Biol.* 158:251–273.

Svedberg, T., and Fahreus, R. 1926. A new method for the determination of the molecular weights of the proteins. *J. Am. Chem. Soc.* 48:430–438.

Szabo, A., and Karplus, M. 1972. A mathematical model for structure-function relations in hemoglobin. *J. Mol. Biol.* 72:163–197.

Szabo, A., and Karplus, M. 1976. Analysis of the interaction of organic phosphates with hemoglobin. *Biochemistry* 15:2869–2877.

Takahashi, K.; Casey, J. L.; and Sturtevant, J. M. 1981. Thermodynamics of the binding of D-glucose to yeast hexokinase. *Biochemistry* 20:4693–4697.

Takano, T.; Kallai, O. B.; Swanson, R.; and Dickerson, R. E. 1973. The structure of ferrocytochrome c at 2.45-Å resolution. *J. Biol. Chem.* 248:5234–5255.

Takano, T., and Dickerson, R. E. 1981. Conformation change of cytochrome c, I: Ferrocytochrome c structure refined at 1.5-Å resolution. *J. Mol. Biol.* 153:95–115.

Takeda, Y.; Ohlendorf, D. H.; Anderson, W. F.; and Matthews, B. W. 1983. DNA-binding proteins. *Science* 221:1020–1026.

Tanford, C. 1969. Extension of the theory of linked functions to incorporate the effects of protein hydration. *J. Mol. Biol.* 39:539–544.

Tyuma, I.; Shimizu, K.; and Imai, K. 1971. Effect of 2,3-diphosphoglycerate on the cooperativity in oxygen binding of human adult hemoglobin. *Biochem. Biophys. Res. Commun.* 43:423–428.

van Bruggen, E. F. J. 1982. In van Holde, K. E., and Miller, K. I. 1982. Haemocyanins. *Quart. Rev. Biophys.* 15:20.

van Bruggen, E. F. J. 1983. An electron microscopist's view of the quaternary structure of arthropodan and molluscan hemocyanins. *Life Chem. Reports.* Suppl. 1:1–14.

van Holde, K. E., and Miller, K. I. 1985. Association-dissociation equilibria of *octopus* hemocyanin. *Biochemistry* 24:4577–4582.

van Holde, K. E., and Miller, K. I. 1986. Oxygen-linked dissociation and oxygen binding by subunits of *octopus dofleini* hemocyanin. In *Invertebrate Oxygen Carriers*. Bernt Linzen, ed. Pp. 417–420. Springer-Verlag, Berlin.

Warburg, O.; Negelein, E.; and Christian, W. 1929. Ueber carbylamin-Haemoglobin und die Photochemische Dissoziation seiner Kohlenoxydverbindung. *Biochem. Z.* 214:26.

Watt, G. D.; Frankel, R. B.; and Papaefthymiou, G. C. 1985. Reduction of mammalian ferritin. *Proc. Natl. Acad. Sci. USA* 82:3640–3643.

Weber, G. 1982. Asymmetric ligand binding by haemoglobin. *Nature* 300:603–607.

Weber, G., and Drickamer, H. G. 1983. The effect of high pressure upon proteins and other biomolecules. *Quart. Rev. Biophys.* 16:89–112.

Weber, P. C., and Salemme, F. R. 1982. Cytochrome c′: A dimeric, high-spin heme protein. In *Electron Transport and Oxygen Utilization*. Chien Ho, ed. Pp. 57–59. Elsevier, North Holland.

White, J. G., and Heagan, B. 1973. Fine structure of hemoglobin polymerization. In *Sickle Cell Disease, Diagnosis, Management, Education, and Research*. H. Abramson, J. F. Bertles, and D. L. Wethers, eds. C. V. Mosby, Saint Louis. P. 108.

Whitehead, E. P. 1980. Protein symmetry and the co-operative ligand-binding behaviour predicted by allosteric Koshland models. *J. Theor. Biol.* 86:45–82.

Wiley, D. C., and Skehel, J. J. 1987. The structure and function of the hemagglutinin membrane glycoprotein of influenza virus. *Ann. Rev. Biochem.* 56:365–394.

Wilson, I. A.; Skehel, J. J.; and Wiley, D. C. 1981. Structure of the haemagglutinin membrane glycoprotein of influenza virus at 3-Å resolution. *Nature* (London) 289:366–373.

Wishner, B. C.; Ward, K. B.; Lattman, E. E.; and Love, W. E. 1975. Crystal structure of sickle-cell deoxyhemoglobin at 5 Å resolution. *J. Mol. Biol.* 98:179–194.

Wittenberg, J. B. 1959. Oxygen transport: A new function proposed for myoglobin. *Biol. Bull.* 117:402–403.

Wyman, J. 1948. Heme proteins. *Adv. Prot. Chem.* 4:407–531.

Wyman, J. 1963. Allosteric effects in hemoglobin. *Cold Spring Harb. Symp. Quant. Biol.* 28:483–489.

Wyman, J. 1964. Linked functions and reciprocal effects in hemoglobin: A second look. *Adv. Prot. Chem.* 19:223–286.

Wyman, J. 1965. The binding potential: A neglected linkage concept. *J. Mol. Biol.* 11:631–644.

Wyman, J. 1967. Allosteric linkage. *J. Am. Chem. Soc.* 89:2202–2218.

Wyman, J. 1968. Regulation in macromolecules as illustrated by haemoglobin. *Quart. Rev. Biophys.* 1:35–80.

Wyman, J. 1972. On allosteric models. *Current Topics in Cell. Reg.* 6:207–223.

Wyman, J. 1975a. A group of thermodynamic potentials applicable to ligand binding by a polyfunctional macromolecule. *Proc. Natl. Acad. Sci. USA* 72:1464–1469.

Wyman, J. 1975b. The turning wheel: A study in steady states. *Proc. Natl. Acad. Sci. USA* 72:3983–3987.

Wyman, J. 1978. The place of symmetry in the study of biological macromolecules. *Biophys. Chem.* 9:1–8.

Wyman, J. 1984. Linkage graphs: A study in the thermodynamics of macromolecules. *Quart. Rev. Biophys.* 17:453–488.

Wyman, J., and Ingalls, E. N. 1941. Interrelationships in the reactions of horse hemoglobin. *J. Biol. Chem.* 139:877–895.

Wyman, J., and Allen, D. W. 1951. The problem of the heme interactions in hemoglobin and the basis of the Bohr effect. *J. Polymer Sci.* 7:499–518.

Wyman, J., and Phillipson, P. 1974. A probabilistic approach to cooperativity of ligand binding by a polyvalent molecule. *Proc. Natl. Acad. Sci. USA* 71:3431–3434.

Wyman, J.; Gill, S. J.; and Colosimo, A. 1979. On thermal transitions in biological macromolecules. *Biophys. Chem.* 10:363–369.

Wyman, J., and Gill, S. J. 1980. Ligand-linked phase changes in a biological system: Applications to sickle cell hemoglobin. *Proc. Natl. Acad. Sci. USA* 77:5239–5242.

Wyman, J.; Bishop, G.; Richey, B.; Spokane, R.; and Gill, S. J. 1982. Examination of Haldane's law. *Biopolymers* 21:1735–1747.

Zhang, R.-g.; Joachimiak, A.; Lawson, C. L.; Schevitz, R. W.; Otwinowski, Z.; and Sigler, P. B. 1987. The crystal structure of *trp* aporepressor at 1.8Å shows how binding tryptophan enhances DNA affinity. *Nature* 327:591–597.

Zinoffsky, O. 1886. Ueber die grosse des Haemoglobinmolekuls. *Hoppe-Seylers Z. Physiol. Chem.* 10:16–34.

Zipp, A., and Kauzmann, W. 1973. Pressure denaturation of metmyoglobin. *Biochemistry* 12:4217–4228.

Zolla, L.; Kuiper, H. A.; Vecchini, P.; Antonini, E.; and Brunori, M. 1978. Dissociation and oxygen-binding behaviour of β-hemocyanin from *Helix pomatia*. *Eur. J. Biochem.* 87:467–473.

Index

NOTE: The *f* following some page numbers refers to a figure on that page.